Grades 4-6 Supplement

Mathematical Reasoning™ Series

📖 Beginning 1 📖 Beginning 2
📖 Level A 📖 Level B 📖 Level C 📖 Level D
📖 Level E 📖 Level F 📖 Level G
📖 Understanding Geometry
📖 Grades 2-4 Supplement 📖 Grades 4-6 Supplement
📖 Middle School Supplement

Written by
Warren Hill
Ronald Edwards

© 2012, 2002, 1992, 1991
THE CRITICAL THINKING CO.™
www.CriticalThinking.com
Phone: 800-458-4849 • Fax: 831-393-3277
P.O. Box 1610 • Seaside • CA 93955-1610
ISBN 978-1-60144-415-8

MIX
Paper from
responsible sources
FSC® C011935

TABLE OF CONTENTS

ABOUT THE AUTHORS

Dr. Warren H. Hill has been a Professor of Mathematics at Westfield State College (Massachusetts) for 20 years. He is a graduate of Peabody College for Teachers and holds doctorates in both mathematics and psychology. Dr. Hill has taught college-level mathematics and teacher-training courses for many years and prior to that had several years of high school-level teaching experience. He is a frequent speaker at both national and international conferences on reading, math, and thinking skills and regularly serves as a consultant and workshop teacher for school districts across the United States. Dr. Hill is the author of several books and numerous articles on mathematics.

Dr. Ronald R. Edwards has been a Professor of Mathematics at Westfield State College (Massachusetts) for 19 years. He holds an A.B. degree from Brown University, an M.A.T. from Wesleyan University, and a Ph.D. from the University of Connecticut. Dr. Edwards currently teaches college-level mathematics, computer science, and teacher training courses and has had several years of high school level teaching experience. He presents national workshops and seminars on computer science and mathematics and is the author of several books and numerous articles on mathematics.

INTRODUCTION

Objective

Mathematical Reasoning™ Grades 4-6 Supplement introduces children in the upper elementary grades to the application of analytical and critical thinking skills within the study of mathematics. The primary goal of the book is not to teach students a set of arithmetic skills, but to encourage them to develop analytical and reasoning skills applicable to a wide range of mathematical concepts. This is achieved through activities that are compatible with the standards developed by the National Council of Teachers of Mathematics.

These activities encourage students to develop investigative, analytical, and explanatory abilities in a cooperative learning environment. In addition, the activities explore a variety of quantitative and spatial relationships that are an essential part of the foundation of mathematics. The systems of whole and rational numbers as well as elementary geometry are used in the activities as vehicles to promote the development of these numerical and spatial concepts. To this end, there are 1374 individual exercises on 283 reproducible student activity sheets. After the teacher or parent has *discussed* the example as well as explained any vocabulary new to the students, then students may proceed to work the next few exercises independently or in a small group. As a result of exploring each exercise to the fullest extent, layer by layer, the students should show significant gains in vocabulary development, substantially increase observational skills, and be able to process mathematical concepts on a much higher level.

The activities are arranged in six sections which address six major strands in the elementary mathematics curriculum:
- Number and Numeration
- Geometry
- Operations
- Measurement
- Relations
- Tables and Graphs

The first two sections develop an understanding of basic number and geometric concepts. The remaining four sections build upon these number and spatial understandings and investigate their relationships and applications in problem solving. To be used effectively, the materials should be followed sequentially. The presentation of the activities in each section assumes students have been exposed to the key concepts developed in earlier sections.

Cognitive Model

Many of the activities in Mathematical Reasoning™ Grades 4-6 Supplement have their origin in the cognitive development of Jean Piaget. A basic tenet of Piaget's cognitive model is that learning is an *interactive* process. Piaget maintained that the goal of education should be to provide the settings and opportunities for the student to become actively involved in the learning process. In a general sense, Piaget would have maintained that learning and intellectual development are not passive, sporadic activities, but dynamic, ongoing processes. The ability to acquire knowledge is built upon the capacity to organize and structure a concept's key components. Furthermore, this process is based upon the development of logical relationships. Thus, it is necessary, first of all, to identify those logical relationships that serve as the foundation of intellectual development, then provide the settings within an academic discipline that will enable the student to acquire proficiency with these relationships.

The application of logic and analytical skills to numerical and spatial concepts is introduced in this book through activities that are designed to focus student attention on the tasks of examining, discussing, and describing numerical and geometric relationships in terms of logical relations. These logical relations include:
- analyzing similarities and differences
- recognizing sequences and patterns
- using numerical and spatial concepts for classification
- applying the concept of analogies to relations and functions

In addition, many of the activities stress using inductive reasoning to extend patterns, make predictions based upon available data, and formulate inferences. The role of deductive reasoning is introduced to students through the use of logical connectives, counterexamples, and the application of the process of elimination to derive solutions to numerical and geometric problems.

The presence of multiple solutions to certain exercises encourages students to realize that mathematics does not necessarily restrict itself to a single simple solution or a single strategy to arrive at a solution. The need to share ideas and compare solutions is of paramount importance. Such analysis and verbalizing results in students developing an appreciation that mathematics is indeed a logical discipline with recognizable patterns, order, and structure.

The Roles of the Teacher and the Student

The activities in *Mathematical Reasoning™ Grades 4-6 Supplement* provide teachers with an opportunity to teach students to *think mathematically.* The teacher's role is changed from simply reciting or explaining mathematical concepts to encouraging learners to explore and interact with these concepts. The teacher is encouraged to employ questioning techniques and discussion strategies that help learners move in a desired direction instead of providing a set of correct answers. The role of the teacher becomes one of developing questioning techniques that allow students to "wrestle" with the task of explaining their reasoning - and providing ample opportunities to do so. This is necessary because a student's understanding of the role of logical relations in mathematics is dependent upon his or her ability to verbalize and explain an underlying mathematical process rather than providing a simple response to an exercise. To achieve the objective of thinking mathematically, students must become active participants in the learning process.

As a corollary to questioning techniques, the teacher must also develop acute listening skills. When an inappropriate response is given, it is often a delicate task to "hear" a student's reasoning and then redirect it toward an appropriate response. The teacher must continually be aware that there may be more than one correct response in some situations. In fact, it may be more appropriate in many cases to think in terms of a "best" response rather than a correct or incorrect response. Unanimous agreement on the best answer is not crucial. What is crucial, however, is that each person understands and appreciates the other's reasoning.

In the case of an unexpected response, the teacher should focus on the student's verbalized explanation or rationale for the answer before discussing its correctness. For example, a typical teacher reaction to an unexpected response might be, "Why did you choose that answer?"

In sum, the role of the teacher is not to put forth a body of information but to serve as a catalyst between the student's intuitive responses and the student's ability to offer a verbal rationale for his or her conclusions. At the same time, the role of the student is not to be passive but to be an active participant in the learning process by applying analysis and reasoning to mathematics and by discussing the reasoning used in solving the activities.

HOW MANY LETTERS?

Find the number of letters in each box. Count the letters only.
Write the answer in the circle.

Example

a	b	e		t
3	2	5		8
c	d	e		f
4	1	6		3

⑧

A–1

A	i	$	?	5
m	t	s	=	4
c	u	E	r	9
M	S	a	p	H

◯

A–2

D	H	=	?		N	Q
t	u	+			T	
A	F	&	$		O	P
e	f	*			J	

◯

A–3

=	=	=	=	=	=
=	o	c	t	o	b
=	c	t	o	b	e
=	t	o	b	e	r

◯

A–4

y	y	y	y	1
w	w	w	2	w
x	x	3	x	x
5	z	z	z	z

◯

A–5

b	+	8	0	L
3	t	1	p	i
E	o	l	d	!
6	B	–	7	$

◯

HOW MANY DIFFERENT LETTERS?

Look at the boxes below. Each box contains a mixture of letters.
Find the number of different letters in each box.
Write the answer in the circle.

Example

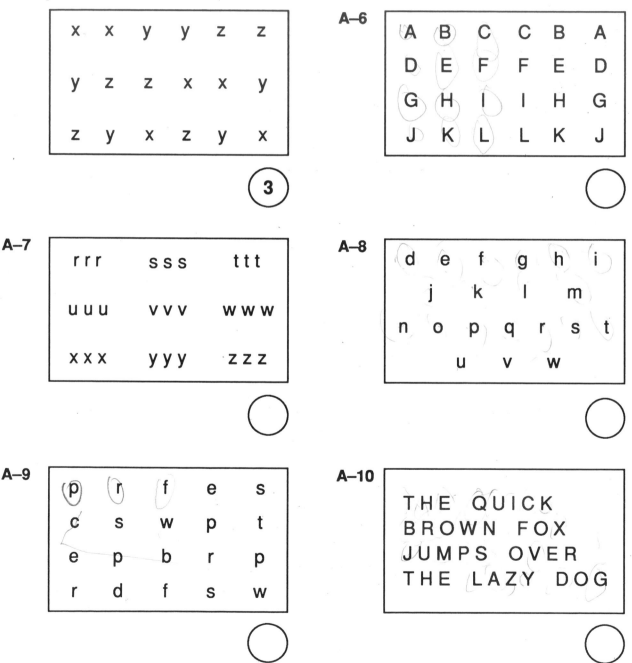

A–6

A–7

A–8

A–9

A–10

THE QUICK
BROWN FOX
JUMPS OVER
THE LAZY DOG

COUNTING THE DOTS

In the triangle write the number of dots pictured in the pattern.
In the circle write the smallest number of dots needed to complete a rectangular pattern of dots.
In the box write the smallest number of dots needed to complete a square pattern of dots.

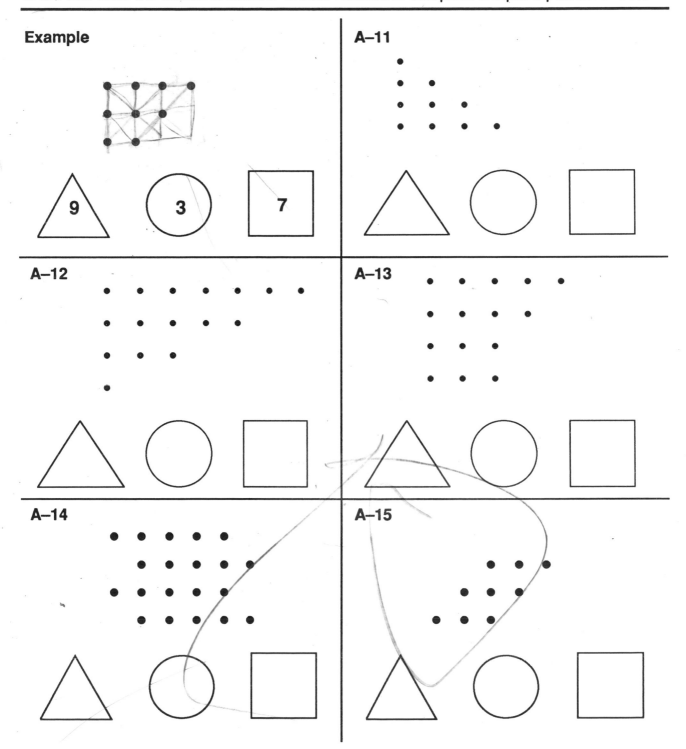

Example

9   3   7

A–11

A–12

A–13

A–14

A–15

COUNTING THE DOTS

Look at the sets below.
Each circle represents 50 dots, each square represents 25 dots, and each triangle represents 5 dots.
What is the total number of dots in each set?

Example

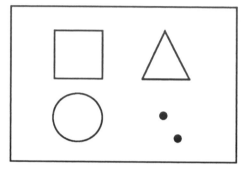

Total = ____82____

A–16

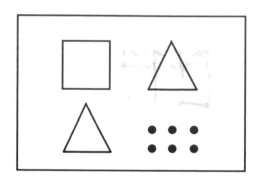

Total = _____

A–17

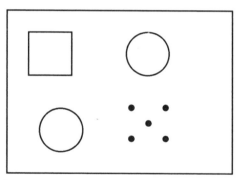

Total = _____

A–18

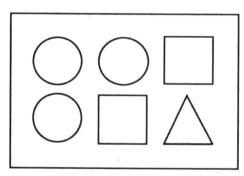

Total = _____

A–19

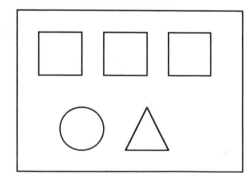

Total = _____

A–20

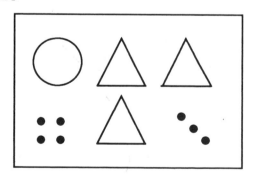

Total = _____

WRITE THE NUMBER

A Japanese abacus is pictured below.
The beads above the crossbar have a value of 5; those below have a value of 1.
Beads that have been moved toward the crossbar of the abacus represent a number.
Write the number that is pictured on the abacus.

Example

173

A–21

A–22

A–23

A–24

A–25

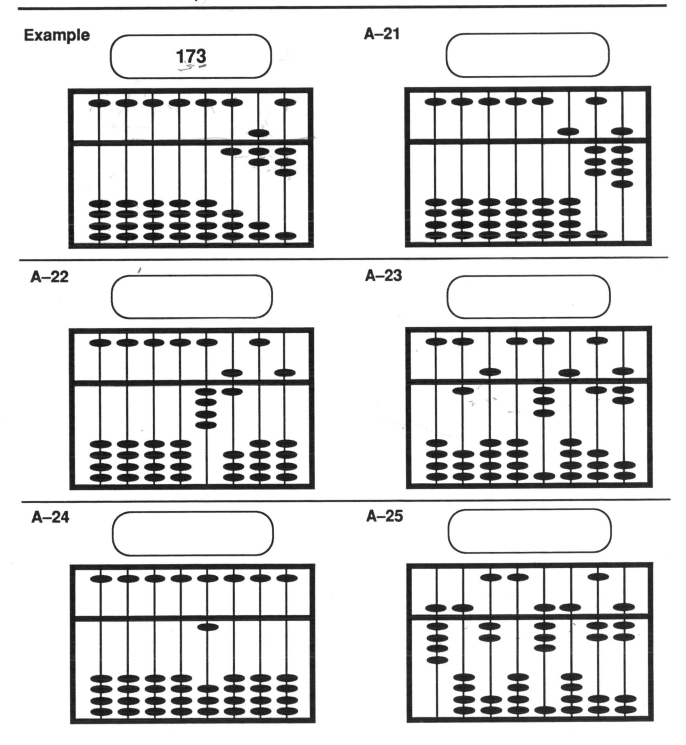

CONSTRUCT THE NUMBER

A Japanese abacus is pictured below.
The beads above the crossbar have a value of 5; those below have a value of 1.
Draw the beads at the crossbar of each abacus to represent the number in the box.

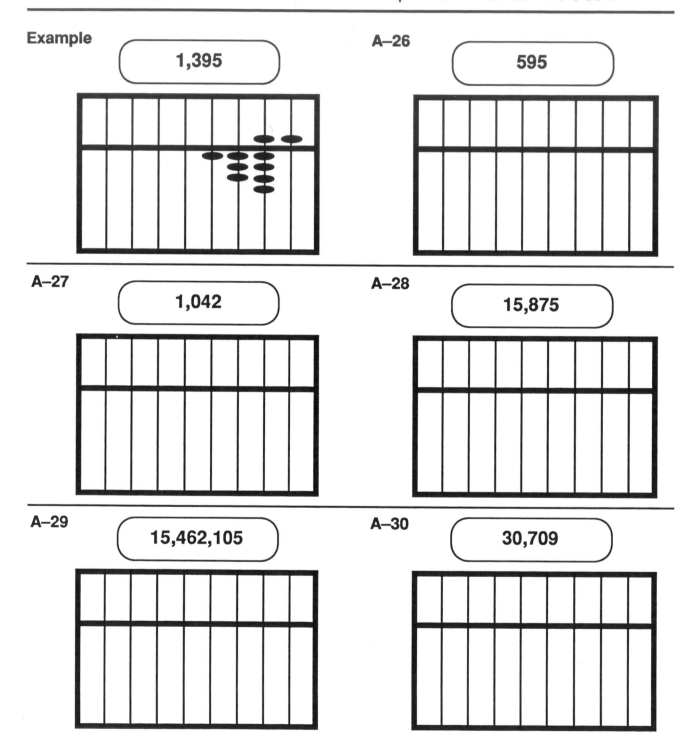

Example 1,395

A–26 595

A–27 1,042

A–28 15,875

A–29 15,462,105

A–30 30,709

CONTINUE THE SEQUENCE

Place numbers in the blank spaces to continue the sequence.

Example	9	11	13	15	<u>17</u>	<u>19</u>	<u>21</u>	<u>23</u>
A–31	11	14	17	20	_____	_____	_____	_____
A–32	37	44	51	58	_____	_____	_____	_____
A–33	50	47	44	41	_____	_____	_____	_____
A–34	17	24	31	38	_____	_____	_____	_____
A–35	25	28	31	34	_____	_____	_____	_____
A–36	97	95	93	91	_____	_____	_____	_____
A–37	108	101	94	87	_____	_____	_____	_____

CONTINUE THE SEQUENCE

Place numbers in the blank spaces to continue the sequence.

A–38	1	2	4	7	11	_____	_____	_____	_____
A–39	5	6	8	11	15	_____	_____	_____	_____
A–40	1	2	5	10	17	_____	_____	_____	_____
A–41	1	3	6	10	15	_____	_____	_____	_____
A–42	9	11	15	21	29	_____	_____	_____	_____
A–43	5	6	9	14	21	_____	_____	_____	_____
A–44	1	4	9	16	25	_____	_____	_____	_____
A–45	2	4	8	16	32	_____	_____	_____	_____

COMPLETING THE SEQUENCE

Place numbers in the blank spaces to complete the sequence.

Example   2   __4__   6   __8__   10   __12__   14

A–46   3   6   _____   _____   _____   18   21

A–47   36   34   32   _____   _____   _____   24   22

A–48   _____   _____   20   _____   12   8   4

A–49   _____   66   _____   60   _____   54   _____   48   45

A–50   _____   10   _____   20   _____   30   _____   40

A–51   _____   90   _____   _____   60   _____   _____   30

A–52   141   _____   _____   126   _____   116   111

COMPLETING THE SEQUENCE

Place numbers in the blank spaces to complete the sequence.

A–53   3   10   17   _____   31   _____   _____   52

A–54   3   _____   9   _____   15   _____   21   _____   27

A–55   4   9   _____   _____   24   _____   _____   39

A–56   95   91   _____   _____   79   _____   _____

A–57   45   _____   31   _____   17   _____   3

A–58   3   _____   _____   18   _____   28   _____   _____   43

A–59   83   _____   _____   74   _____   68   _____

A–60   64   _____   _____   _____   56   _____

SEQUENCES OF NUMBERS

Each exercise below begins a sequence.
The three dots mean that the sequence continues.
Circle the numbers that belong to the sequence.

Example

2, 5, 8, 11, 14, • • •

a. (38)   b. 36

c. 24   d. (23)

A–61

9, 13, 17, 21, • • •

a. 32   b. 33

c. 40   d. 41

A–62

10, 13, 16, 19 • • •

a. 21   b. 36

c. 28   d. 38

A–63

6, 8, 11, 15, 20, • • •

a. 27   b. 25

c. 33   d. 36

A–64

9, 12, 15, 18, 21, • • •

a. 42   b. 25

c. 44   d. 30

SEQUENCES OF NUMBERS

Each exercise below begins a sequence.
The three dots mean that the sequence continues.
Circle the row that belongs to the sequence.

Example

1, 2, 4, 5, 7, 8, • • •

a. 21, 22, 24, 25

b. 17, 18, 19, 20

c. 22, 23, 25, 26

A–65

1, 2, 3, 5, 6, 7, 9, 10, 11 • • •

a. 28, 29, 30

b. 31, 32, 33

c. 21, 22, 23

A–66

1, 2, 5, 6, 9, 10, 13, 14, • • •

a. 25, 26, 29, 30

b. 19, 20, 23, 24

c. 25, 28, 31, 34

A–67

1, 2, 6, 7, 11, 12, 16, 17, • • •

a. 23, 24, 28, 29

b. 18, 22, 23, 27

c. 31, 32, 36, 37

A–68

1, 2, 4, 7, 8, 11, 13, 14, 16, • • •

a. 18, 19, 22, 25

b. 19, 22, 23, 26

c. 23, 24, 26, 28

NUMBER PROPERTIES

Circle all the numbers that satisfy the rule.

Example: A number that is divisible by 5 and is between 18 and 30.

15   23   (20)   30   (25)

A–69 A number that is a multiple of 3 and a multiple of 4.

24   9   56   42   17

A–70 A number that is even and is between 78 and 85.

77   81   84   86   78

A–71 A number that is greater than the number of days in any month and has a factor of 6.

30   36   54   33   42

A–72 A number that is 2 times a single-digit number and is greater than 14.

14   18   17   15   20

A–73 A number that has a factor of 4 and is between 64 and 74.

60   68   70   88   64

NUMBER PROPERTIES

Circle all the numbers that satisfy the rule.

Example: A number that is odd or is a multiple of 3.

  22   34

A-74   A number that is odd and is a multiple of 3.

72   39   22   34   25

A-75   A number that is divisible by 6 or is between 29 and 31.

27   28   30   36   31

A-76   A number that is divisible by 5 or is divisible by 7

16   35   18   28   20

A-77   A number that is divisible by 5 and is divisible by 7

16   35   18   28   20

A-78   A number that is less than the number of digits in any zip code and is not a prime number.

7   4   3   6   8

NUMBER PROPERTIES

Circle all the numbers that satisfy the rule.

A-79   A number that is a multiple of 2 and has an 8 in tens place.

   78   80   8   888   881

A-80   A number that has two digits whose sum is 9 and has a factor of 3.

   33   18   182   36   108

A-81   A number that is less than the number of months in the year or is between 37 and 42.

   26   41   0   8   12

A-82   A number that is greater than the number of vowels in the alphabet or is between 10 and 15.

   4   18   14   5   6

A-83   A number that is less than the number of months in the year and is between 37 and 42.

   26   41   0   8   12

A-84   A number that is greater than the number of digits in any local telephone number and is a prime number.

   5   7   29   49   53

NUMBER PROPERTIES

All of the numbers in circle A are between 25 and 40.
All of the numbers in circle B are between 30 and 50.
Write each number below in the correct region of the diagram.

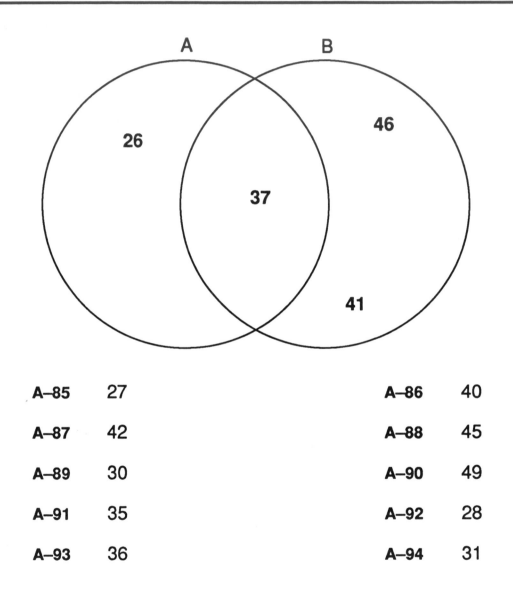

A–85	27	A–86	40
A–87	42	A–88	45
A–89	30	A–90	49
A–91	35	A–92	28
A–93	36	A–94	31

A–95   What numbers are in both circle A and circle B? _____

_____

A–96   What other numbers between 25 and 50 could be placed
in both circle A and circle B? _____

COMMON FACTORS

All of the numbers in circle A have a factor of 6.
All of the numbers in circle B have a factor of 4.
Write each number below in the correct region of the diagram.

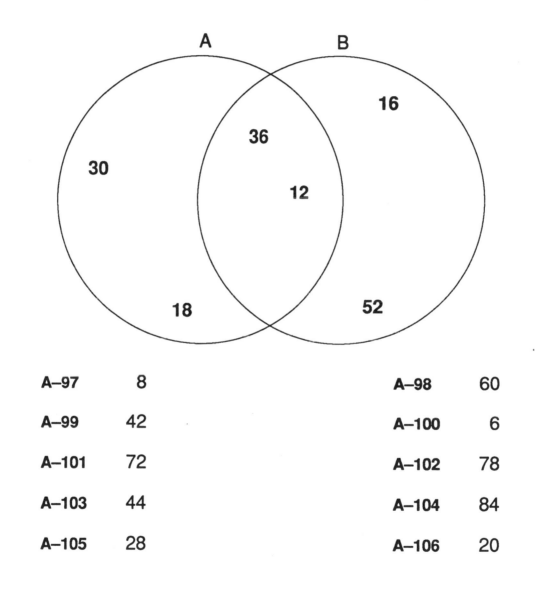

A–97	8		A–98	60
A–99	42		A–100	6
A–101	72		A–102	78
A–103	44		A–104	84
A–105	28		A–106	20

A–107   What numbers are in both circle A and circle B? _____

_____

A–108   List two other numbers between 1 and 100 that could be placed in both circle A and circle B. _____

FRACTIONAL PARTS

In the box write the fraction that tells what part of the figure is shaded.

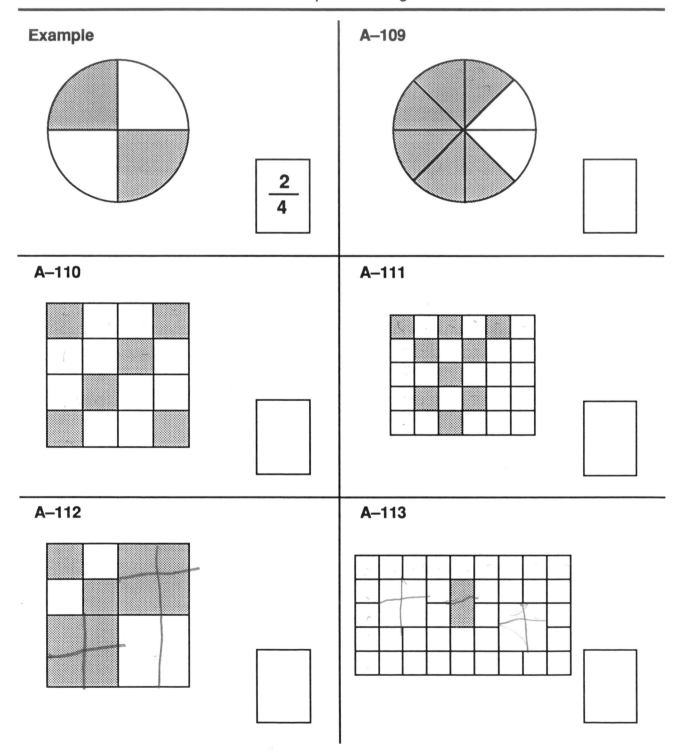

Example

$$\frac{2}{4}$$

A–109

A–110

A–111

A–112

A–113

FRACTIONAL PARTS

Shade each figure to match the given fraction.

Example

$\dfrac{3}{4}$

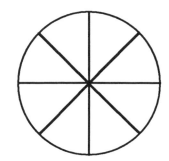

A–114

$\dfrac{5}{8}$

A–115

$\dfrac{7}{12}$

A–116

$\dfrac{2}{3}$

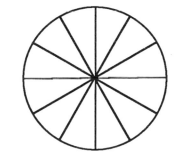

A–117

$\dfrac{3}{8}$

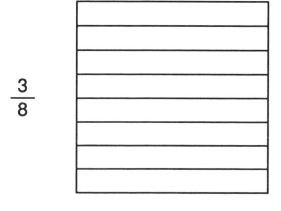

A–118

$\dfrac{3}{5}$

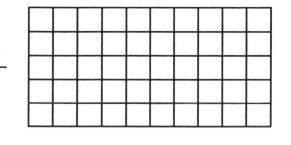

ESTIMATING FRACTIONAL PARTS

Circle the fraction which estimates what part of the figure is shaded.

Example

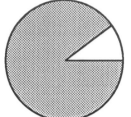

	a.	b.	c.	d.
	$\dfrac{1}{10}$	$\dfrac{1}{5}$	$\dfrac{5}{10}$	$\left(\dfrac{9}{10}\right)$

A–119

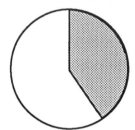

	a.	b.	c.	d.
	$\dfrac{1}{4}$	$\dfrac{2}{4}$	$\dfrac{3}{5}$	$\dfrac{2}{5}$

A–120

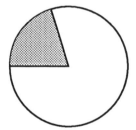

	a.	b.	c.	d.
	$\dfrac{1}{10}$	$\dfrac{1}{4}$	$\dfrac{4}{5}$	$\dfrac{1}{5}$

A–121

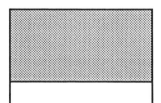

	a.	b.	c.	d.
	$\dfrac{3}{8}$	$\dfrac{3}{4}$	$\dfrac{1}{4}$	$\dfrac{1}{2}$

A–122

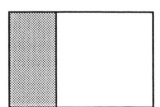

	a.	b.	c.	d.
	$\dfrac{1}{3}$	$\dfrac{1}{4}$	$\dfrac{2}{3}$	$\dfrac{3}{4}$

ESTIMATING FRACTIONAL PARTS

Circle the figure whose shaded part matches the given fraction.

Example

$\dfrac{2}{3}$ a.   b.   c.   d.

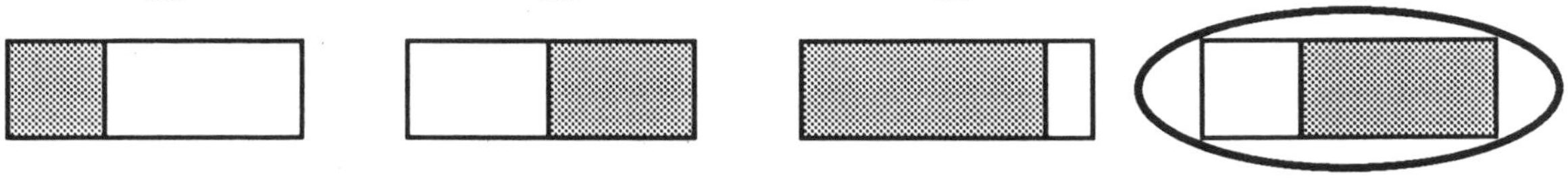

A–123

$\dfrac{3}{8}$ a.   b.   c.   d.

A–124

$\dfrac{1}{4}$ a.   b.   c.   d.

A–125

$\dfrac{7}{8}$ a.   b.   c.   d.

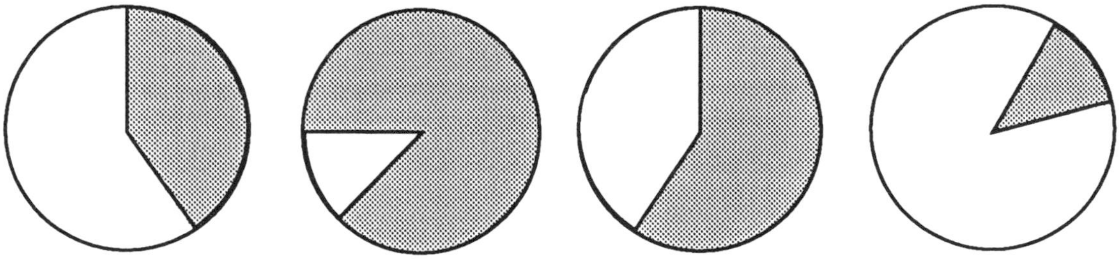

A–126

$\dfrac{3}{10}$ a.   b.   c.   d.

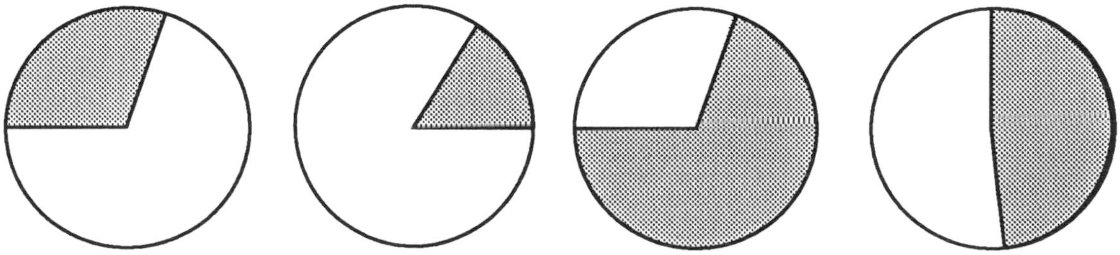

SEQUENCES OF FRACTIONS

Place fractions in the blank spaces to complete the sequence.

Example	$\frac{1}{2}$	$\frac{1}{3}$	$\frac{1}{4}$	$\frac{1}{5}$	$\frac{1}{6}$	$\frac{1}{7}$
A–127	$\frac{5}{6}$	$\frac{5}{7}$	$\frac{5}{8}$	$\frac{5}{9}$	——	——
A–128	$\frac{11}{10}$	$\frac{9}{10}$	$\frac{7}{10}$	$\frac{5}{10}$	——	——
A–129	$\frac{2}{4}$	——	$\frac{6}{8}$	——	$\frac{10}{12}$	$\frac{12}{14}$
A–130	$\frac{1}{2}$	$\frac{2}{3}$	——	$\frac{4}{5}$	——	——
A–131	——	——	$\frac{3}{6}$	$\frac{4}{8}$	$\frac{5}{10}$	$\frac{6}{12}$
A–132	$\frac{1}{3}$	——	$\frac{3}{9}$	——	$\frac{5}{15}$	——
A–133	——	——	$\frac{15}{20}$	$\frac{20}{25}$	$\frac{25}{30}$	$\frac{30}{35}$

SEQUENCES AND PATTERNS OF FRACTIONS

Fill in the blanks with the fractions that complete the sequences or patterns of fractions.

Example

$\frac{1}{2}$	$\frac{1}{4}$	$\frac{1}{6}$	$\frac{1}{8}$	$\frac{1}{10}$
$\frac{2}{4}$	$\frac{2}{8}$	$\frac{2}{12}$	$\frac{2}{16}$	$\frac{2}{20}$

A–134

$\frac{1}{3}$		$\frac{1}{5}$	$\frac{1}{6}$	
$\frac{3}{9}$	$\frac{3}{12}$		$\frac{3}{18}$	

A–135

	$\frac{3}{6}$		$\frac{5}{8}$	$\frac{6}{9}$
	$\frac{6}{12}$	$\frac{8}{14}$		$\frac{12}{18}$

A–136

$\frac{1}{2}$		$\frac{3}{4}$
$\frac{2}{4}$	$\frac{4}{6}$	
$\frac{3}{6}$		$\frac{9}{12}$

A–137

	$\frac{1}{6}$	
$\frac{2}{6}$		$\frac{2}{18}$
	$\frac{3}{18}$	

DECIMAL NUMBERS

A Japanese abacus is pictured below.
The beads above the crossbar have a value of 5; those below the bar have a value of 1.
The dotted line represents the **units** column.
Circle the decimal number that is pictured on the abacus.

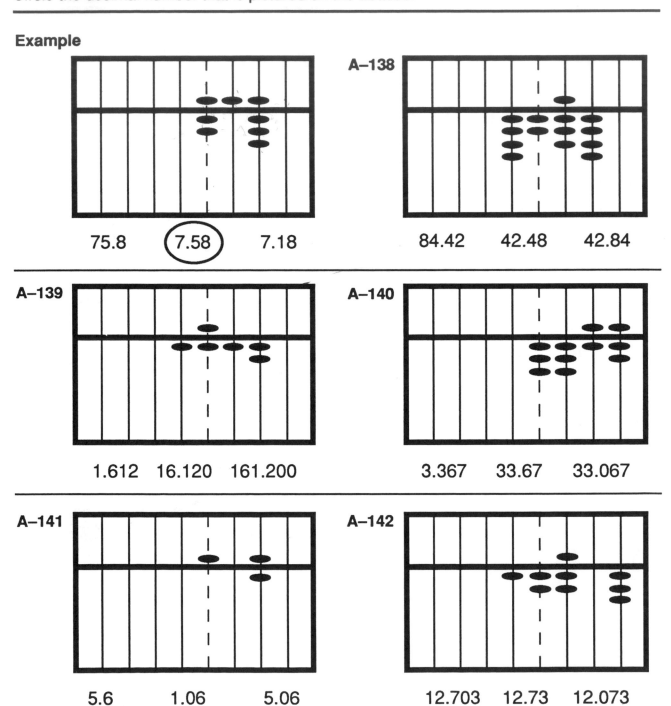

Example

75.8   (7.58)   7.18

A–138

84.42   42.48   42.84

A–139

1.612   16.120   161.200

A–140

3.367   33.67   33.067

A–141

5.6   1.06   5.06

A–142

12.703   12.73   12.073

DECIMAL NUMBERS

A Japanese abacus is pictured below.
The beads above the crossbar have a value of 5; those below the bar have a value of 1.
The dotted line represents the **units** column.
Match the decimal number with the value that is pictured on the abacus.

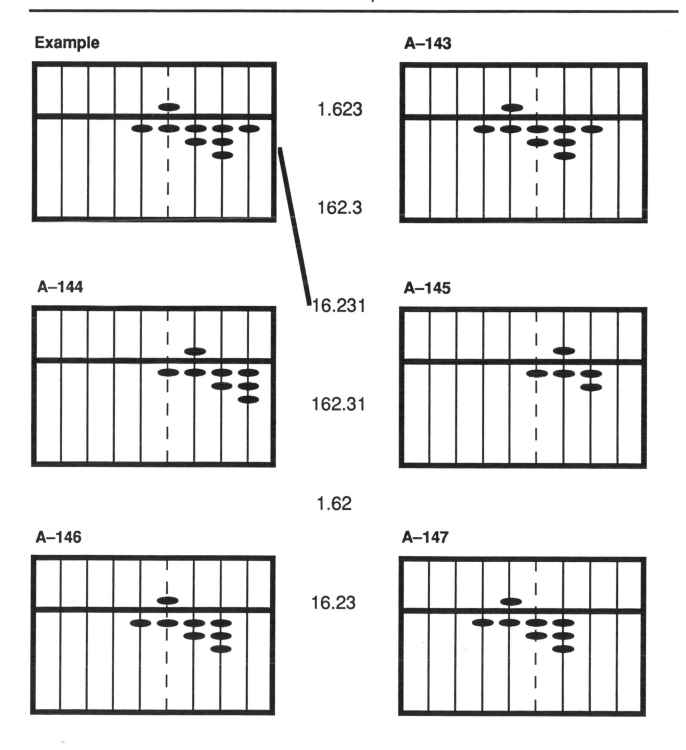

Example

1.623

162.3

A–143

A–144

16.231

A–145

162.31

1.62

A–146

16.23

A–147

DECIMAL NUMBERS

A Japanese abacus is pictured below.
The beads above the crossbar have a value of 5; those below the bar have a value of 1.
The dotted line represents the **units** column.
Write the decimal number that is pictured on the abacus.

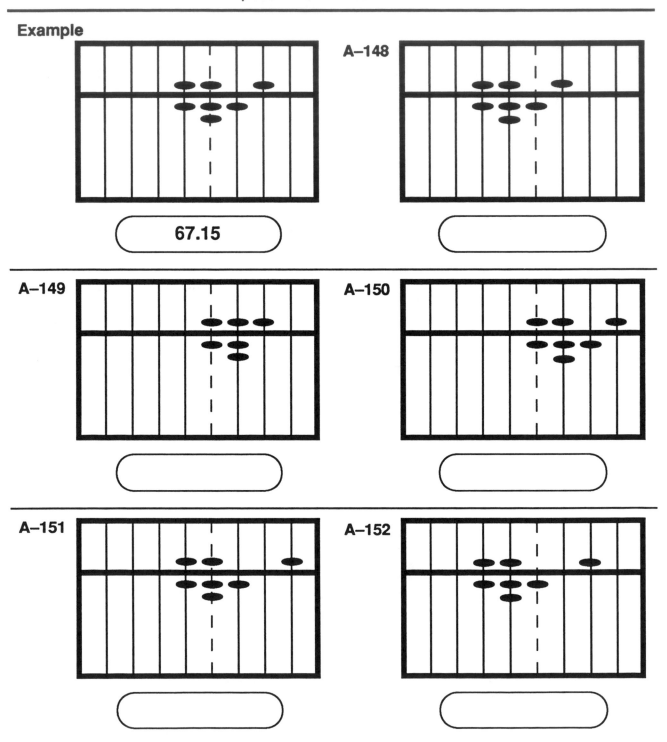

Example

67.15

A–148

A–149

A–150

A–151

A–152

DECIMAL NUMBERS

A Japanese abacus is pictured below.
The beads above the crossbar have a value of 5; those below the bar have a value of 1.
The dotted line represents the **units** column.
Draw beads at the crossbar of each abacus to represent the decimal number in the box.

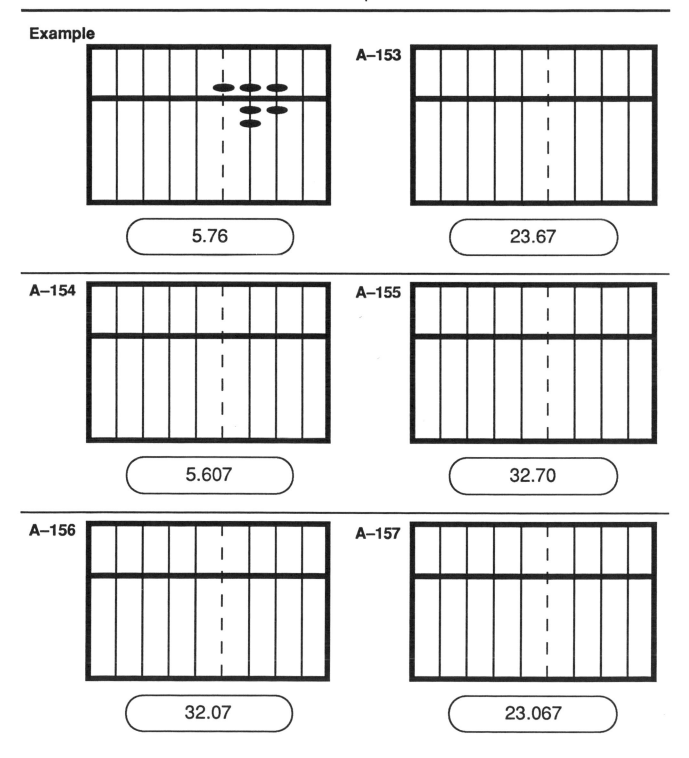

Example

5.76

A–153

23.67

A–154

5.607

A–155

32.70

A–156

32.07

A–157

23.067

DECIMAL NUMBERS

A Japanese abacus is pictured below.
The beads above the crossbar have a value of 5; those below the bar have a value of 1.
The dotted line represents the **units** column.
Draw beads at the crossbar of each abacus to represent the decimal number in the box.

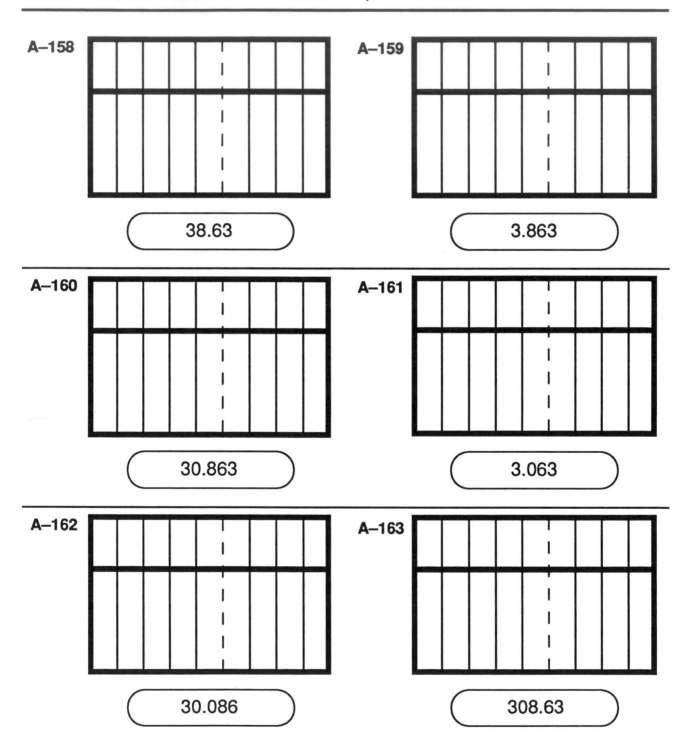

A–158

38.63

A–159

3.863

A–160

30.863

A–161

3.063

A–162

30.086

A–163

308.63

NAMING POINTS ON THE NUMBER LINE

The points on the number line represent consecutive counting numbers.
Fill in the boxes with the correct numbers.

Example

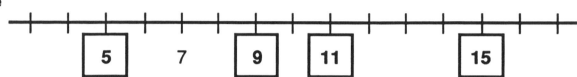

A–164

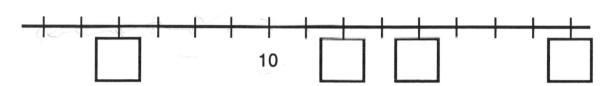

A–165

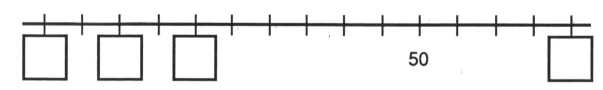

A–166

WHICH NUMBER DOES NOT FIT?

A part of the number line is shown.
Circle all the numbers that do not fit on that part of the number line.

Example

50 60 70

a. 58   b. **(78)**

c. **(48)**   d. 68

A–167

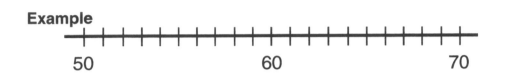

117 127 137

a. 129   b. 201

c. 136   d. 108

A–168

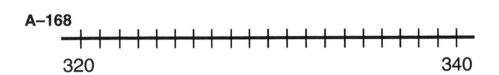

320 340

a. 350   b. 329

c. 318   d. 339

A–169

880 895

a. 950   b. 902

c. 885   d. 897

A–170

1999 2010

a. 2000   b. 1990

c. 2109   d. 1890

A–171

4985 4995

a. 4899   b. 5000

c. 4000   d. 4999

WHAT IS THE NUMBER?

Look at the numbers on the number line.
The arrow is pointing to a missing number.
Write the missing number as a fraction.

Example

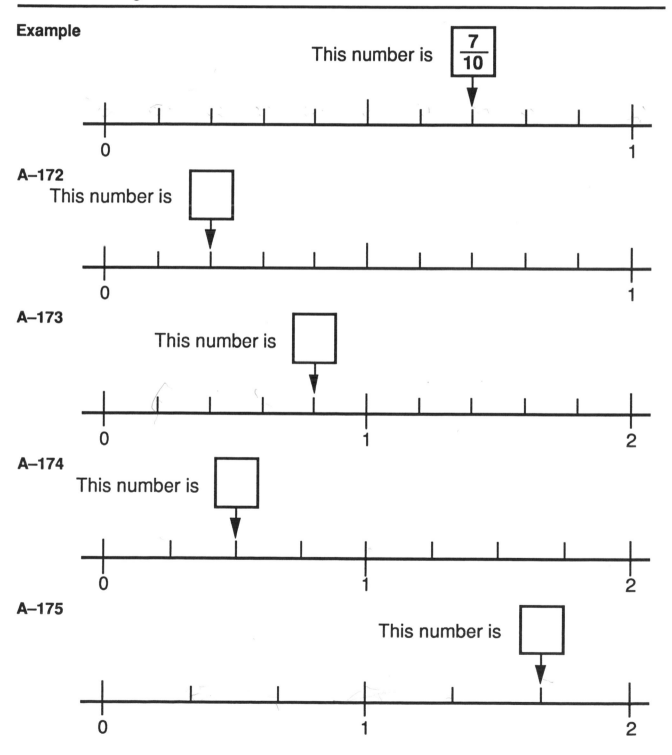

A–172

A–173

A–174

A–175

ESTIMATING WITH FRACTIONS

The arrow indicates a point on the number line.
Circle the number that is closest to that point.

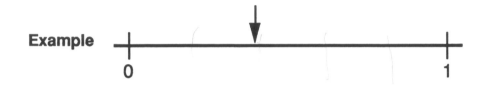

Example

0   1

a. $\frac{1}{2}$ b. $\frac{1}{4}$

c. $\frac{2}{3}$ d. $\frac{2}{5}$

A–176

0   1

a. $1\frac{1}{4}$ b. $\frac{7}{8}$

c. $\frac{7}{10}$ d. $\frac{1}{3}$

A–177

0   1   2

a. $\frac{1}{4}$ b. $1\frac{1}{2}$

c. $\frac{1}{3}$ d. $\frac{2}{4}$

A–178

0   1   2

a. $\frac{1}{3}$ b. $\frac{1}{2}$

c. $\frac{1}{8}$ d. $\frac{2}{3}$

A–179

0   1   2

a. $\frac{1}{2}$ b. $1\frac{3}{6}$

c. $2\frac{1}{2}$ d. $1\frac{1}{4}$

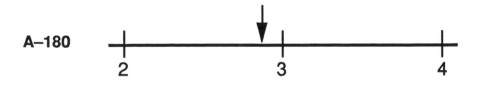

A–180

2   3   4

a. $2\frac{2}{3}$ b. $3\frac{1}{8}$

c. $2\frac{7}{8}$ d. $\frac{9}{10}$

NAMING POINTS ON THE NUMBER LINE

Two numbers appear on each number line.
Write the missing numbers as decimals.

Example

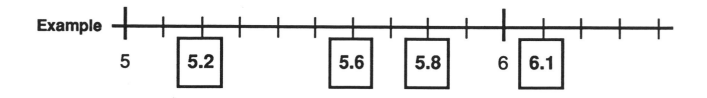

5   **5.2**   **5.6**   **5.8**   6   **6.1**

A–181

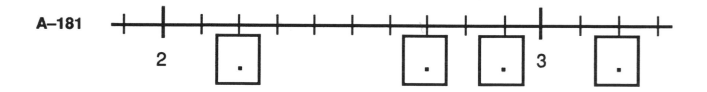

2   .   .   .   3   .

A–182

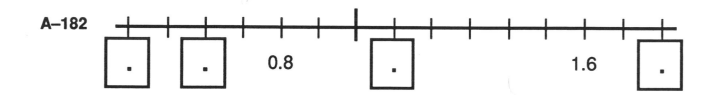

.   .   0.8   .   1.6   .

A–183

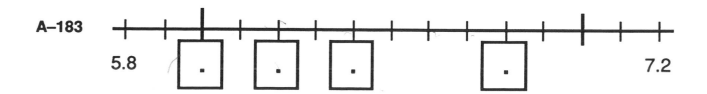

5.8   .   .   .   .   7.2

ESTIMATING WITH DECIMALS

The arrow indicates a point on the number line.
Circle the number that is closest to that point.

Example

a.   8.2   b.   8.8

c.   7.5   d.   (7.8)

A–184

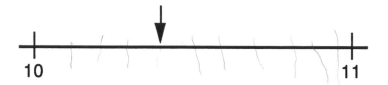

a.   10.1   b.   10.5

c.   10.4   d.   11.6

A–185

a.   23.1   b.   24.5

c.   24.1   d.   23.5

A–186

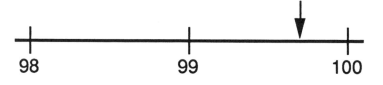

a.   99.7   b.   98.9

c.   100.2   d.   99.5

A–187

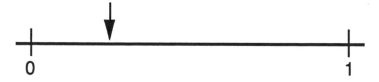

a.   1.25   b.   1.75

c.   0.80   d.   0.25

A–188

a.   45.05   b.   45.50

c.   45.30   d.   46.90

WHOLE NUMBER PLACE VALUE

Write the whole number that is described below.

Example	ten greater than 3,587	**3,597**
A–189	one hundred less than 3,642	_____
A–190	one thousand greater than 6,942	_____
A–191	one hundred less than 4,060	_____
A–192	ten thousand greater than 89,742	_____
A–193	ten less than 408	_____
A–194	one hundred less than 3,009	_____
A–195	ten more than 89,990	_____

DECIMAL NUMBER PLACE VALUE

Write the decimal number that is described below.

Example	one-tenth less than 4.24	__4.14__
A–196	one-hundredth more than 0.087	_____
A–197	one-thousandth less than 3.1415	_____
A–198	one-hundredth more than 2.890	_____
A–199	one hundred less than 710.08	_____
A–200	one-tenth more than 3.99	_____
A–201	one-tenth less than 2.075	_____
A–202	one thousand more than 9,888.088	_____

READING NUMERALS

Circle the numeral that is stated in words.

Example: one thousand, forty-two

1,420   (1,042)   142,000

A–203   two million, eighty thousand, seven hundred five

2,800,705   280,705   2,080,705

A–204   one hundred eighteen and thirty-four hundredths

118,340.0   118.034   118.34

A–205   one and five thousandths

1.050   1.005   0.105

A–206   twenty-six thousand and sixty-two hundredths

26,000.62   26,000.062   2,600.62

A–207   twenty-six thousand, sixty-two

2,600,062   260,062   26,062

A–208   five hundred fifty-five and fifty-five thousandths

555.055   555.550   5,055.055

WRITING NUMERAL NAMES

Write the numerals in words.

Example	29.086	<u>twenty-nine and eighty-six thousandths</u>
A–209	2,084.35	
A–210	25,025.025	
A–211	1.008	
A–212	208,750	
A–213	9.99	
A–214	3.0750	

FRACTIONS – GREATER THAN / LESS THAN

Circle all the fractions that are **greater than** the fraction in the square.

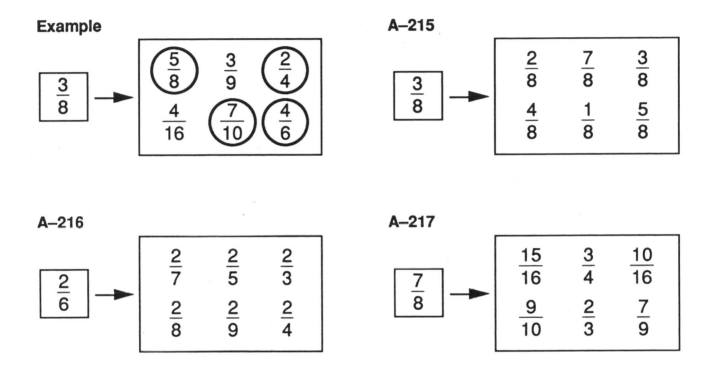

Example

$\frac{3}{8} \rightarrow$

$\frac{5}{8}$	$\frac{3}{9}$	$\frac{2}{4}$
$\frac{4}{16}$	$\frac{7}{10}$	$\frac{4}{6}$

A–215

$\frac{3}{8} \rightarrow$

$\frac{2}{8}$	$\frac{7}{8}$	$\frac{3}{8}$
$\frac{4}{8}$	$\frac{1}{8}$	$\frac{5}{8}$

A–216

$\frac{2}{6} \rightarrow$

$\frac{2}{7}$	$\frac{2}{5}$	$\frac{2}{3}$
$\frac{2}{8}$	$\frac{2}{9}$	$\frac{2}{4}$

A–217

$\frac{7}{8} \rightarrow$

$\frac{15}{16}$	$\frac{3}{4}$	$\frac{10}{16}$
$\frac{9}{10}$	$\frac{2}{3}$	$\frac{7}{9}$

Circle all the fractions that are **less than** the fraction in the square.

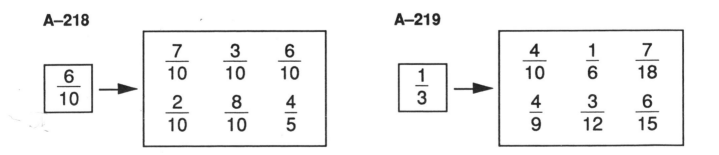

A–218

$\frac{6}{10} \rightarrow$

$\frac{7}{10}$	$\frac{3}{10}$	$\frac{6}{10}$
$\frac{2}{10}$	$\frac{8}{10}$	$\frac{4}{5}$

A–219

$\frac{1}{3} \rightarrow$

$\frac{4}{10}$	$\frac{1}{6}$	$\frac{7}{18}$
$\frac{4}{9}$	$\frac{3}{12}$	$\frac{6}{15}$

FRACTIONS – GREATER THAN / LESS THAN / EQUAL

Write a whole number in the square to make a true statement.

Example

$$\frac{2}{4} > \boxed{\frac{2}{5}}$$

A–220

$$\frac{2}{3} = \frac{\boxed{}}{12}$$

A–221

$$\frac{5}{9} < \frac{\boxed{}}{9}$$

A–222

$$\frac{5}{6} > \frac{\boxed{}}{6}$$

A–223

$$\frac{1}{2} < \frac{\boxed{}}{8}$$

A–224

$$\frac{4}{\boxed{}} > \frac{4}{6}$$

A–225

$$\frac{12}{15} = \frac{\boxed{}}{5}$$

A–226

$$\frac{5}{\boxed{}} < \frac{\boxed{}}{8}$$

DECIMAL NUMBERS – GREATER THAN / LESS THAN

The dotted line on the abacus represents the **units** column.
A decimal number is pictured on the left abacus.
Draw beads on the right abacus to make a number **less than** the given decimal number.
Write the decimal numbers in the boxes.

Example

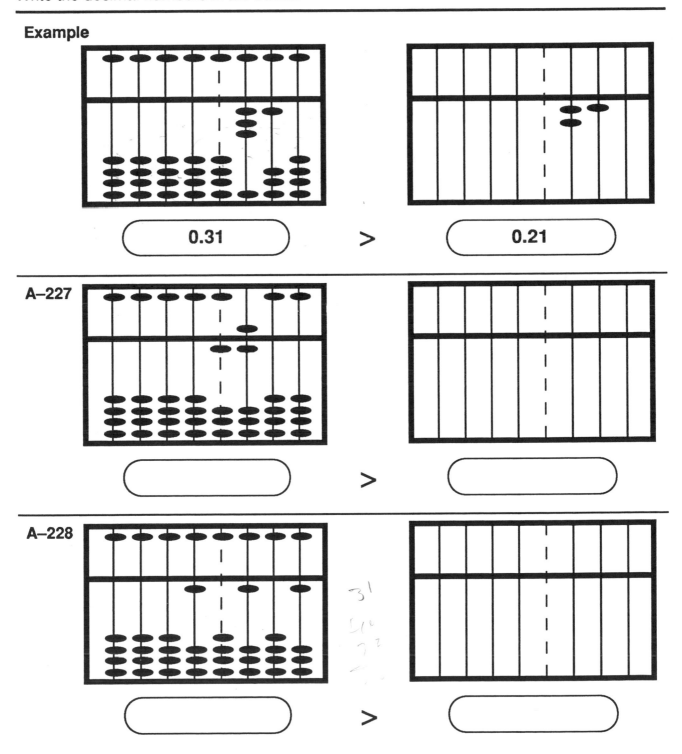

$$0.31 \quad > \quad 0.21$$

A–227

$$> $$

A–228

$$> $$

DECIMAL NUMBERS – GREATER THAN / LESS THAN

Write a digit in each blank to make three different decimal numbers **greater than** the number in the box.

Example	3.819	3.__9__19	3.8__2__0	__4__.819

A–229	0.222	0.2____2	0.22____	0.____3____

A–230	5.869	5.____89	5.8____9	5.____89

Write a digit in each blank to make three different decimal numbers **less than** the number in the box.

A–231	1.31	1.____1	____.31	1.3____

A–232	13.09	1____.09	13.0____	1____.____9

A–233	3.22	3.____4	3.2____	3.____4

FRACTIONS – BETWEEN

Write three different fractions that are between the two given fractions.

			$\frac{1}{6}$	$\frac{1}{5}$	$\frac{1}{4}$
Example	$\frac{1}{7}$	$\frac{1}{3}$			
A–234	$\frac{2}{9}$	$\frac{6}{9}$			
A–235	$\frac{1}{6}$	$\frac{10}{12}$			
A–236	$\frac{2}{8}$	$\frac{3}{4}$			
A–237	$\frac{1}{5}$	$\frac{8}{10}$			
A–238	$\frac{1}{2}$	$\frac{5}{6}$			
A–239	$\frac{1}{4}$	$\frac{1}{2}$			

DECIMAL NUMBERS – BETWEEN

Write three different decimal numbers that are between the two given numbers.

Example	12.49	12.53	**12.50**	**12.51**	**12.52**
A–240	9.98	10.06	_____	_____	_____
A–241	0.49	0.55	_____	_____	_____
A–242	1.4	1.9	_____	_____	_____
A–243	2.108	2.112	_____	_____	_____
A–244	0.4	0.49	_____	_____	_____
A–245	1.5	1.7	_____	_____	_____

ESTIMATING DECIMALS

Circle the number nearest in value to the number in the box.

Example	2.9 →	1	③	30	2	20
A–246	3.4 →	3	30	4	40	2
A–247	0.6 →	0	2	20	1	10
A–248	9.8 →	9	90	8	80	10
A–249	1.2 →	0	1	10	2	12
A–250	6.6 →	6	60	7	70	10
A–251	19.8 →	18	180	19	20	10

ESTIMATING DECIMALS

Circle the number nearest in value to the number in the box.

Example	0.18 →	0.0	0.3	1.0	(0.2)	2.0
A–252	4.75 →	4.0	4.8	5.0	5.8	5.7
A–253	9.09 →	10.0	9.0	9.1	10.1	9.9
A–254	8.91 →	9.0	9.1	8.0	8.9	9.9
A–255	1.24 →	1.4	0.9	10.0	1.0	1.1
A–256	0.99 →	0.1	1.9	10.0	1.5	1.1
A–257	19.49 →	18.0	18.5	19.0	18.4	19.4

ESTIMATING FRACTIONS

The number line shows the location of tenths.

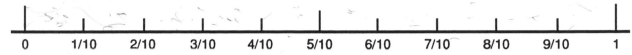

0   1/10   2/10   3/10   4/10   5/10   6/10   7/10   8/10   9/10   1

Circle the fraction nearest in value to the fraction in the box.

Example | $\dfrac{1}{3}$ → | $\dfrac{1}{10}$ | $\dfrac{3}{10}$ | $\dfrac{5}{10}$ | $\dfrac{7}{10}$ | $\dfrac{9}{10}$

A–258 | $\dfrac{5}{12}$ → | $\dfrac{1}{10}$ | $\dfrac{2}{10}$ | $\dfrac{3}{10}$ | $\dfrac{4}{10}$ | $\dfrac{6}{10}$

A–259 | $\dfrac{2}{3}$ → | $\dfrac{3}{10}$ | $\dfrac{5}{10}$ | $\dfrac{7}{10}$ | $\dfrac{8}{10}$ | $\dfrac{9}{10}$

A–260 | $\dfrac{3}{4}$ → | $\dfrac{3}{10}$ | $\dfrac{4}{10}$ | $\dfrac{5}{10}$ | $\dfrac{6}{10}$ | $\dfrac{8}{10}$

A–261 | $\dfrac{4}{5}$ → | $\dfrac{5}{10}$ | $\dfrac{6}{10}$ | $\dfrac{7}{10}$ | $\dfrac{8}{10}$ | $\dfrac{9}{10}$

A–262 | $\dfrac{1}{8}$ → | $\dfrac{1}{10}$ | $\dfrac{3}{10}$ | $\dfrac{4}{10}$ | $\dfrac{6}{10}$ | $\dfrac{8}{10}$

ESTIMATING FRACTIONS

The number line shows the location of some decimal numbers.

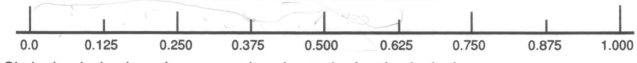

Circle the decimal number nearest in value to the fraction in the box.

Example	$\dfrac{2}{3}$ →	0.250	(0.625)	0.875	0.375
A–263	$\dfrac{1}{4}$ →	0.125	0.375	0.250	0.875
A–264	$\dfrac{1}{5}$ →	0.250	0.875	0.125	0.375
A–265	$\dfrac{3}{8}$ →	0.125	0.375	0.625	0.875
A–266	$\dfrac{9}{10}$ →	0.875	0.125	0.625	0.375
A–267	$\dfrac{8}{10}$ →	0.250	0.625	0.875	0.750

ESTIMATING DECIMAL NUMBERS

Circle the decimal number which best estimates the number of shaded rectangles.

Example

1.7   3.8   **4.3**   4.7

A–268

0.4   2.5   5.2   2.8

A–269

3.0   0.5   3.5   4.0

A–270

3.5   0.6   4.3   5.5

A–271

1.8   0.5   1.2   1.0

ESTIMATING FRACTIONS

Circle the fraction which best estimates the number of shaded rectangles.

Example

$2\frac{1}{2}$　$3\frac{3}{4}$　$\boxed{2\frac{1}{4}}$　2

A–272

$6\frac{7}{8}$　$7\frac{1}{8}$　$\frac{1}{8}$　$7\frac{7}{8}$

A–273

5　$\frac{1}{6}$　1　$1\frac{1}{4}$

A–274

$\frac{7}{18}$　3　$\frac{11}{2}$　$\frac{7}{2}$

A–275

$\frac{3}{4}$　$\frac{1}{4}$　$\frac{9}{4}$　$\frac{3}{10}$

ESTIMATING FRACTIONS

Compare the number of shaded rectangles to the total number of rectangles in each exercise.

Circle the fraction which best estimates the fractional part of the total number of rectangles that is shaded.

Example

$$\frac{11}{16} \qquad 2\frac{1}{2} \qquad \frac{3}{8} \qquad \boxed{\frac{5}{16}}$$

A–276

$$2\frac{1}{2} \qquad \frac{5}{10} \qquad \frac{5}{8} \qquad \frac{3}{5}$$

A–277

$$\frac{1}{3} \qquad 1 \qquad \frac{1}{2} \qquad \frac{2}{3}$$

A–278

$$5\frac{1}{2} \qquad \frac{11}{20} \qquad \frac{9}{20} \qquad \frac{3}{5}$$

A–279

$$\frac{2}{3} \qquad \frac{1}{3} \qquad \frac{1}{2} \qquad 2$$

ESTIMATING FRACTIONS

Circle the fraction which best estimates the part of the rectangle that is shaded.

Example

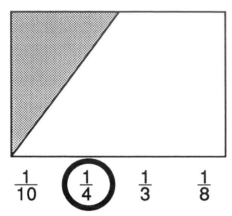

$$\frac{1}{10} \quad \left(\frac{1}{4}\right) \quad \frac{1}{3} \quad \frac{1}{8}$$

A–280

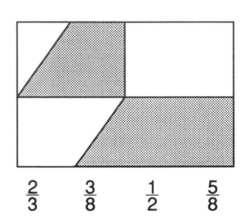

$$\frac{2}{3} \quad \frac{3}{8} \quad \frac{1}{2} \quad \frac{5}{8}$$

A–281

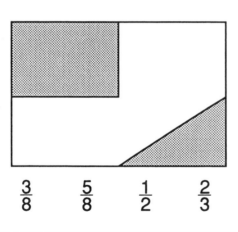

$$\frac{3}{8} \quad \frac{5}{8} \quad \frac{1}{2} \quad \frac{2}{3}$$

A–282

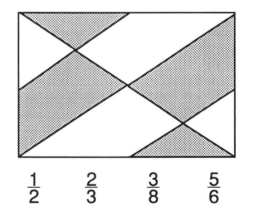

$$\frac{1}{2} \quad \frac{2}{3} \quad \frac{3}{8} \quad \frac{5}{6}$$

A–283

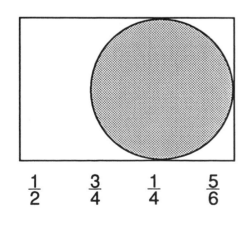

$$\frac{1}{2} \quad \frac{3}{4} \quad \frac{1}{4} \quad \frac{5}{6}$$

A–284

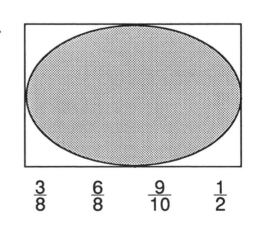

$$\frac{3}{8} \quad \frac{6}{8} \quad \frac{9}{10} \quad \frac{1}{2}$$

EQUIVALENT FRACTIONS

Circle all the fractions that tell what part of the figure is shaded.

Example

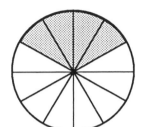

a. $\frac{4}{8}$ b. $\frac{4}{12}$

c. $\frac{4}{6}$ d. $\frac{1}{3}$

A–285

a. $\frac{2}{4}$ b. $\frac{1}{3}$

c. $\frac{2}{6}$ d. $\frac{2}{3}$

A–286

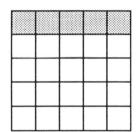

a. $\frac{1}{4}$ b. $\frac{5}{25}$

c. $\frac{5}{20}$ d. $\frac{1}{5}$

A–287

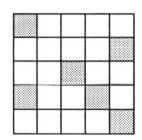

a. $\frac{6}{19}$ b. $\frac{6}{25}$

c. $\frac{1}{5}$ d. $\frac{60}{100}$

A–288

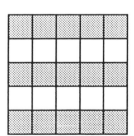

a. $\frac{3}{5}$ b. $\frac{2}{3}$

c. $\frac{20}{25}$ d. $\frac{15}{25}$

A–289

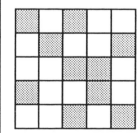

a. $\frac{10}{15}$ b. $\frac{10}{25}$

c. $\frac{2}{5}$ d. $\frac{40}{100}$

EQUIVALENT FRACTIONS

In each row circle all the fractions that are equivalent to the fraction in the box.

Example $\boxed{\dfrac{1}{4}} \longrightarrow$ $\dfrac{1}{8}$ $\dfrac{2}{4}$ $\boxed{\dfrac{2}{8}}$ $\dfrac{1}{2}$ $\boxed{\dfrac{5}{20}}$

A–290 $\boxed{\dfrac{2}{3}} \longrightarrow$ $\dfrac{2}{6}$ $\dfrac{6}{9}$ $\dfrac{4}{9}$ $\dfrac{4}{6}$ $\dfrac{6}{12}$

A–291 $\boxed{\dfrac{5}{6}} \longrightarrow$ $\dfrac{5}{10}$ $\dfrac{5}{12}$ $\dfrac{10}{12}$ $\dfrac{3}{6}$ $\dfrac{15}{24}$

A–292 $\boxed{\dfrac{6}{8}} \longrightarrow$ $\dfrac{6}{12}$ $\dfrac{9}{12}$ $\dfrac{3}{4}$ $\dfrac{12}{24}$ $\dfrac{12}{16}$

A–293 $\boxed{\dfrac{2}{10}} \longrightarrow$ $\dfrac{2}{5}$ $\dfrac{1}{5}$ $\dfrac{1}{10}$ $\dfrac{3}{20}$ $\dfrac{5}{25}$

A–294 $\boxed{\dfrac{3}{10}} \longrightarrow$ $\dfrac{3}{20}$ $\dfrac{6}{10}$ $\dfrac{6}{50}$ $\dfrac{9}{30}$ $\dfrac{30}{100}$

EQUIVALENT FRACTIONS

Each set contains four equivalent fractions.
Place an **X** on all the fractions that are not equivalent to those in the set.

Example

$\{\dfrac{4}{6}, \dfrac{6}{9}, \dfrac{12}{18}, \dfrac{16}{24}\}$

a. $\dfrac{10}{15}$ b. $\cancel{\dfrac{9}{12}}$

c. $\cancel{\dfrac{6}{12}}$ d. $\dfrac{2}{3}$

A–295

$\{\dfrac{4}{5}, \dfrac{12}{15}, \dfrac{20}{25}, \dfrac{24}{30}\}$

a. $\dfrac{8}{10}$ b. $\dfrac{8}{20}$

c. $\dfrac{15}{20}$ d. $\dfrac{28}{35}$

A–296

$\{\dfrac{5}{8}, \dfrac{20}{32}, \dfrac{15}{24}, \dfrac{25}{40}\}$

a. $\dfrac{30}{48}$ b. $\dfrac{25}{64}$

c. $\dfrac{5}{16}$ d. $\dfrac{10}{16}$

A–297

$\{\dfrac{8}{10}, \dfrac{24}{30}, \dfrac{12}{15}, \dfrac{40}{50}\}$

a. $\dfrac{4}{5}$ b. $\dfrac{4}{10}$

c. $\dfrac{16}{20}$ d. $\dfrac{20}{25}$

A–298

$\{\dfrac{5}{10}, \dfrac{10}{20}, \dfrac{4}{8}, \dfrac{15}{30}\}$

a. $\dfrac{3}{4}$ b. $\dfrac{6}{12}$

c. $\dfrac{10}{15}$ d. $\dfrac{1}{2}$

DECIMAL NUMBERS

Circle the decimal number that tells what part of the figure is shaded.

Example

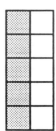

a. 0.1   b. 0.2

c. 0.5   d. 0.4

A–299

a. 0.4   b. 0.3

c. 0.2   d. 0.6

A–300

a. 0.7   b. 0.5

c. 0.2   d. 0.3

A–301

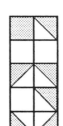

a. 0.3   b. 0.7

c. 0.4   d. 0.6

A–302

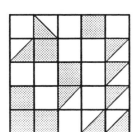

a. 0.60   b. 0.20

c. 0.40   d. 0.14

A–303

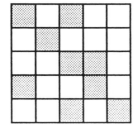

a. 0.90   b. 0.18

c. 0.36   d. 0.64

DECIMAL NUMBERS

Each large square represents one unit.
Shade a portion of the figure to match the decimal number.

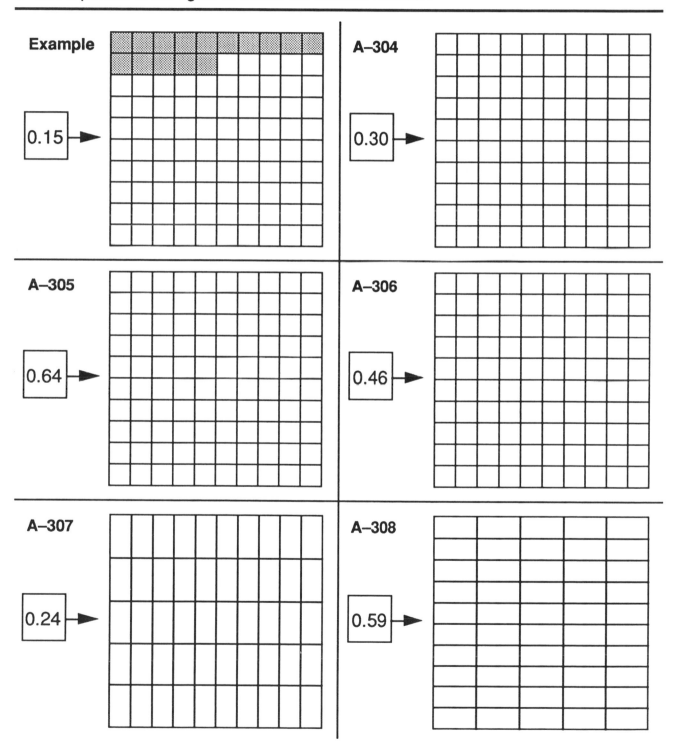

FRACTIONS AND DECIMAL NUMBERS

Circle all the decimal numbers and fractions that tell what part of the figure is shaded.

Example

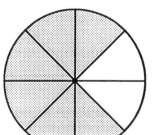

a. $\dfrac{4}{6}$ b. $\boxed{\dfrac{2}{5}}$

c. $\boxed{0.4}$ d. $\boxed{\dfrac{8}{20}}$

A–309

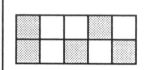

a. $\dfrac{1}{2}$ b. $\dfrac{4}{10}$

c. $\dfrac{5}{10}$ d. 0.5

A–310

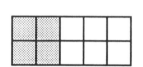

a. $\dfrac{4}{10}$ b. 0.4

c. $\dfrac{2}{5}$ d. 0.04

A–311

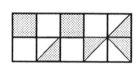

a. $\dfrac{11}{100}$ b. 0.5

c. $\dfrac{3}{10}$ d. $\dfrac{1}{2}$

A–312

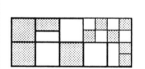

a. 0.8 b. 0.75

c. $\dfrac{6}{8}$ d. $\dfrac{3}{4}$

A–313

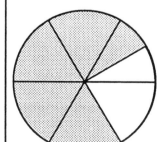

a. $\dfrac{2}{3}$ b. $\dfrac{9}{12}$

c. 0.75 d. $\dfrac{3}{4}$

FRACTIONS AND DECIMAL NUMBERS

The figure in each exercise represents one unit.
Shade a portion of the figure to match the number in the box.

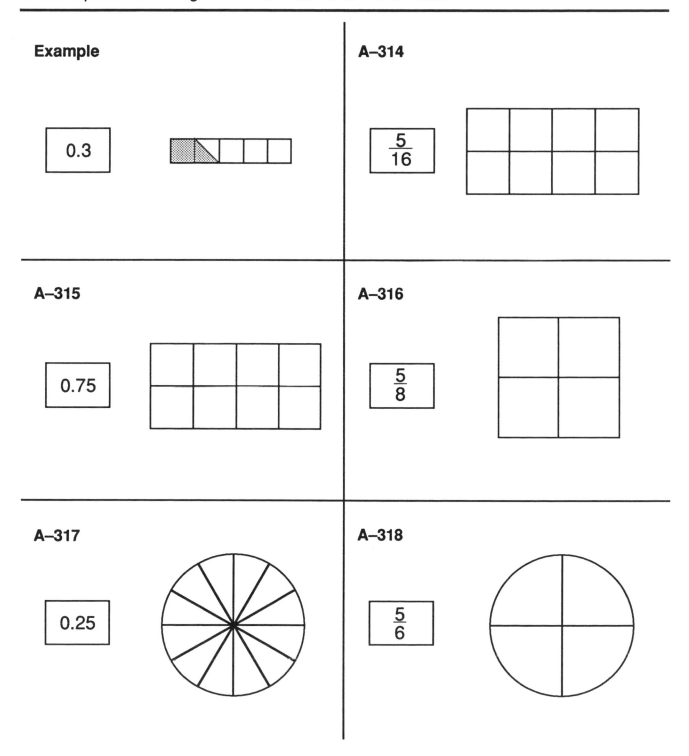

FRACTIONS AND DECIMAL NUMBERS

Circle the decimal number that is equal to the fraction.

Example

$\frac{3}{4}$

7.5	1.33
0.075	(0.75)

A–319

$\frac{5}{8}$

0.0625	0.625
1.60	6.25

A–320

$\frac{3}{2}$

0.15	0.015
0.666	1.5

A–321

$\frac{4}{16}$

0.025	4.00
0.25	2.5

A–322

$2\frac{1}{5}$

0.454	2.2
0.022	0.22

A–323

$\frac{9}{12}$

1.333	7.5
0.075	0.75

FRACTIONS AND DECIMAL NUMBERS

Circle all the fractions that are equal to the decimal number.

Example

0.5

$$\frac{1}{3} \qquad \frac{4}{20} \qquad \frac{4}{7}$$

$$\boxed{\frac{1}{2}} \qquad \frac{5}{25} \qquad \boxed{\frac{5}{10}}$$

A–324

0.75

$$\frac{7}{10} \qquad \frac{3}{4} \qquad \frac{5}{10}$$

$$\frac{6}{8} \qquad \frac{1}{2} \qquad \frac{75}{100}$$

A–325

0.35

$$\frac{3}{10} \qquad \frac{35}{100} \qquad \frac{5}{100}$$

$$\frac{14}{40} \qquad \frac{7}{20} \qquad \frac{35}{10}$$

A–326

0.875

$$\frac{7}{8} \qquad \frac{5}{100} \qquad \frac{85}{100}$$

$$\frac{15}{16} \qquad \frac{85}{10} \qquad \frac{875}{1000}$$

A–327

3.2

$$\frac{32}{10} \qquad 3\frac{1}{5} \qquad \frac{320}{100}$$

$$\frac{32}{100} \qquad 3\frac{2}{10} \qquad 3\frac{2}{5}$$

A–328

1.25

$$1\frac{1}{4} \qquad \frac{125}{100} \qquad 1\frac{1}{2}$$

$$1\frac{25}{100} \qquad \frac{3}{2} \qquad \frac{5}{4}$$

FRACTIONS AND DECIMAL NUMBERS

Circle all the values that are equal to the number in the box.

Example	$\boxed{\dfrac{3}{4}}$	$\boxed{0.75}$	7.5	$\boxed{\dfrac{6}{8}}$	$\boxed{\dfrac{9}{12}}$	0.075
A–329	$\boxed{\dfrac{5}{8}}$	$\dfrac{10}{15}$	$\dfrac{14}{16}$	6.25	0.625	0.0625
A–330	$\boxed{0.45}$	$\dfrac{9}{20}$	$\dfrac{4}{10}$	$\dfrac{45}{100}$	$\dfrac{45}{10}$	4.50
A–331	$\boxed{4.6}$	$\dfrac{46}{10}$	4.60	$\dfrac{46}{100}$	$4\dfrac{6}{10}$	0.46
A–332	$\boxed{\dfrac{9}{5}}$	0.18	$1\dfrac{4}{5}$	$1\dfrac{8}{10}$	1.8	18.0
A–333	$\boxed{0.375}$	$\dfrac{375}{1000}$	3.75	$\dfrac{3}{8}$	$\dfrac{5}{16}$	0.3750
A–334	$\boxed{2\dfrac{3}{20}}$	$\dfrac{43}{20}$	21.5	2.15	$\dfrac{23}{20}$	0.215
A–335	$\boxed{\dfrac{195}{100}}$	1.95	$\dfrac{195}{10}$	$1\dfrac{9}{20}$	$1\dfrac{95}{100}$	0.195

CONSTRUCTING FIGURES

Eight points are labeled on each geoboard design.
Draw the figure that is the union of the segments listed.

Example $\overline{GI}, \overline{IC}, \overline{BC}, \overline{GB}$

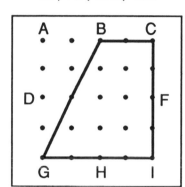

B–1 $\overline{BC}, \overline{GH}, \overline{BG}, \overline{HC}$

B–2 $\overline{HC}, \overline{CA}, \overline{HG}, \overline{GA}$

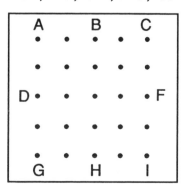

B–3 $\overline{HC}, \overline{IH}, \overline{CI}$

B–4 $\overline{GI}, \overline{BC}, \overline{GB}, \overline{HC}, \overline{CI}$

B–5 $\overline{AC}, \overline{CI}, \overline{IG}, \overline{AG}, \overline{BG}, \overline{CH}$

CONSTRUCTING FIGURES

Draw the figure that is the union of Figures 1, 2, and 3.
Name any triangles in the completed figure that are not already listed.

Example

Figure 1: triangle GHB

Figure 2: triangle CIH

Figure 3: quadrilateral   BCIH

Name the triangles: __**Triangle CBH**__

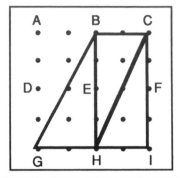

B–6

Figure 1: quadrilateral GICB

Figure 2: triangle GIC

Figure 3: triangle   GHC

Name the triangles: _____

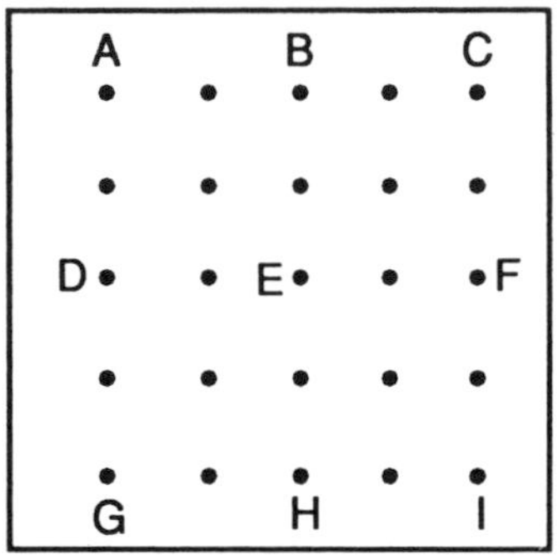

B–7

Figure 1: triangle ACI

Figure 2: triangle GAE

Figure 3: triangle   ACE

Name the triangles: _____

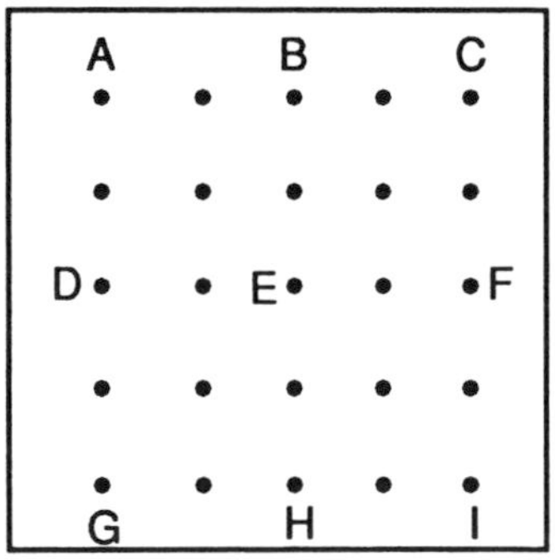

B–8

Figure 1: triangle GAC

Figure 2: triangle IAC

Figure 3: triangle   GIA

Name the triangles: _____

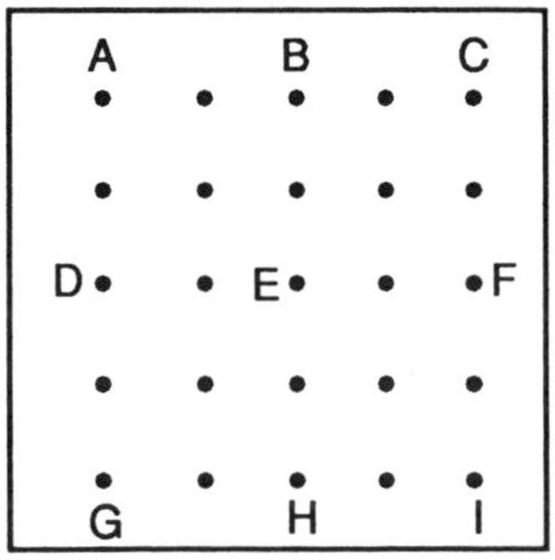

COMPARING LENGTHS

Circle the letter of each statement that is true.

Example

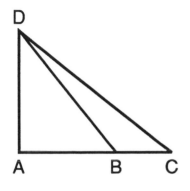

Figure DAC is a right triangle.

a. $\overline{DC}$ is longer than $\overline{AD}$.　**b.** $\overline{AB}$ is shorter than $\overline{DB}$.

c. $\overline{DB}$ is shorter than $\overline{AD}$.　**d.** $\overline{DC}$ is longer than $\overline{BD}$.

e. $\overline{BC}$ is shorter than $\overline{AC}$.　f. $\overline{AC}$ is shorter than $\overline{AB}$.

B–9

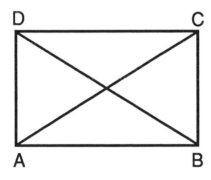

Figure ABCD is a rectangle.

a. $\overline{AD}$ is congruent to $\overline{BC}$.　b. $\overline{AC}$ is longer than $\overline{BD}$.

c. $\overline{AB}$ is shorter than $\overline{BC}$.　d. $\overline{AB}$ is shorter than $\overline{BD}$.

e. $\overline{AC}$ is shorter than $\overline{BC}$.　f. $\overline{AB}$ is congruent to $\overline{DC}$.

B–10

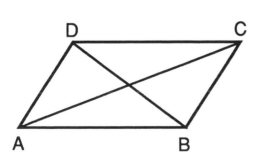

Figure ABCD is a parallelogram.

a. $\overline{AD}$ is longer than $\overline{AB}$.　b. $\overline{BD}$ is longer than $\overline{BC}$.

c. $\overline{AB}$ is shorter than $\overline{AC}$.　d. $\overline{AD}$ is congruent to $\overline{BC}$.

e. $\overline{AB}$ is shorter than $\overline{DC}$.　f. $\overline{AC}$ is congruent to $\overline{BD}$.

COMPARING PATHS

Use X's to indicate the shortest path from A to B.

Example

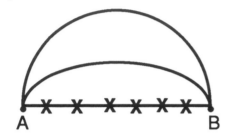

B–11

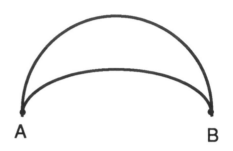

B–12

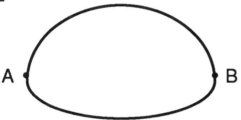

B–13

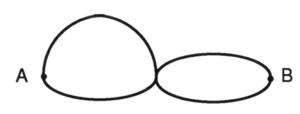

B–14

B–15

B–16

B–17

COMPARING LENGTHS

The center of each circle is "O."
Circle the letter in front of each statement that is true.

Example

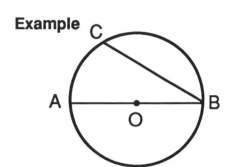

a. $\overline{AB}$ is longer than $\overline{CB}$. b. $\overline{BC}$ is shorter than $\overarc{BC}$.

c. $\overline{OB}$ is longer than $\overline{CB}$. d. $\overarc{AC}$ is longer than $\overarc{BC}$.

e. $\overline{AO}$ is congruent to $\overline{OB}$. f. $\overline{AB}$ is equal to $\overarc{AB}$.

B–18

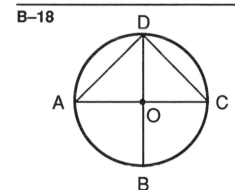

$\overline{AC}$ and $\overline{BD}$ are perpendicular line segments.

a. $\overline{CD}$ is congruent to $\overarc{CD}$. b. $\overline{AC}$ is congruent to $\overline{BD}$.

c. $\overline{AD}$ is congruent to $\overline{DC}$. d. $\overline{AD}$ is shorter than $\overarc{DC}$.

e. $\overline{AD}$ is longer than $\overarc{AD}$. f. $\overline{AO}$ is congruent to $\overline{OD}$.

B–19

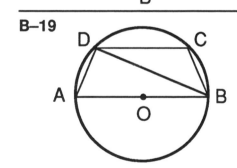

ABCD is an isosceles trapezoid.

a. $\overline{AB}$ is shorter than $\overline{BD}$. b. $\overline{DC}$ is shorter than $\overarc{DC}$.

c. $\overline{DC}$ is congruent to $\overline{AB}$. d. $\overline{AD}$ is congruent to $\overline{CB}$.

e. $\overarc{AD}$ is shorter than $\overarc{CB}$. f. $\overline{AD}$ is congruent to $\overarc{DC}$.

B–20

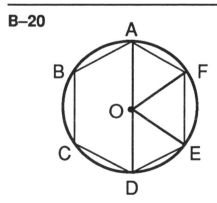

The six points are equally spaced around the circle.

a. $\overline{OD}$ is shorter than $\overline{OF}$. b. $\overline{AD}$ is shorter than $\overline{BC}$.

c. $\overline{AB}$ is congruent to $\overline{CD}$. d. $\overarc{AB}$ is congruent to $\overarc{CD}$.

e. $\overline{AO}$ is longer than $\overline{OE}$. f. $\overline{CD}$ is shorter than $\overarc{AB}$.

COMPARING LENGTHS

The center of each circle is "O."
Circle the letter in front of each statement that is true.

Example

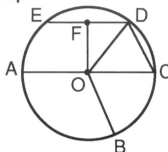

$\overline{AC}$ is parallel to $\overline{ED}$.

a. $\overline{OD}$ is congruent to $\overline{OB}$.   b. $\overline{OF}$ is shorter than $\overline{OD}$.

c. $\overline{AO}$ is congruent to $\overline{OF}$.   d. $\overline{ED}$ is shorter than $\overset{\frown}{ED}$.

e. $\overset{\frown}{AE}$ is congruent to $\overset{\frown}{DC}$.   f. $\overset{\frown}{AE}$ is longer than $\overset{\frown}{DC}$.

B–21

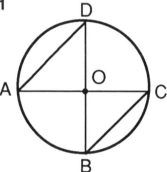

$\overline{AC}$ and $\overline{BD}$ are perpendicular line segments.

a. $\overline{AD}$ is congruent to $\overline{BC}$.   b. $\overline{AO}$ is congruent to $\overline{AD}$.

c. $\overset{\frown}{AD}$ is shorter than $\overset{\frown}{BC}$.   d. $\overline{BD}$ is longer than $\overline{AC}$.

e. $\overset{\frown}{BC}$ is longer than $\overline{AD}$.   f. $\overset{\frown}{DC}$ is shorter than $\overset{\frown}{AB}$.

B–22

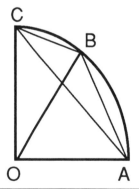

$\overset{\frown}{AC}$ is $\frac{1}{4}$ of a circle with the center at "O."

a. $\overline{OC}$ is shorter than $\overline{AC}$.   b. $\overset{\frown}{AC}$ is longer than $\overline{AC}$.

c. $\overline{AB}$ is congruent to $\overline{BC}$.   d. $\overline{AB}$ is congruent to $\overset{\frown}{BC}$.

e. $\overline{AC}$ is shorter than $\overset{\frown}{AB}$.   f. $\overline{OB}$ is longer than $\overline{OC}$.

B–23

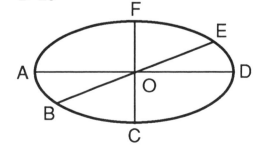

The curved figure is an ellipse.

a. $\overline{OF}$ is longer than $\overline{AO}$.   b. $\overline{OF}$ is congruent to $\overline{OE}$.

c. $\overline{AD}$ is shorter than $\overline{FC}$.   d. $\overline{AD}$ is longer than $\overline{BE}$.

e. $\overline{BO}$ is shorter than $\overline{OD}$.   f. $\overline{BO}$ is congruent to $\overline{OF}$.

COMPARING CHORDS

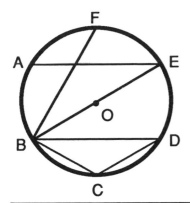

The center of the circle is "O."
The six other points are equally spaced around the circle.
Six chords connect these points.

Example   Name the longest chord in the circle.   **BE**

B–24   Name the shortest chord in the circle.   _____

B–25   Name a diameter of the circle.   _____

B–26   Name two radii of the circle.   _____

B–27   Name a chord the same length as $\overline{BC}$.   _____

B–28   Name a chord the same length as $\overline{AE}$.   _____

B–29   Name a chord shorter than the path from
B to C to D.   _____

B–30   Name a path longer than the path
from F to B to D.   _____

CONSTRUCTING FIGURES

The six points are equally spaced around the circle.
Draw each figure described using the given six points.

Example

A diameter containing point A

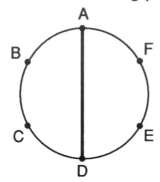

B–31

An equilateral triangle

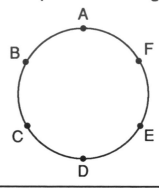

B–32

The longest path using only the points F, B, and C

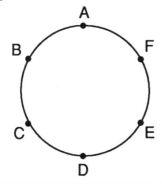

B–33

A rectangle

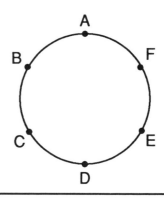

B–34

The longest path using only the points B, C, D, and F

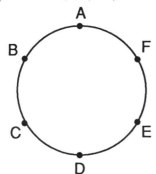

B–35

A scalene triangle

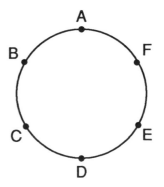

COMPARING ANGLES

Circle the letter in front of each statement that is true.

Example

$\overline{AB}$ and $\overline{DO}$ are perpendicular line segments.

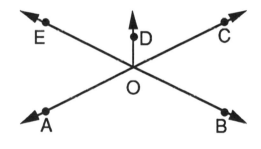

(a.) ∠DOB is congruent to ∠AOD.

(b.) ∠COB is less than ∠DOB.

c. ∠COB is greater than ∠AOD.

(d.) ∠AOC is greater than ∠DOB.

e. ∠DOC is greater than ∠AOD.

B–36

a. ∠COB is congruent to ∠EOA.

b. ∠EOC is less than ∠DOC.

c. ∠AOB is greater than ∠EOD.

d. ∠COB is less than ∠AOB.

e. ∠AOD is less than ∠DOC.

B–37

$\overline{AD}$ and $\overline{BE}$ are perpendicular line segments.

a. ∠COB is greater than ∠DOB.

b. ∠EOD is congruent to ∠DOB.

c. ∠EOF is greater than ∠FOA.

d. ∠AOF is less than ∠DOE.

e. ∠EOC is congruent to ∠BOF.

COMPARING ANGLES

Circle the letter in front of each statement that is true.

Example   Figure ABCD is a rectangle.

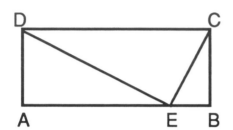

    (a.) ∠DAE is congruent to ∠EBC.

    b. ∠ADE is congruent to ∠ECB.

    (c.) ∠ADC is greater than ∠ADE.

    d. ∠AED is congruent to ∠CEB.

B–38   Figure ABCD is a rectangle and Figure BEO is a right triangle.

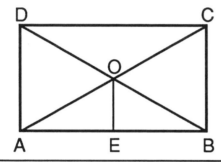

    a. ∠DOC is congruent to ∠COB.

    b. ∠AOD is congruent to ∠COB.

    c. ∠OAE is congruent to ∠OBE.

    d. ∠AEO is less than ∠EBC.

B–39   Figure ABCD is a trapezoid and Figure DAB is a right triangle.

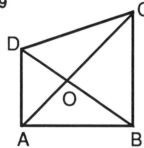

    a. ∠BCD is less than ∠CDA.

    b. ∠DOA is less than ∠COB.

    c. ∠DAB is congruent to ∠ABC.

    d. ∠ABC is greater than ∠CAB.

B–40   Figure CAB is a right triangle.

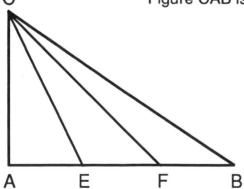

    a. ∠CEA is greater than ∠CFA.

    b. ∠CEF is less than ∠CAE.

    c. ∠CEF is less than ∠CFB.

    d. ∠ACF is greater than ∠ACE.

ISOMETRIC GRIDS

Each array of dots forms an isometric grid.
Connect dots to construct each of the polygons.

Example An equilateral triangle

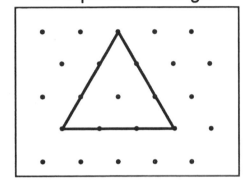

B–41 A right triangle

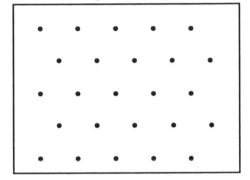

B–42 A regular hexagon

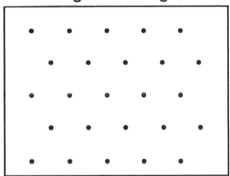

B–43 A rectangle

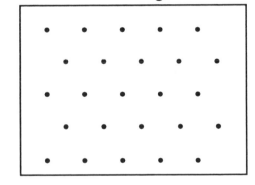

B–44 A trapezoid

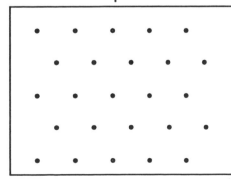

B–45 A parallelogram

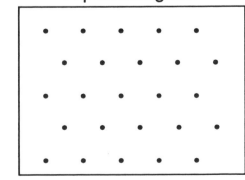

COMPARING ANGLES

Each figure below is shown on an isometric grid.
Circle both angles if they are congruent.
If they are not congruent, circle the greater angle.

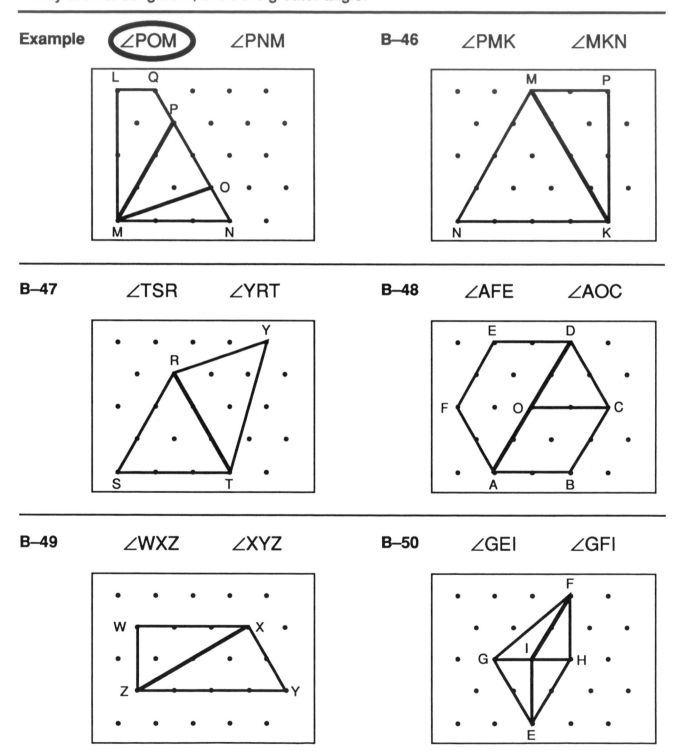

Example   (∠POM)   ∠PNM   **B–46**   ∠PMK   ∠MKN

B–47   ∠TSR   ∠YRT   **B–48**   ∠AFE   ∠AOC

B–49   ∠WXZ   ∠XYZ   **B–50**   ∠GEI   ∠GFI

CONSTRUCTING ANGLES

The quadrilateral ABCD is drawn on the isometric grid. Construct each of the following angles.

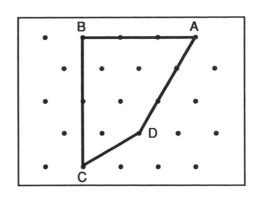

Example   ∠RST, which is the same size as ∠DAB

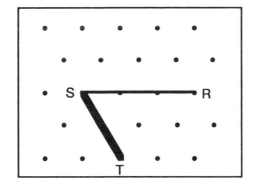

B–51   ∠PQR, which is twice the size of ∠BAD

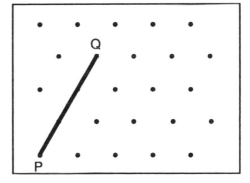

B–52   ∠KLM, which is the same size as ∠ABC

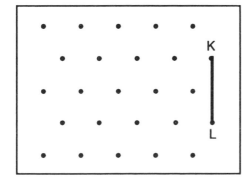

B–53   ∠FGH, which is half the size of ∠BAD

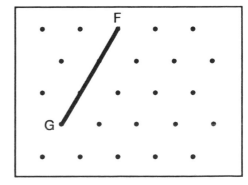

CONSTRUCTING POLYGONS

Each array of dots forms an isometric grid.
Construct the figures described.

Example A trapezoid with $\overline{XY}$ as one of the parallel sides

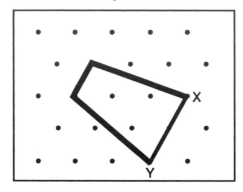

B–54 An equilateral triangle with $\overline{PQ}$ as a side

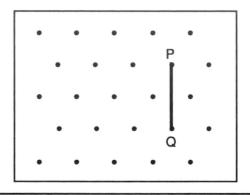

B–55 An isosceles triangle with $\overline{RS}$ as the shortest side

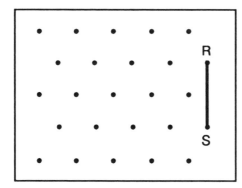

B–56 An equilateral triangle with $\overline{AB}$ as one side

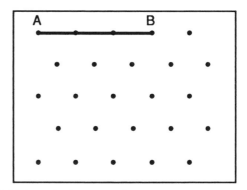

B–57 A scalene triangle with $\overline{MN}$ as one side

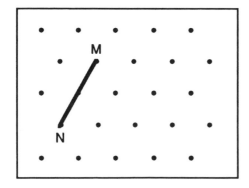

B–58 A right triangle with $\overline{CD}$ as one leg

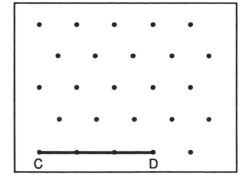

CONSTRUCTING POLYGONS

Each array of dots forms an isometric grid. Using triangle ABC, construct polygons that satisfy each condition.

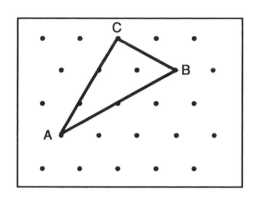

Example   Triangle RST so that the measure of ∠R is twice that of ∠A

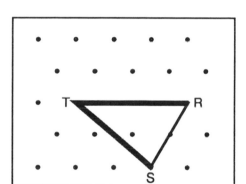

B–59   Triange DEF, which is the same size and shape as triangle ABC

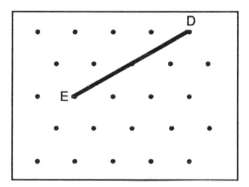

B–60   Triangle LMN so that the measure of ∠L is four times greater than that of ∠A

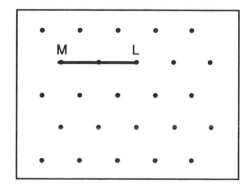

B–61   Isosceles triangle PQR so that the measure of ∠Q is the same as ∠B

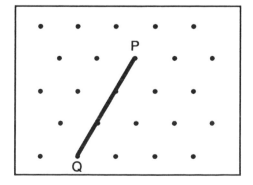

DECOMPOSING POLYGONS

Using diagonals that do not intersect inside the polygon, separate each polygon into the figures listed.

Example Three triangles	**B–62** Three triangles different from those in the Example
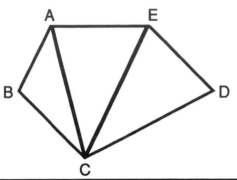	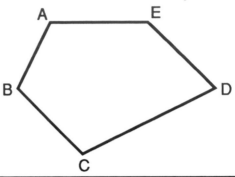

B–63 A quadrilateral and a triangle	**B–64** A quadrilateral and a triangle different from those constructed in B–63
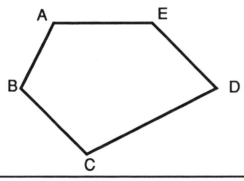	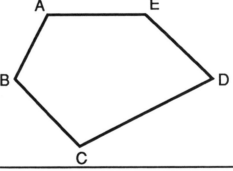

B–65 A quadrilateral and two triangles	**B–66** A quadrilateral and two triangles different from those constructed in B–65
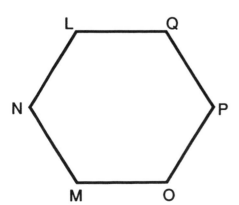	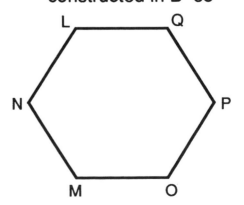

DECOMPOSING POLYGONS

Five numbered figures appear on the geoboard design.
Decompose each polygon into either three or four of these figures.
Number the pieces to match the given figures.

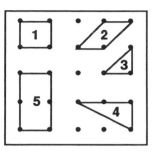

Example

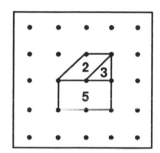

B–67

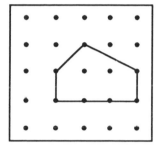

B–68

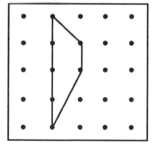

B–69

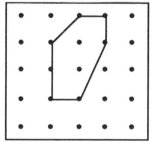

B–70

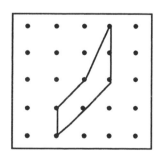

B–71

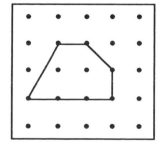

LOCATING POLYGONS

Each polygon has been subdivided into smaller figures.
Each region is identified with a number.
Name the polygon that is formed by combining the indicated regions.

Example

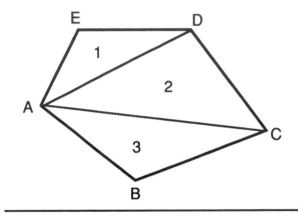

Regions	
1	**triangle**
1 and 2	**quadrilateral**
2 and 3	**quadrilateral**

B–72

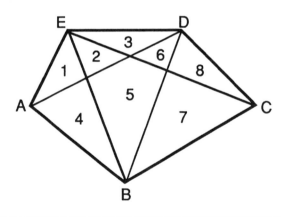

Regions	
1 and 2	
4 and 5	
4, 5, and 7	
3, 6, and 8	
1, 2, 3, 4, 5, and 6	

B–73

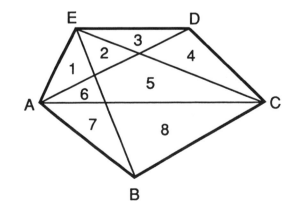

Regions	
5 and 6	
5 and 8	
2, 3, 4, and 5	
4 and 5	
2 and 3	

LOCATING POLYGONS

Each polygon has been subdivided into smaller regions.
Each region is identified with a number.

Example

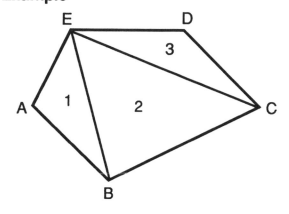

Find two quadrilaterals that can be formed by combining regions.
Name the regions.

1 and 2

2 and 3

B–74

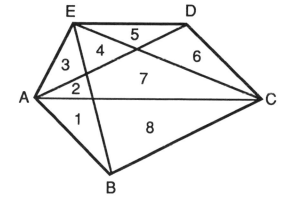

Find four quadrilaterals that can be formed by combining two or more regions.
Name the regions .

_____   _____

_____   _____

B–75

Find four quadrilaterals that can be formed by combining two or more regions.
Name the regions .

_____   _____

_____   _____

MATCHING SHAPES

Select figure a or b or c to complete the shading of the given figure.

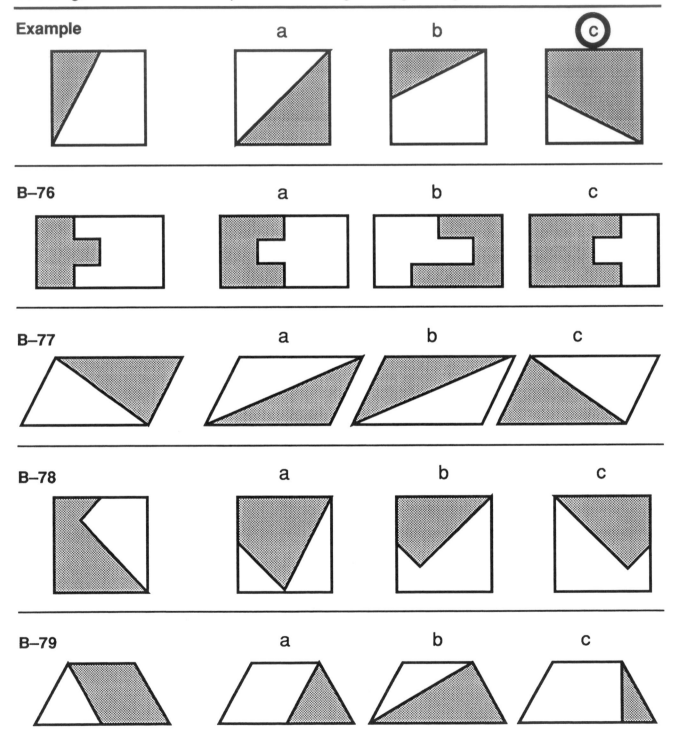

CONGRUENT FIGURES

Compare Figure 1 and Figure 2.

Figure 1

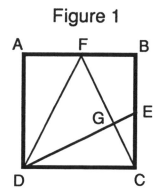

Figure 2

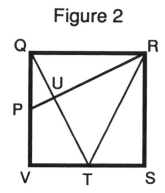

Name a shape in Figure 2 that is congruent to the shape in Figure 1.

Example	Figure 1: △DFC	Figure 2: △**RTQ**
B–80	Figure 1: △ECD	Figure 2: _____
B–81	Figure 1: △FGD	Figure 2: _____
B–82	Figure 1: $\overline{GD}$	Figure 2: _____
B–83	Figure 1: Quadrilateral ABED	Figure 2: _____
B–84	Figure 1: Quadrilateral FDEB	Figure 2: _____

PROPERTIES OF POLYGONS

Place an X inside each polygon that is described by the statement.

Example

A polygon with four congruent sides or four congruent angles.

B–85

A polygon that is not a quadrilateral and has at least one right angle.

B–86

A polygon that has all sides congruent or all angles congruent.

B–87

A polygon that is a parallelogram and is not a rectangle.

PROPERTIES OF POLYGONS

Write the letter of each polygon that is described by the statement.

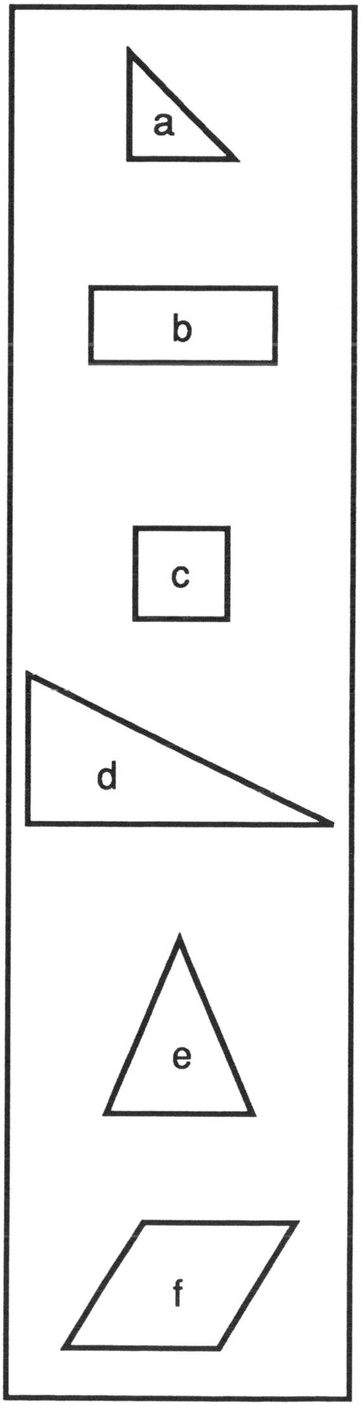

Example

The polygon is a parallelogram and has four congruent sides.

c and f

B–88

The polygon is a triangle and has two congruent sides.

B–89

The polygon is a rectangle and has all sides congruent.

B–90

The polygon is not a parallelogram and has one right angle.

B–91

The polygon is a right triangle and has two congruent sides.

B–92

The polygon is a rhombus and has a right angle.

PROPERTIES OF POLYGONS

Describe the properties of each polygon using the list below.
Write the numbers of the properties below each polygon.

SIDES	ANGLES	PARALLEL
1. all congruent	4. all congruent	7. opposite sides
2. at least two congruent	5. at least two congruent	8. exactly two sides
3. none congruent	6. at least one right	9. no sides

Example

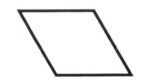

1, 2, 5, 7

B–93

_____

B–94

_____

B–95

_____

B–96

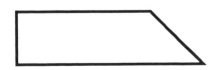

_____

B–97

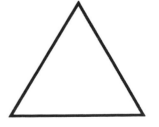

_____

PROPERTIES OF POLYGONS

Draw a polygon that has the properties described.

Example

A polygon that is a parallelogram and has a right angle

B–98

A polygon that is a quadrilateral and has two parallel sides

B–99

A polygon that is a right triangle and has two congruent sides

B–100

A polygon that is a parallelogram and has four congruent sides

B–101

A polygon that is a quadrilateral and has two sets of parallel sides

B–102

A polygon that is a triangle and has exactly two congruent sides

CLASSIFYING POLYGONS

Circle the letter in front of each word that makes the following statement true.

"Pictured is a set of _____."

Underline the word which best describes the set.

Example

a. polygons   b. rectangles
c. quadrilaterals   d. squares
e. parallelograms   f. trapezoids
g. triangles   h. rhombuses
i. regular polygons

B–103

a. polygons   b. rectangles
c. quadrilaterals   d. squares
e. parallelograms   f. trapezoids
g. triangles   h. rhombuses
i. regular polygons

B–104

a. polygons   b. rectangles
c. quadrilaterals   d. squares
e. parallelograms   f. trapezoids
g. triangles   h. rhombuses
i. regular polygons

B–105

a. polygons   b. rectangles
c. quadrilaterals   d. squares
e. parallelograms   f. trapezoids
g. triangles   h. rhombuses
i. regular polygons

PROPERTIES OF POLYGONS

Each polygon belongs in one of the regions in the diagram.
Place the number of the region inside each polygon.

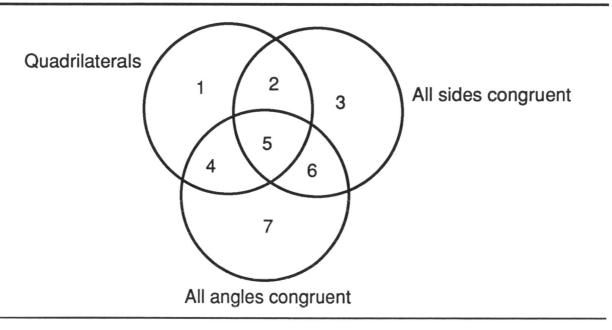

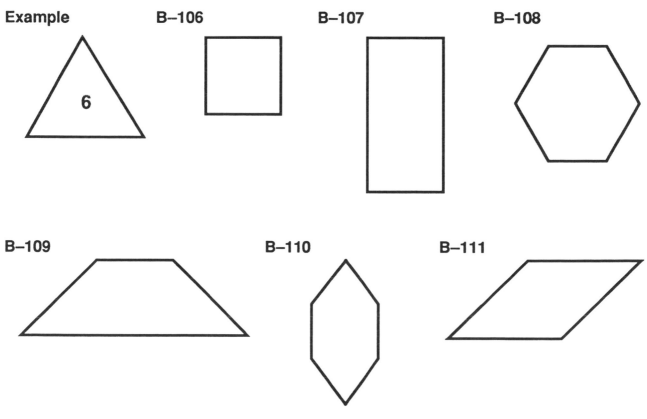

CLASSIFYING POLYGONS

List the numbers of all polygons that fit the following descriptions.

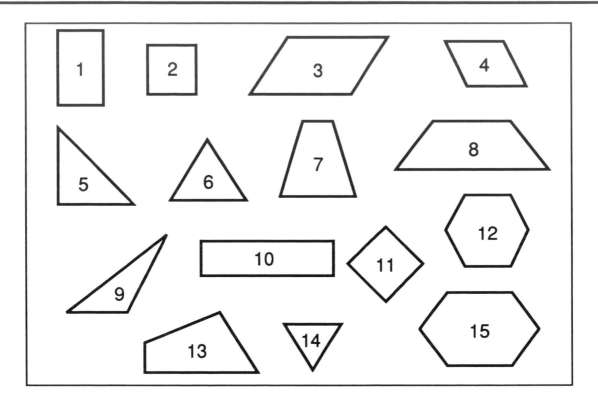

Example

A polygon with at least one pair of parallel sides and an angle greater than a right angle

3, 4, 7, 8, 12, 15

B–112

A parallelogram with no right angles

_____

B–113

A polygon with all sides congruent

_____

B–114

A quadrilateral that has a right angle and no two sides parallel

_____

B–115

A quadrilateral that has at least one pair of parallel sides and is not a rectangle

_____

DESCRIBING SETS OF POLYGONS

Write a description for the set of polygons chosen from those below.

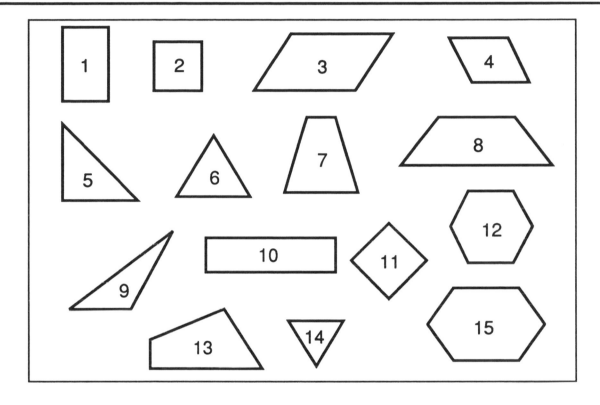

Example   Polygons: 1, 2, 10, 11 __**Quadrilaterals with all right angles**__
                                         (or rectangles)

B–116   Polygons: 5, 6, 14 _____

_____

B–117   Polygons: 1, 2, 5, 10, 11, 13 _____

_____

B–118   Polygons: 12, 15 _____

_____

B–119   Polygons: 2, 4, 11 _____

_____

DIVIDING A SET INTO SUBSETS

Divide the set below into three disjoint subsets.
Describe each subset and list the numbers of the polygons that belong to each set.

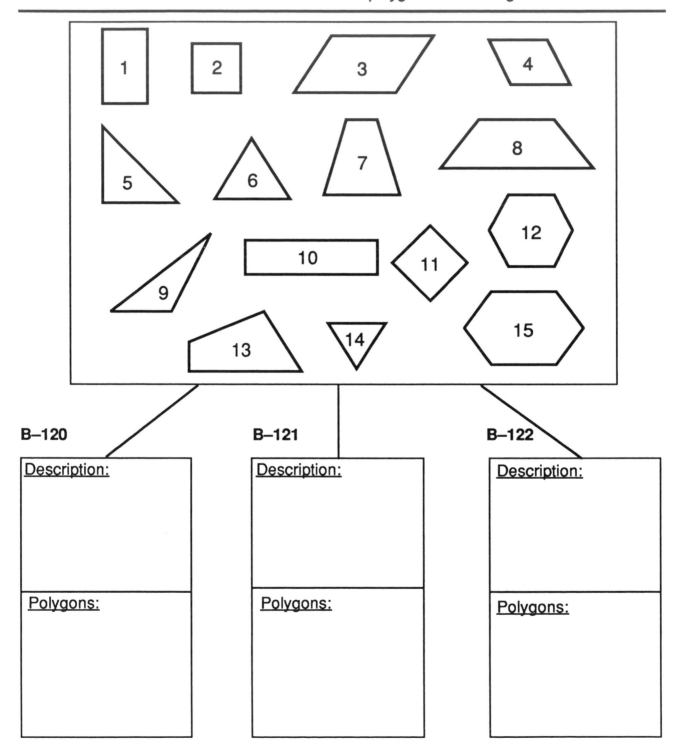

B–120

Description:

Polygons:

B–121

Description:

Polygons:

B–122

Description:

Polygons:

PROPERTIES OF POLYGONS

Each square represents a set of polygons.
Place an X in each region that could be the location of the polygon described.

**All rectangles
are parallelograms.**

Example

A polygon that is not
a parallelogram

B–123

A parallelogram that
is not a rectangle

B–124

A parallelogram that
is a rectangle

B–125

A polygon that is
not a rectangle

B–126

A polygon that is
a paralleolgram

**All squares
are rhombuses.**

B–127

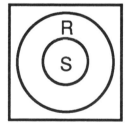

A rhombus that is
a square

B–128

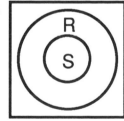

A polygon that is
not a rhombus

B–129

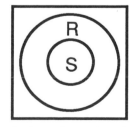

A rhombus that is
not a square

B–130

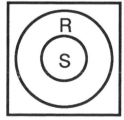

A polygon that is
a rhombus

B–131

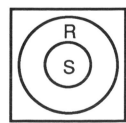

A polygon that is
not a square

PROPERTIES OF POLYGONS

Each rectangle represents a set of polygons.
Write the number of the region into which each polygon should be placed.

Example

Some quadrilaterals (Q)
have all sides congruent(C).

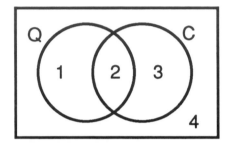

__2__ a. A quadrilateral that is a square

__2__ b. A rhombus that is not a square

__1__ c. A rectangle that is not a square

__4__ d. A hexagon with sides that are not congruent

__3__ e. An equilateral triangle

__1__ f. A parallelogram that is not a rectangle

B–132

Some right triangles (R)
are isosceles triangles (I).

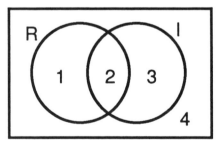

_____ a. A quadrilateral that is a square

_____ b. A right triangle with no congruent sides

_____ c. An isosceles triangle with no right angles

_____ d. An isosceles triangle with one right angle

_____ e. An equilateral triangle

_____ f. A scalene triangle with no right angles

B–133

Some parallelograms (P)
have all angles congruent (C).

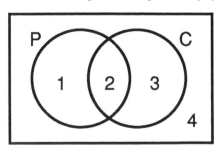

_____ a. A quadrilateral that is a square

_____ b. A quadrilateral that is a trapezoid

_____ c. A rectangle that is not a square

_____ d. A rhombus that is not a square

_____ e. An equilateral triangle

_____ f. A parallelogram that is not a rhombus

SIMILAR FIGURES

Similar figures have the same shape.
Draw a figure on the dot paper that is similar to the given figure.
Make the figure as large as possible.

Example

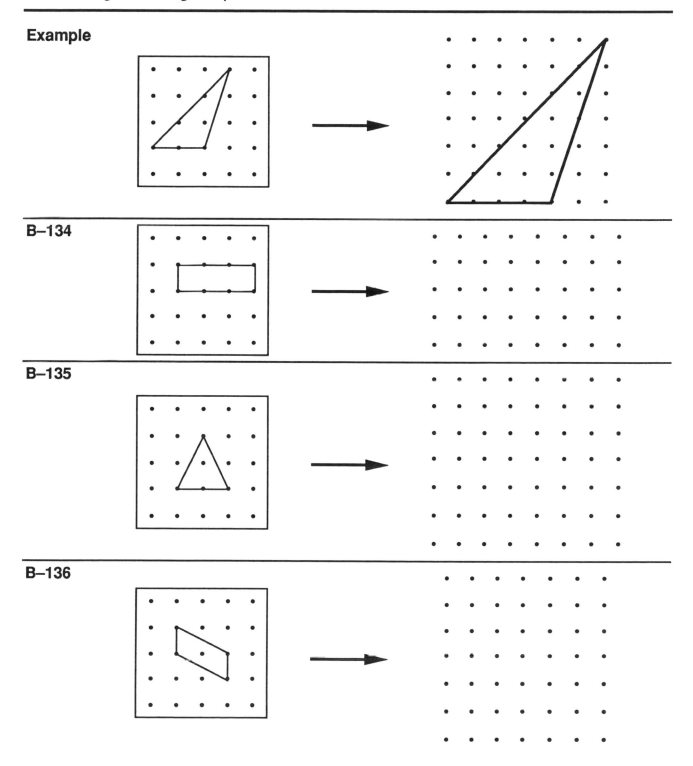

B–134

B–135

B–136

SIMILAR FIGURES

Similar figures have the same shape.
Connect dots on the geoboard design to make a figure similar to the given figure.
Make the figure as small as possible.

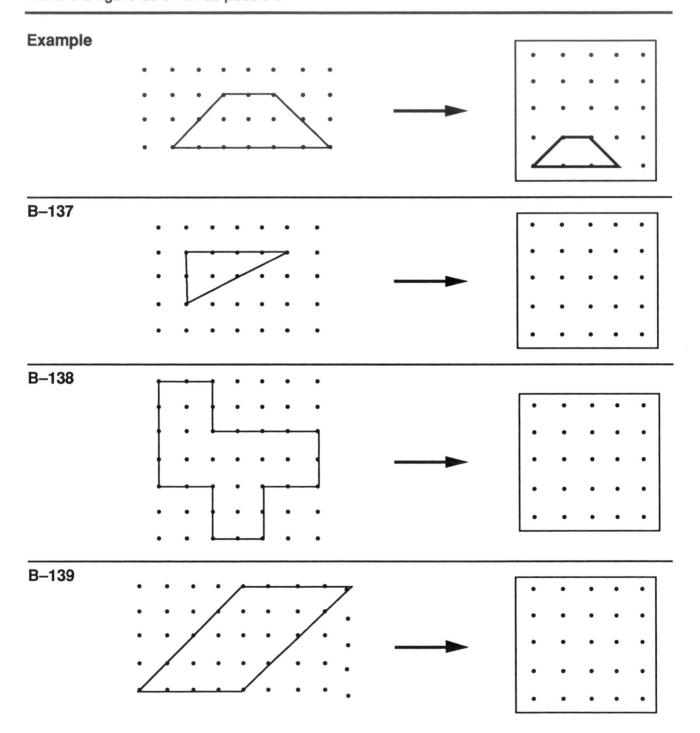

Example

B–137

B–138

B–139

TRANSLATIONS

A figure is pictured before a translation.
Draw the figure after the translation indicated.

Example

Translate the figure

four units to the right.

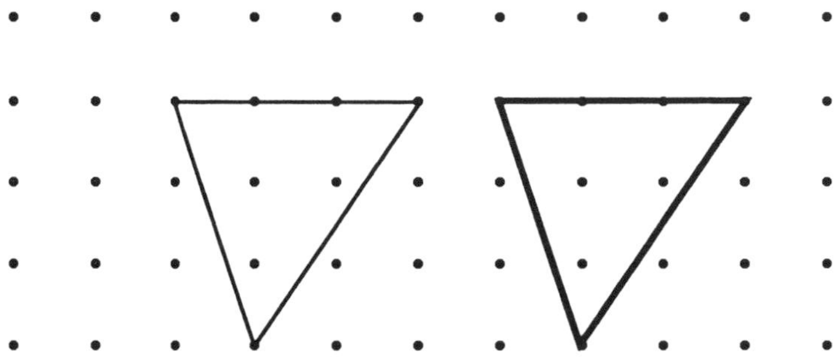

B–140

Translate the figure

five units to the left.

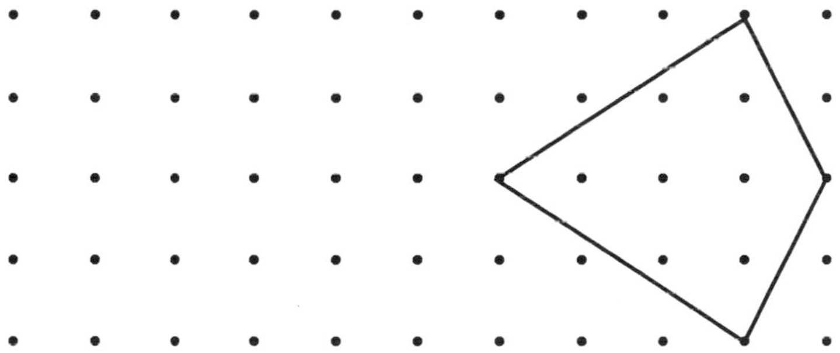

B–141

Translate the figure

one unit down and

six units to the right.

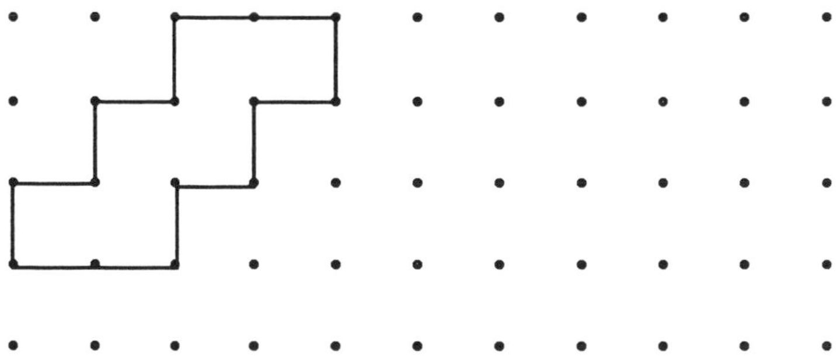

B–142

Translate the figure

one unit up and

three units to the left.

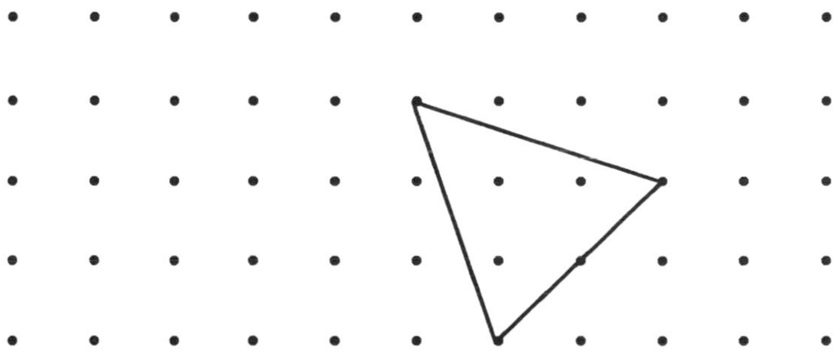

REFLECTIONS

Use the line AB as the line of reflection.
Draw the given figure after a reflection across line AB.

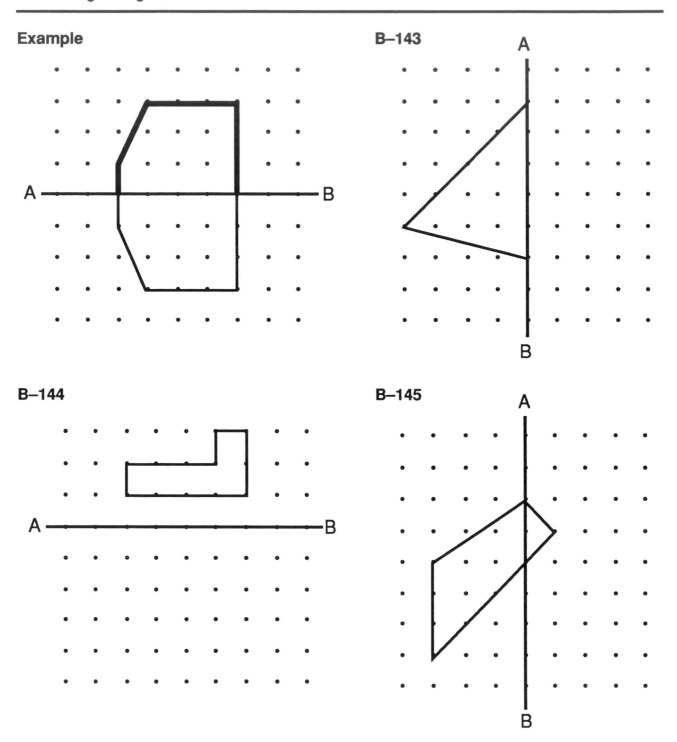

Example

B–143

B–144

B–145

REFLECTIONS

Use the line AB as the line of reflection.
Draw the given figure after a reflection across line AB.

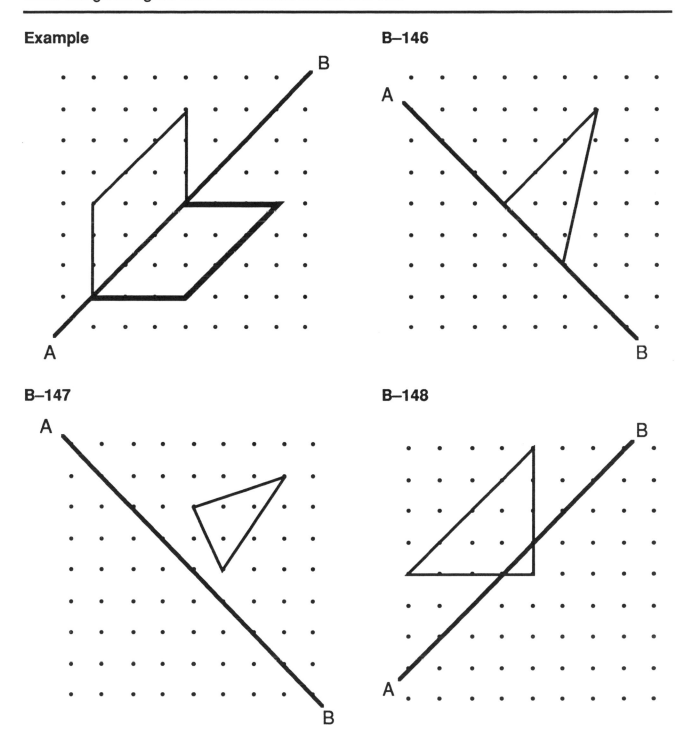

Example

B–146

B–147

B–148

ROTATIONS

Rotate each figure a quarter turn around the center dot on the geoboard.
Draw the rotated figure and label the points to match the given figure.

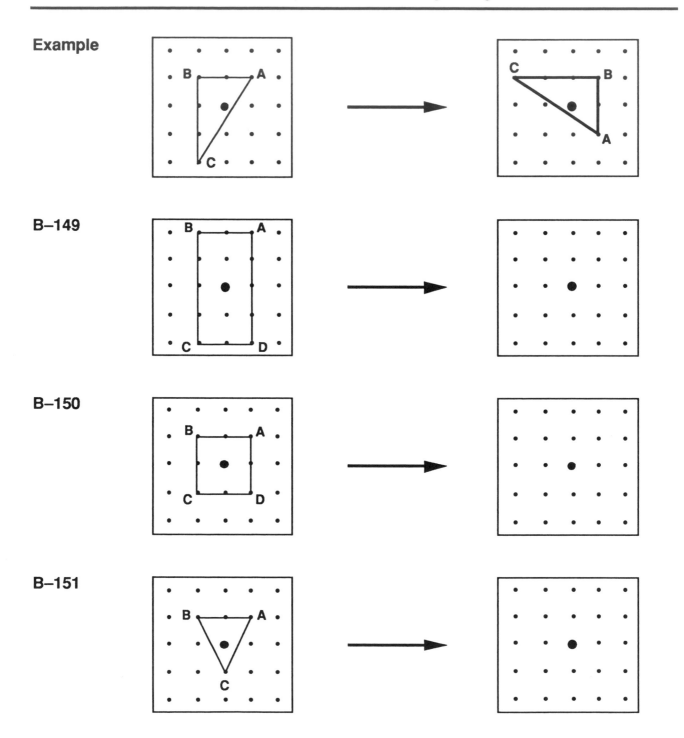

Example

B–149

B–150

B–151

ROTATIONS

Rotate each figure a half turn around the center dot on the geoboard.
Draw the rotated figure and label the points to match the given figure.

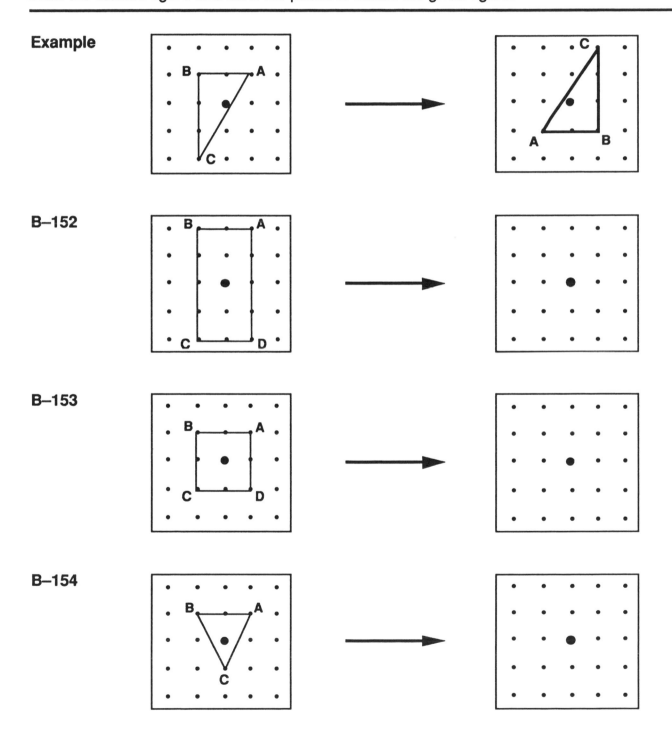

CONSTRUCTING FIGURES

The dotted line is the line of reflection and the center dot is the center of rotation.
Draw each figure after the indicated reflections or clockwise rotations.
Label the figures that you draw.

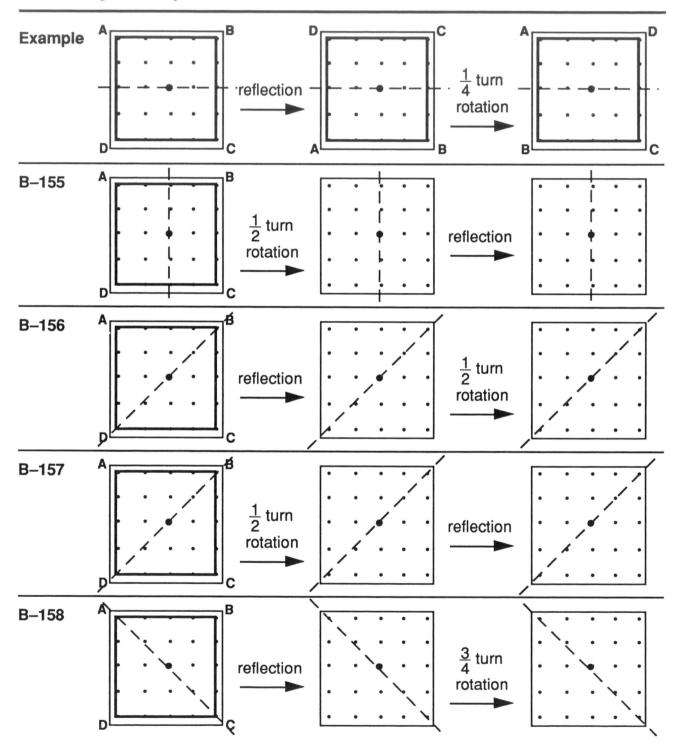

REFLECTIONS AND ROTATIONS

Name a single motion that transforms Figure A into Figure B.
For rotations identify the amount of rotation in a clockwise direction.
For reflections indicate the line of reflection.

Example	FIGURE A	FIGURE B	MOTION

Example

FIGURE A: A-B / D-C (square)

FIGURE B: D-C / A-B (square)

MOTION: __reflection__ __horizontal line__

B–159

FIGURE A: A-B / D-C

FIGURE B: C-D / B-A

B–160

FIGURE A: A-B / D-C

FIGURE B: A-D / B-C

B–161

FIGURE A: A-B / D-C

FIGURE B: D-A / C-B

B–162

FIGURE A: A-B / D-C

FIGURE B: B-A / C-D

LINE SYMMETRY

Half of a symmetric figure is drawn.
The dotted line is the line of symmetry.
Draw the other half of the figure.

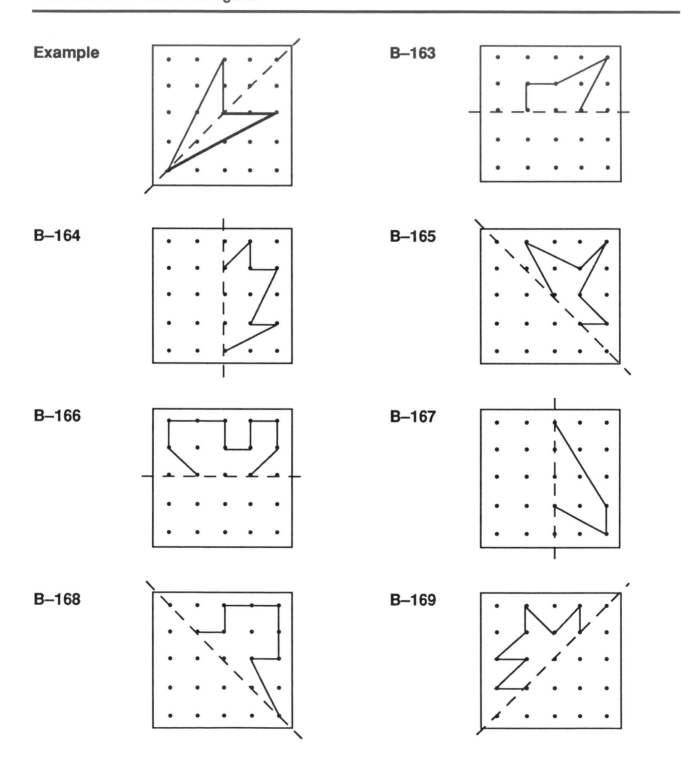

Example

B–163

B–164

B–165

B–166

B–167

B–168

B–169

LINE SYMMETRY

Draw all possible lines of symmetry for each figure.
Write the number of lines of symmetry in the box below the figure.
Write a "0" in the box if the figure does not have line symmetry.

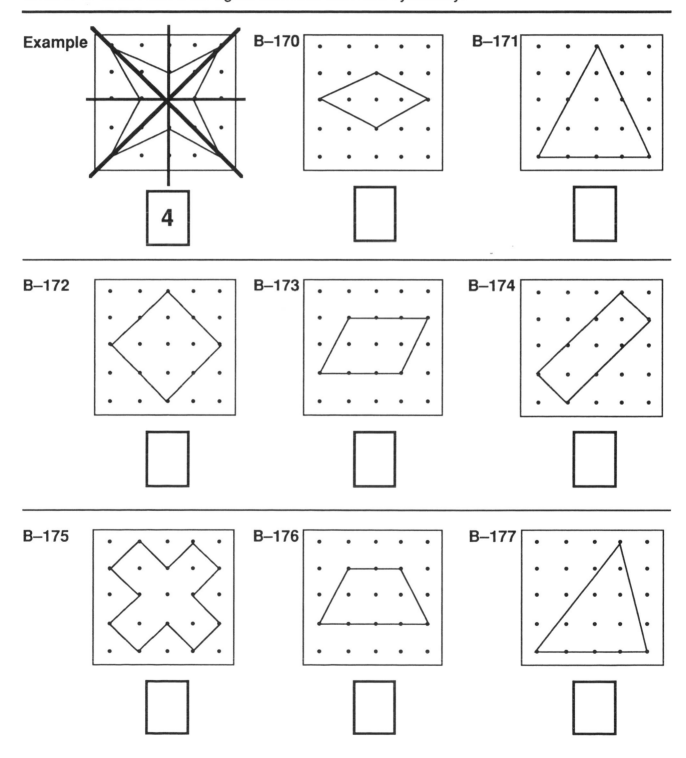

Example

4

B–170

B–171

B–172

B–173

B–174

B–175

B–176

B–177

ROTATIONAL SYMMETRY

Use the center dot as the point of rotation.
Reproduce the given figure as often as possible using the turn listed for the figure.

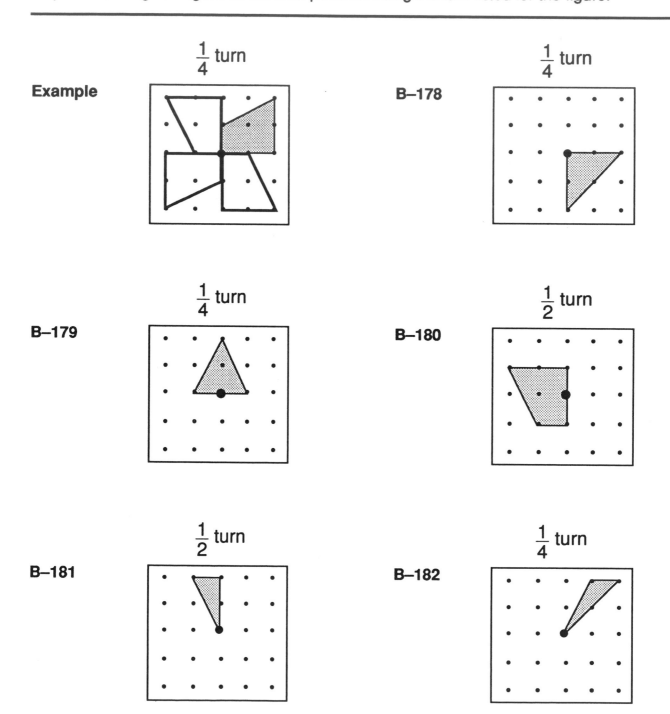

ROTATIONAL SYMMETRY

Each figure has rotational symmetry with the center dot as the point of rotation.
In the box, write the smallest turn that illustrates this symmetry.

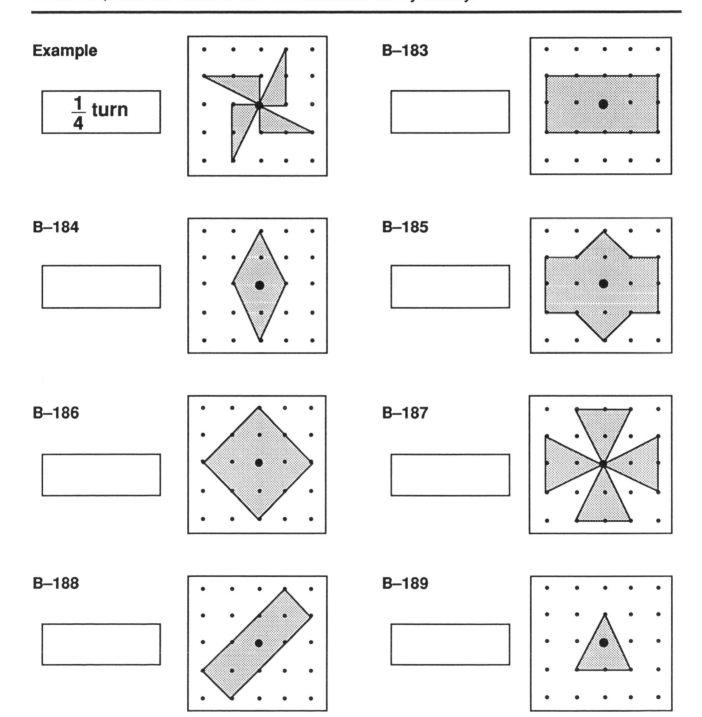

Example

$\frac{1}{4}$ **turn**

B–183

B–184

B–185

B–186

B–187

B–188

B–189

SHRINKING POLYGONS

The polygons in each sequence are shrinking.
Draw the missing polygon in each sequence

Example

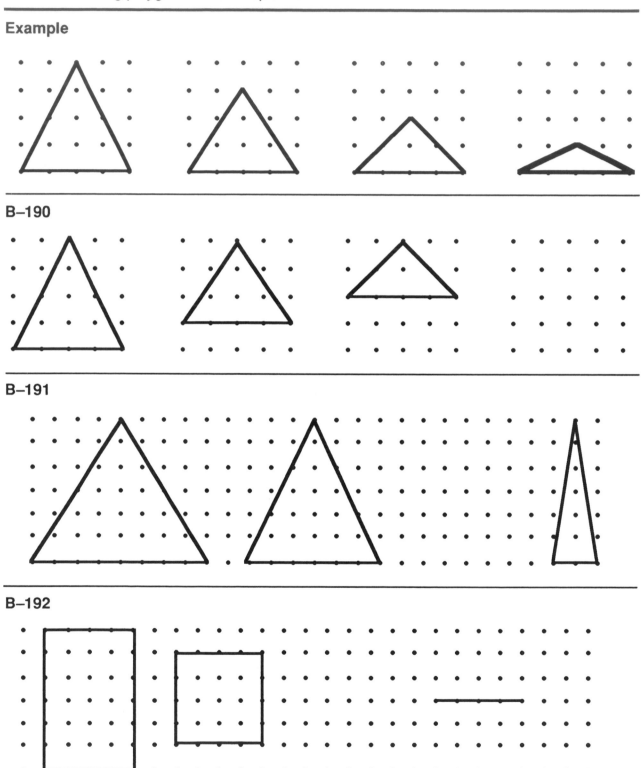

B–190

B–191

B–192

STRETCHING POLYGONS

The polygons in each sequence are stretching.
Draw the missing polygon in each sequence

Example

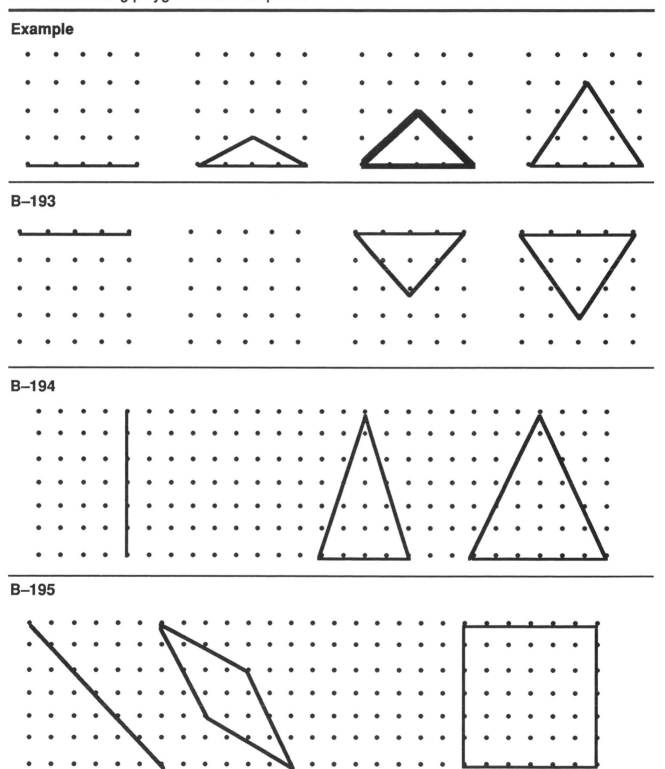

B–193

B–194

B–195

ROTATING POLYGONS

As each polygon is turned around the dotted line, its shadow changes shape. Match each polygon with its sequence of shadows.

Example

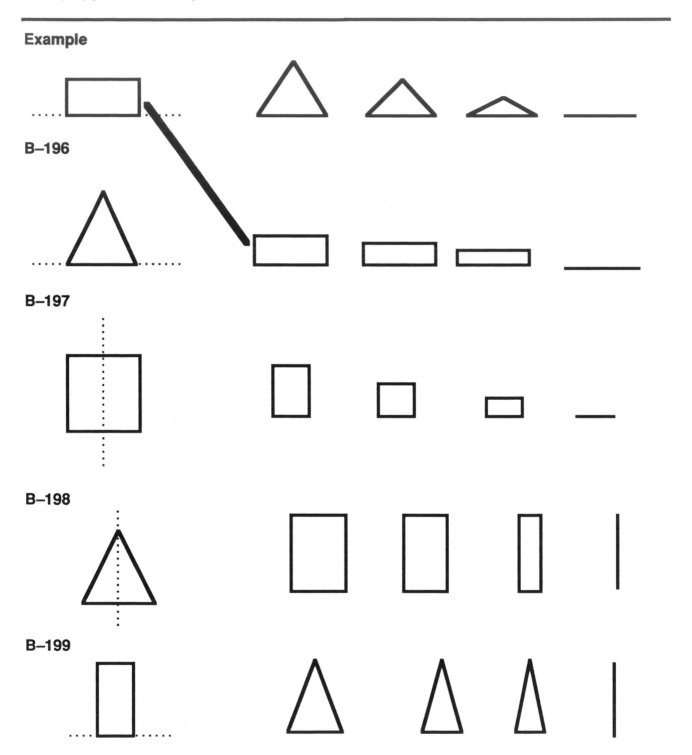

B–196

B–197

B–198

B–199

ROTATING POLYGONS

As each figure is turned around the dotted line, its shadow changes shape.
Match the figure with its sequence of shadows.

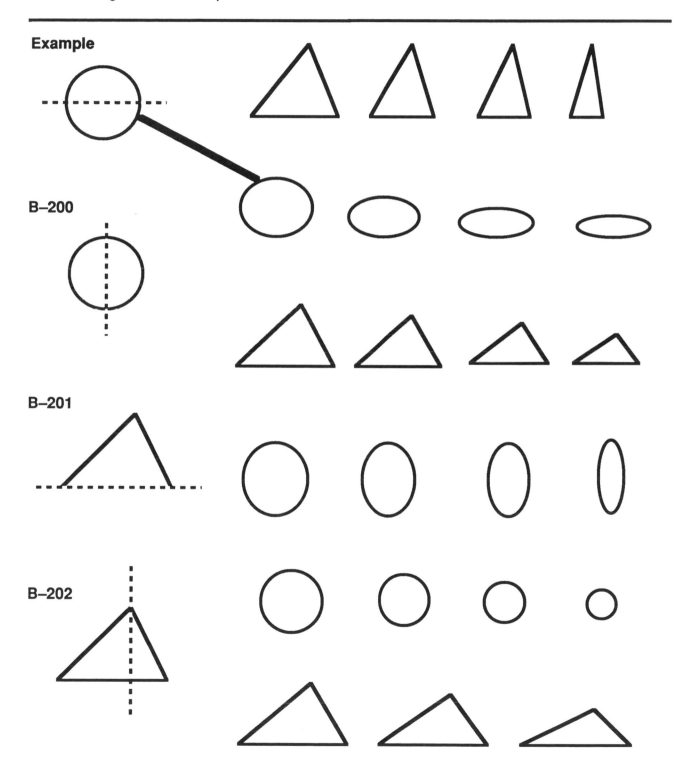

Example

B–200

B–201

B–202

DECOMPOSING SOLIDS

Each given solid can be separated into two different solids.
Write the numbers of these two solids in the boxes.

Example

B–203 | 1 | + | 2 |

B–204 | ☐ | + | ☐ |

B–205 | ☐ | + | ☐ |

B–206 | ☐ | + | ☐ |

1.

2.

3.

4.

5.

COMPOSITION OF SOLIDS

Find the solid that can be formed by combining the two given solids.
Write its number in the box.

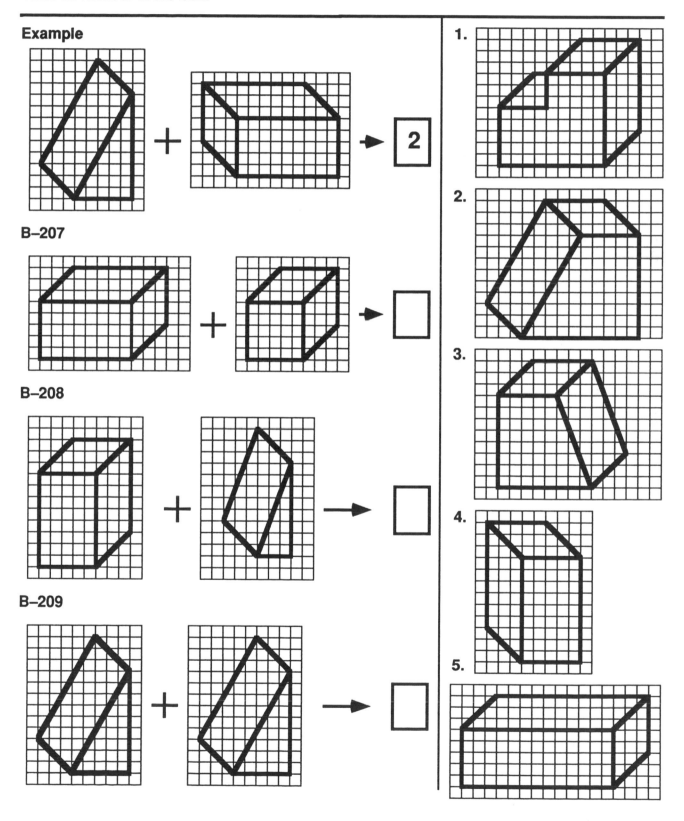

Example

B–207

B–208

B–209

1.

2.

3.

4.

5.

MAKING SOLIDS BY FOLDING

When folded along the connecting lines, each pattern of squares will form a cube.
The letter "B" in a square marks the bottom of the cube.
Place a "T" in a square to mark the top of each cube

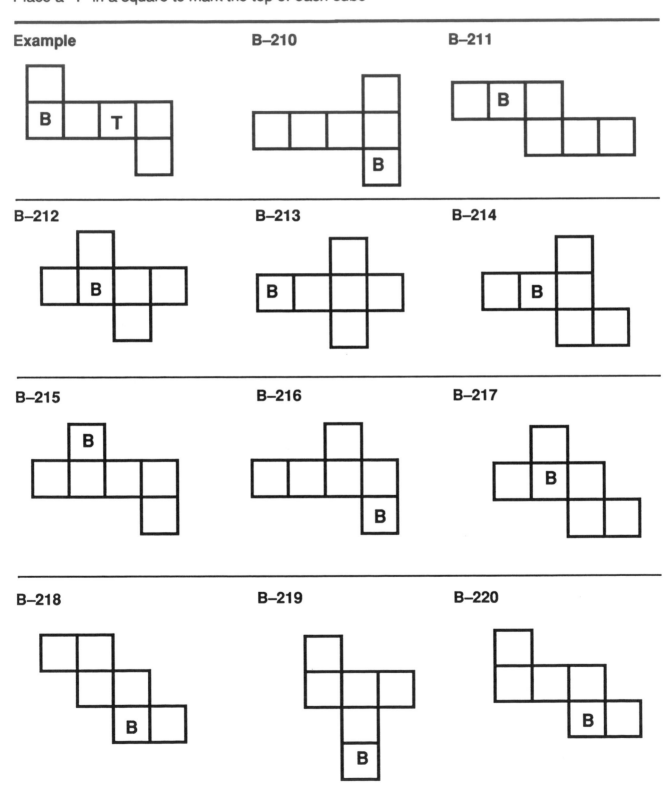

Example

B–210

B–211

B–212

B–213

B–214

B–215

B–216

B–217

B–218

B–219

B–220

MAKING SOLIDS BY FOLDING

When folded, each pattern forms a rectangular solid.
"B" marks the base of the solid formed, and the other 5 faces are numbered.
Number the faces of each solid to correspond to the numbers on the pattern.

Example

B–221

B–222

B–223

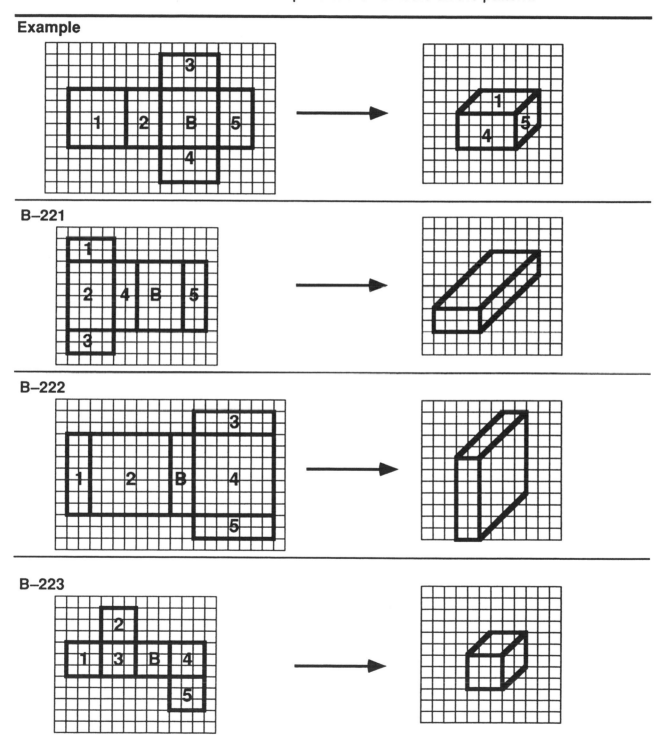

MAKING SOLIDS BY FOLDING

When folded, each pattern forms a solid.
Draw lines connecing each pattern to its corresponding solid.

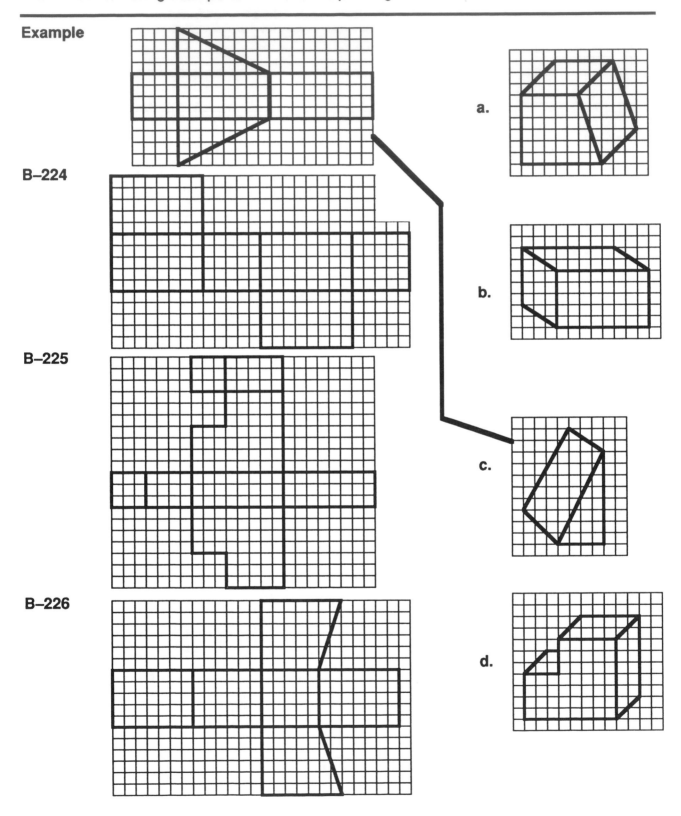

Example

B–224

B–225

B–226

a.

b.

c.

d.

SEPARATING REGIONS

The two circles in the diagram at right partition the box into 3 separate regions.
Each region has been numbered.
Number each region in the boxes below, and write the number of separate regions above the box.

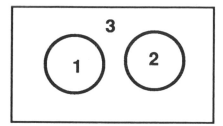

Example __4__

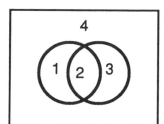

B–227 _____

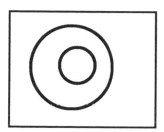

B–228 _____

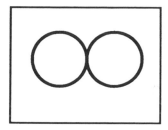

B–229 _____

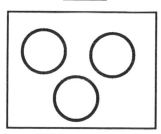

B–230 _____

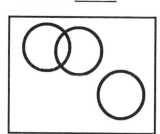

B–231 _____

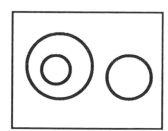

B–232 _____

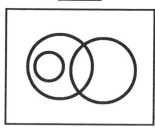

B–233 _____

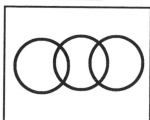

B–234 _____

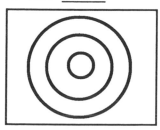

SEPARATING REGIONS

Two circles have been drawn in each box.
Draw a third circle that will partition the box into the number of regions indicated.
Number the regions in each exercise.

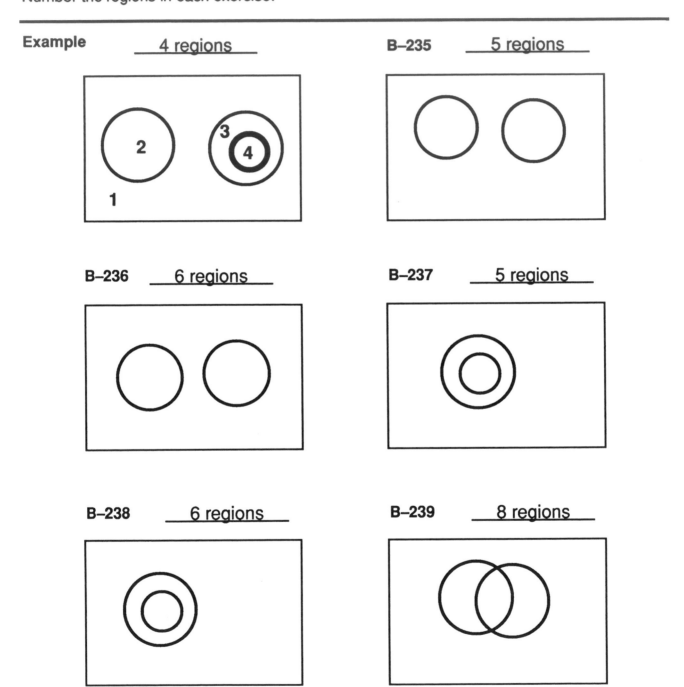

Example ___4 regions___

B–235 ___5 regions___

B–236 ___6 regions___

B–237 ___5 regions___

B–238 ___6 regions___

B–239 ___8 regions___

SEPARATING REGIONS

Four circles partition each box into separate regions.
Number each region in the box, and write the number of separate regions above the box.

Example　　　　7

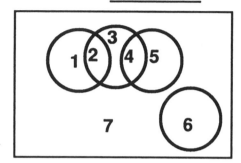

B–240

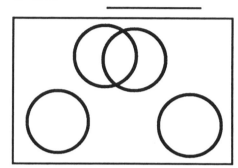

B–241

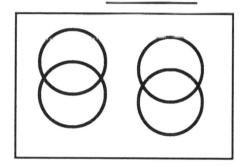

B–242

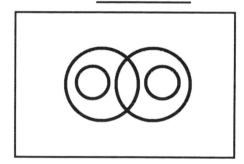

B–243

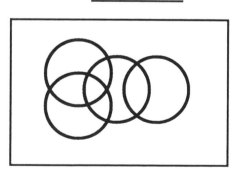

B–244

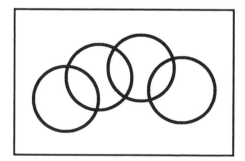

SEPARATING REGIONS

Three circles have been drawn in each box.
Draw a fourth circle that will partition the box into the number of regions indicated.
Number the regions in each exercise.

Example _____5 regions_____

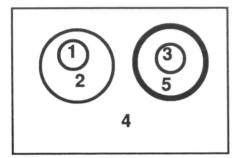

B–245 _____6 regions_____

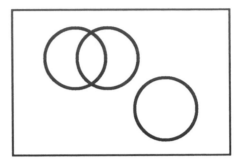

B–246 _____7 regions_____

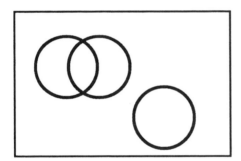

B–247 _____10 regions_____

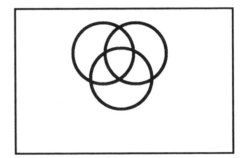

B–248 _____9 regions_____

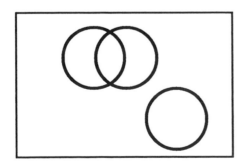

B–249 _____11 regions_____

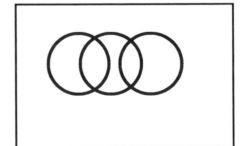

TRACING NETWORKS

The points in each network are labeled.
Beginning at point A, determine whether it is possible to
trace the network using each line exactly once.
Number the lines to indicate the path followed.

Example

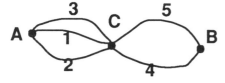

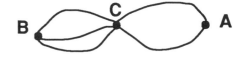

Is it possible? **YES**

Is it possible? **NO**

B–250

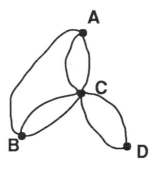

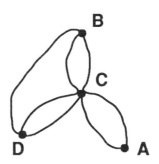

Is it possible? _____

Is it possible? _____

B–251

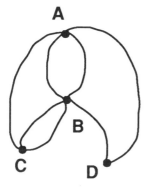

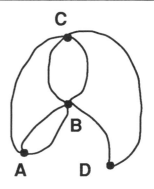

Is it possible? _____

Is it possible? _____

TRACING NETWORKS

The points in each network are labeled.
Determine whether it is possible to begin at one of the points and
trace the network using each line exactly once.
If it is possible, name the beginning point and end point, and
number the lines to indicate the path followed.

Example

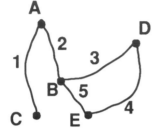

Is it possible? **YES**

Starting Point **C**   End Point **B**

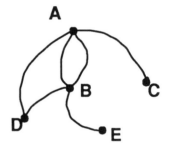

Is it possible? **NO**

Starting Point ____   End Point ____

B–252

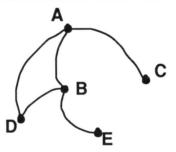

Is it possible? _____

Starting Point ____   End Point ____

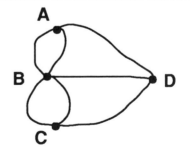

Is it possible? _____

Starting Point ____   End Point ____

B–253

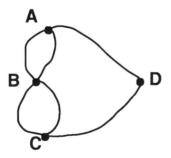

Is it possible? _____

Starting Point ____   End Point ____

Is it possible? _____

Starting Point ____   End Point ____

DRAWING PATHS

Each figure represents the floor plan of a building, and the openings represent doorways.
Each room is labelled with the letter B, C, or D, and the outside is labelled with the letter A.
Determine if a path can be drawn from A, passing through each door exactly once.
If it is possible, draw the path.

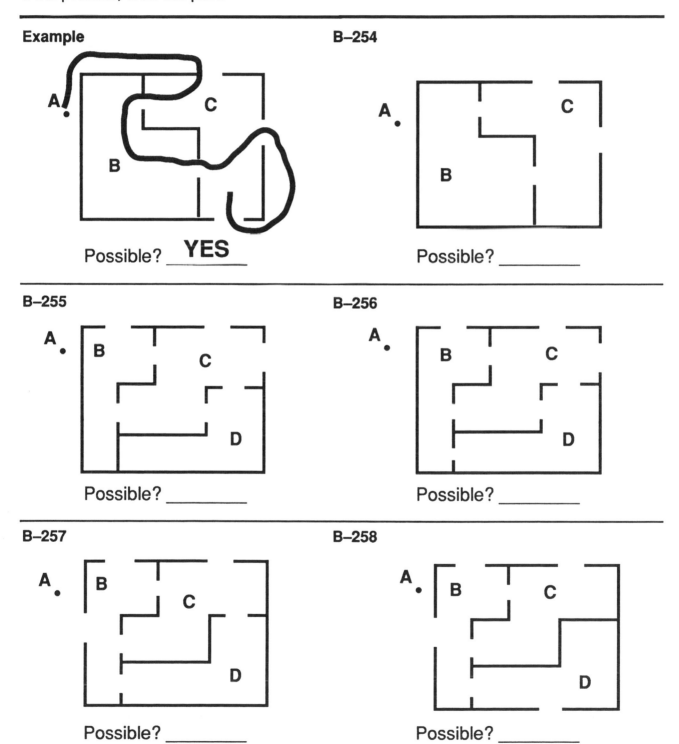

Example

A

C

B

Possible? __**YES**__

B–254

A

C

B

Possible? _____

B–255

A B

C

D

Possible? _____

B–256

A B C

D

Possible? _____

B–257

A B

C

D

Possible? _____

B–258

A B C

D

Possible? _____

DRAWING PATHS

Each figure represents the floor plan of a building, and the openings represent doorways.
Each room is labelled with the letter B, C, D, or E, and the outside is labelled with the letter A.
Determine if a path can be drawn, passing through each door exactly once.
If it is possible, draw the path.

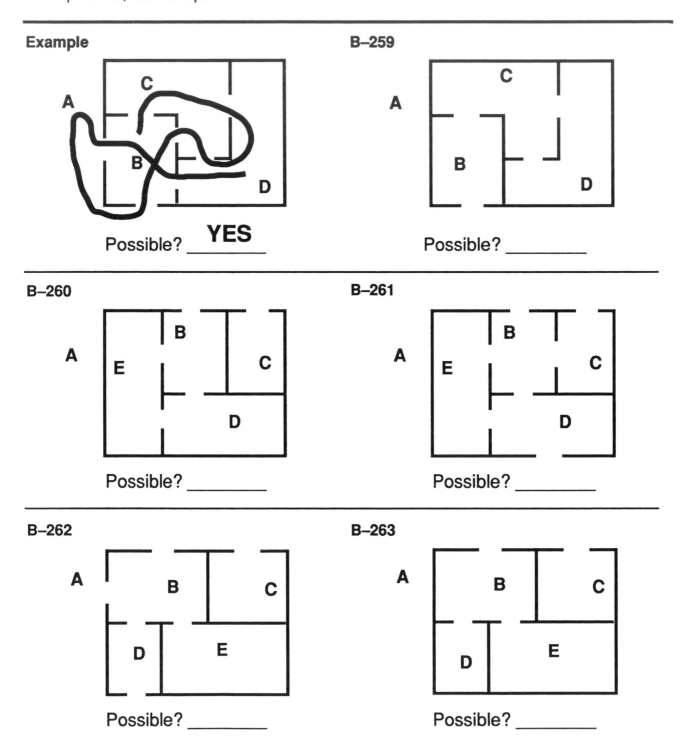

Example

Possible? **YES**

B–259

Possible? _____

B–260

Possible? _____

B–261

Possible? _____

B–262

Possible? _____

B–263

Possible? _____

COUNTING ARRAYS

Find the number of columns and rows in each array of cubes.
Circle all of the expressions that tell how many cubes are in each array.

Example

Number of Rows = **4**

Number of Columns = **3**

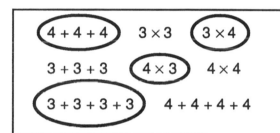

C–1

Number of Rows = _____

Number of Columns = _____

4 + 4 + 4 + 4	5 × 5	4 × 5
5 + 5 + 5 + 5	5 × 4	4 × 4
5 + 5 + 5 + 5 + 5	4 + 4 + 4 + 4 + 4	

C–2

Number of Rows = _____

Number of Columns = _____

6 + 6 + 6 + 6	5 × 6	5 × 5
6 + 6 + 6 + 6 + 6		6 × 6
5 + 5 + 5 + 5 + 5 + 5		6 × 5

C–3

Number of Rows = _____

Number of Columns = _____

8 + 8 + 8 + 8	4 × 8	3 × 8
8 + 8 + 8	8 × 4	8 × 8
4 + 4 + 4 + 4 + 4 + 4 + 4 + 4		

COUNTING ARRAYS

Circle the letters of the expressions that tell how many cubes are in the pair of arrays.

Example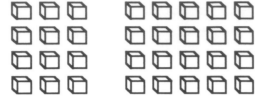

     (a.) $(4 \times 3) + (4 \times 5)$

     b. $5 \times (4 + 3)$

     c. $(3 \times 3) + (4 \times 4)$

     (d.) $4 \times (3 + 5)$

C–4

     a. $(5 \times 3) + (3 \times 5)$

     b. $5 \times (6 + 3)$

     c. $(6 \times 5) + (6 \times 3)$

     d. $(5 \times 6) + (5 \times 3)$

C–5

     a. $(7 \times 4) + (7 \times 6)$

     b. $7 \times (4 + 7)$

     c. $7 \times (4 + 6)$

     d. $(4 \times 6) + (5 \times 7)$

C–6

     a. $(4 \times 4) + (6 \times 6)$

     b. $(4 \times 6) + (4 \times 6)$

     c. $4 \times (6 + 6)$

     d. $6 \times (4 + 4)$

COMPUTING ARRAYS

Each circle represents a set of objects.
The number in each circle tells how many objects are in the set.
Circle all the expressions that tell the total number of objects in each exercise.

Example

a. 7 + 7 + 7   **(b.)** 7 × (3 + 3)

c. 7 × 3   **(d.)** 7 + 7 + 7 + 7 + 7 + 7

e. 7 × 7   **(f.)** 7 × 6

C–7

a. 5 + 5 + 5   b. 5 × (2 + 3)

c. 5 × (3 + 3)   d. 5 + 5 + 5 + 5 + 5 + 5

e. 5 × 6   f. 5 × 3

C–8

a. 7 + 7 + 7   b. 4 × (4 + 2)

c. 4 × (3 + 2)   d. (4 × 4) + 2

e. 4 × 6   f. 4 + 4 + 4 + 4 + 4 + 4

C–9

a. 2 × (5 + 3)   b. 8 × (5 + 3)

c. 2 × (6 + 2)   d. 8 × 2

e. 5 × 2   f. 2 × 8

C–10

a. 9 × (5 + 4)   b. 9 × 4

c. 9 × 9   d. 9 × (8 + 1)

e. 9 × 5   f. 9 × (4 + 3)

COMPUTING ARRAYS

Each circle represents a set of objects.
The number in each circle tells how many objects are in the set.
Circle all the expressions that tell the total number of objects in each exercise.

Example

a. 3×8 **b.** $3 \times (4 + 3)$

c. $3 \times (5 + 3)$ **d.** $(3 \times 4) + (3 \times 3)$

e. $3 \times (6 + 1)$ f. $4 \times (3 + 4)$

C–11

a. $6 \times (4 + 3)$ b. $(6 \times 6) + (6 \times 1)$

c. 6×8 d. $6 \times (4 + 4)$

e. $(6 \times 4) + (6 \times 3)$ f. $6 \times (6 + 1)$

C–12

a. 8×8 b. 8×5

c. $8 \times (6 + 2)$ d. $8 \times (5 + 3)$

e. $(8 \times 6) + (8 \times 2)$ f. $8 \times (6 + 3)$

C–13

a. 5×5 b. $(5 \times 4) + (5 \times 4)$

c. $5 \times (4 + 2)$ d. $5 \times (4 + 4)$

e. $5 \times (3 + 5)$ f. $5 \times (6 + 2)$

C–14

a. $4 \times (6 + 4)$ b. $4 \times (6 + 6)$

c. $4 \times (5 + 5)$ d. $(4 \times 6) + (4 \times 4)$

e. $2 \times (4 + 5)$ f. $(4 \times 5) + (4 \times 5)$

MULTIPLYING FRACTIONS

In each exercise rectangles are subdivided into equal parts.
Circle the number sentence that tells how many rectangles can be made
with the shaded subdivisions.

Example

a. $\dfrac{1}{3} \times 1 = \dfrac{1}{3}$ b. $\dfrac{1}{3} \times 3 = 1$

ⓒ $\dfrac{1}{3} \times 6 = 2$ d. $\dfrac{2}{3} \times 6 = 4$

C–15

a. $\dfrac{1}{2} \times 4 = 2$ b. $\dfrac{1}{4} \times 4 = 1$

c. $\dfrac{3}{4} \times 4 = 3$ d. $\dfrac{1}{4} \times 1 = \dfrac{1}{4}$

C–16

a. $\dfrac{1}{3} \times 3 = 1$ b. $\dfrac{2}{3} \times 1 = \dfrac{2}{3}$

c. $\dfrac{1}{3} \times 2 = \dfrac{2}{3}$ d. $\dfrac{2}{3} \times 3 = 2$

C–17

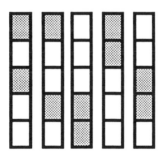

a. $\dfrac{2}{5} \times 5 = 2$ b. $\dfrac{3}{5} \times 5 = 3$

c. $\dfrac{2}{5} \times 1 = \dfrac{2}{5}$ d. $\dfrac{1}{5} \times 5 = 1$

C–18

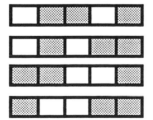

a. $\dfrac{2}{5} \times 4 = 1\dfrac{3}{5}$ b. $\dfrac{1}{5} \times 4 = \dfrac{4}{5}$

c. $\dfrac{3}{5} \times 4 = 2\dfrac{2}{5}$ d. $\dfrac{3}{5} \times 3 = 1\dfrac{4}{5}$

MULTIPLYING FRACTIONS

Circle the number sentences that describe the fractional part of the rectangle that is shaded.

Example

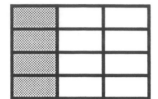

  (a.) $\dfrac{1}{3} \times 1 = \dfrac{1}{3}$ b. $\dfrac{2}{3} \times 1 = \dfrac{2}{3}$

  (c.) $\dfrac{4}{12} \times 1 = \dfrac{4}{12}$ d. $\dfrac{4}{12} \times 12 = 4$

C–19

   a. $\dfrac{2}{3} \times 12 = 8$ b. $\dfrac{1}{3} \times 1 = \dfrac{1}{3}$

   c. $\dfrac{3}{4} \times 1 = \dfrac{3}{4}$ d. $\dfrac{2}{3} \times 1 = \dfrac{2}{3}$

C–20

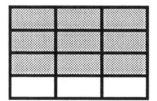

   a. $\dfrac{3}{4} \times 1 = \dfrac{3}{4}$ b. $\dfrac{1}{4} \times 1 = \dfrac{1}{4}$

   c. $\dfrac{9}{12} \times 1 = \dfrac{9}{12}$ d. $\dfrac{9}{12} \times 12 = 9$

C–21

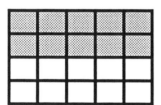

   a. $\dfrac{10}{20} \times 20 = 10$ b. $\dfrac{2}{5} \times 1 = \dfrac{2}{5}$

   c. $\dfrac{2}{4} \times 1 = \dfrac{2}{4}$ d. $\dfrac{1}{2} \times 1 = \dfrac{1}{2}$

C–22

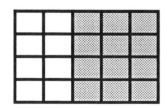

   a. $\dfrac{12}{20} \times 20 = 12$ b. $\dfrac{3}{5} \times 1 = \dfrac{3}{5}$

   c. $\dfrac{2}{5} \times 1 = \dfrac{2}{5}$ d. $\dfrac{12}{20} \times 1 = \dfrac{12}{20}$

MULTIPLYING FRACTIONS

Shade in a fractional part of the rectangle to match the number sentence.

Example

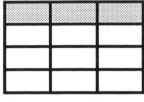

$$\frac{1}{4} \times 1 = \frac{1}{4}$$

C–23

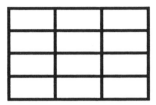

$$\frac{2}{3} \times 1 = \frac{2}{3}$$

C–24

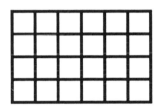

$$\frac{6}{24} \times 1 = \frac{6}{24}$$

C–25

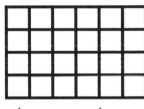

$$\frac{4}{6} \times 1 = \frac{4}{6}$$

C–26

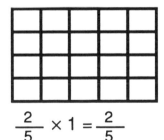

$$\frac{2}{5} \times 1 = \frac{2}{5}$$

C–27

$$\frac{3}{4} \times 1 = \frac{3}{4}$$

C–28

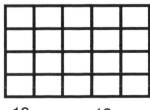

$$\frac{12}{20} \times 1 = \frac{12}{20}$$

C–29

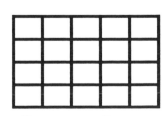

$$\frac{5}{20} \times 1 = \frac{5}{20}$$

MULTIPLYING FRACTIONS

Circle the fraction that matches the fractional part of each rectangle that is shaded.
Circle the fraction that matches the fractional part of the rectangle containing "Xs."
Circle the number sentence that tells the fractional part of the rectangle
that is shaded and has "Xs."

Example

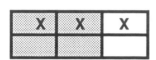

Shaded	"Xs"	Number sentence
$\dfrac{1}{2}$	$\boxed{\dfrac{1}{2}}$	$\boxed{\dfrac{1}{2} \times \dfrac{2}{3} = \dfrac{2}{6}}$
$\boxed{\dfrac{2}{3}}$	$\dfrac{1}{3}$	$\dfrac{2}{6} \times \dfrac{1}{3} = \dfrac{2}{18}$
$\dfrac{3}{6}$	$\dfrac{2}{6}$	$\dfrac{3}{6} \times \dfrac{2}{6} = \dfrac{6}{36}$

C–30

Shaded	"Xs"	Number sentence
$\dfrac{1}{9}$	$\dfrac{1}{9}$	$\dfrac{1}{9} \times \dfrac{1}{3} = \dfrac{1}{27}$
$\dfrac{2}{3}$	$\dfrac{1}{3}$	$\dfrac{2}{3} \times \dfrac{2}{3} = \dfrac{4}{9}$
$\dfrac{1}{3}$	$\dfrac{2}{3}$	$\dfrac{1}{3} \times \dfrac{1}{3} = \dfrac{1}{9}$

C–31

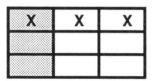

Shaded	"Xs"	Number sentence
$\dfrac{2}{4}$	$\dfrac{2}{4}$	$\dfrac{1}{3} \times \dfrac{2}{6} = \dfrac{1}{18}$
$\dfrac{2}{6}$	$\dfrac{2}{3}$	$\dfrac{2}{6} \times \dfrac{2}{4} = \dfrac{4}{24}$
$\dfrac{1}{3}$	$\dfrac{2}{6}$	$\dfrac{1}{2} \times \dfrac{2}{3} = \dfrac{2}{6}$

C–32

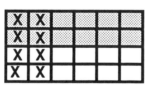

Shaded	"Xs"	Number sentence
$\dfrac{3}{4}$	$\dfrac{1}{2}$	$\dfrac{3}{4} \times \dfrac{2}{3} = \dfrac{6}{12}$
$\dfrac{3}{5}$	$\dfrac{4}{10}$	$\dfrac{3}{5} \times \dfrac{4}{10} = \dfrac{12}{50}$
$\dfrac{3}{9}$	$\dfrac{2}{3}$	$\dfrac{2}{3} \times \dfrac{3}{5} = \dfrac{6}{15}$

MULTIPLYING FRACTIONS

Circle the letter of the number sentence that tells the fractional part of the rectangle that is shaded and has "Xs."

Example

a. $\dfrac{2}{4} \times \dfrac{1}{3} = \dfrac{2}{12}$

b. $\dfrac{4}{12} \times \dfrac{2}{12} = \dfrac{8}{24}$

ⓒ $\dfrac{2}{4} \times \dfrac{2}{3} = \dfrac{4}{12}$

C–33

a. $\dfrac{4}{6} \times \dfrac{3}{4} = \dfrac{12}{24}$

b. $\dfrac{2}{12} \times \dfrac{3}{12} = \dfrac{6}{24}$

c. $\dfrac{1}{4} \times \dfrac{2}{6} = \dfrac{2}{24}$

C–34

a. $\dfrac{1}{4} \times \dfrac{3}{5} = \dfrac{3}{20}$

b. $\dfrac{2}{5} \times \dfrac{1}{4} = \dfrac{2}{20}$

c. $\dfrac{3}{4} \times \dfrac{2}{5} = \dfrac{6}{20}$

C–35

a. $\dfrac{2}{4} \times \dfrac{1}{5} = \dfrac{2}{20}$

b. $\dfrac{4}{5} \times \dfrac{3}{4} = \dfrac{12}{20}$

c. $\dfrac{2}{4} \times \dfrac{4}{5} = \dfrac{8}{20}$

C–36

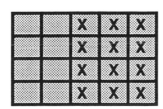

a. $\dfrac{3}{5} \times 1 = \dfrac{12}{20}$

b. $\dfrac{3}{4} \times 1 = \dfrac{15}{20}$

c. $\dfrac{2}{5} \times 1 = \dfrac{5}{20}$

MULTIPLYING FRACTIONS

Shade in a fractional part of the rectangle to match the first fraction.
Put "Xs" in a fractional part of the rectangle to match the second fraction.
Use the rectangle to complete the number sentence.

Example

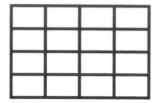

$$\frac{3}{5} \times \frac{3}{4} = \frac{9}{20}$$

C–37

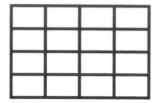

$$\frac{3}{4} \times \frac{1}{4} = \underline{\quad\quad}$$

C–38

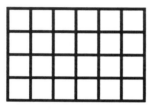

$$\frac{3}{6} \times \frac{1}{4} = \underline{\quad\quad}$$

C–39

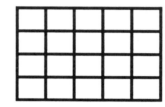

$$\frac{1}{4} \times \frac{2}{5} = \underline{\quad\quad}$$

C–40

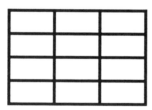

$$\frac{1}{3} \times \frac{2}{4} = \underline{\quad\quad}$$

C–41

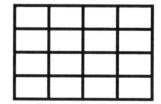

$$\frac{1}{4} \times \frac{1}{4} = \underline{\quad\quad}$$

C–42

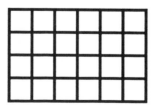

$$\frac{5}{6} \times \frac{4}{4} = \underline{\quad\quad}$$

C–43

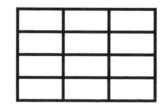

$$\frac{4}{4} \times \frac{2}{3} = \underline{\quad\quad}$$

MODELS FOR DIVISION

The number in each circle tells the number of objects in that circle.
Circle the model that illustrates the solution to each question.
In the box, write a number sentence that describes the model.

Example   A taxi service sends 6 vans to transport 24 people to a meeting.
How many people should ride in each van?

$$24 \div 6 = 4$$

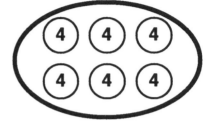

C–44   A bottled water distributor is able to pack 6 jugs of water in each box.
How many boxes will be needed to package 2 dozen jugs of water?

C–45   A local newspaper purchases 24 tons of paper.
If its trucks can carry 6 tons of paper, how many trips
are needed to deliver the paper to its printing plant?

C–46   A butcher wants to divide 24 pounds of hamburger into 6 packages.
How many pounds should be placed in each package?

MODELS FOR DIVISION

The number in each circle tells the number of objects in that circle.
Circle the model that illustrates the solution to each question.
In the box, write a number sentence that describes the model.

Example   A cake recipe requires 8 eggs.
If a chef has 2 dozen eggs, how many cakes can she make?

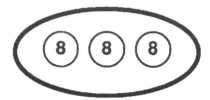

$24 \div 8 = 3$

C–47   Each student needs 4 cubes to make a pattern.
If the teacher has a set of 20 cubes, how many students can make the pattern?

C–48   A chef wants to make 8 omelets from 2 dozen eggs.
How many eggs can he put in each omelet?

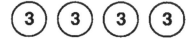

C–49   A teacher wants to divide a set of 20 cubes between 4 students.
How many cubes will each student receive?

C–50   Books are on sale for $5.00 per book. How many books could be purchased
with $30.00?

COMPUTATIONS WITH PARENTHESES

Circle the answer to each computation.

		a.	b.	c.	d.
Example	$(24 \div 4) + 2 =$	3	4	⑧	10
C–51	$24 \div (4 + 2) =$	3	4	8	10
C–52	$(24 - 4) \times 2 =$	16	18	24	40
C–53	$24 - (4 \times 2) =$	16	18	24	40
C–54	$24 + (4 + 2) =$	14	30	32	96
C–55	$(24 + 4) + 2 =$	14	30	32	96
C–56	$(24 - 4) - 2 =$	18	20	22	26
C–57	$24 - (4 - 2) =$	18	20	22	26
C–58	$(24 \div 4) \div 2 =$	3	4	12	14
C–59	$24 \div (4 \div 2) =$	3	4	12	14
C–60	$(24 \times 4) \times 2 =$	172	176	183	192
C–61	$24 \times (4 \times 2) =$	172	176	183	192

COMPUTATIONS WITH PARENTHESES

Insert parentheses to make each statement true.

Example

$24 + (4 \div 2) = 26$

C–62

$24 + 4 \times 2 = 56$

C–63

$24 \times 4 - 2 = 94$

C–64

$24 \div 4 - 2 = 12$

C–65

$24 \times 4 \div 2 = 48$

C–66

$6 = 12 \div 4 - 2$

C–67

$27 = 28 - 4 - 3$

C–68

$4 = 28 \div 4 + 3$

C–69

$3 + 4 \times 2 = 8 + 3$

C–70

$12 \div 2 = 5 \times 0 + 6$

C–71

$3 + 4 \times 2 = 18 \div 2 + 5$

C–72

$12 - 8 - 4 = 16 \div 4 \div 2$

COMPLETING COMPUTATIONS

Use the numbers in the set below to complete each computation.
In each exercise use a different number in each box.

$$\begin{array}{cccc} 0 & 1 & 2 & 3 \\ 4 & 6 & 8 & 12 \end{array}$$

Example

$(12 \div \boxed{4}) - 2 = 1$

C–73

$6 = 12 \div (4 - \boxed{})$

C–74

$(3 \times \boxed{}) \div \boxed{} = 2$

C–75

$(\boxed{} \div 3) - 4 = \boxed{}$

C –76

$\boxed{} = 8 - (\boxed{} + 1)$

C–77

$(\boxed{} - 6) \times 3 = 9 \times \boxed{}$

C–78

$\boxed{} - (\boxed{} - \boxed{}) = 6$

C –79

$3 \times \boxed{} = (\boxed{} + 6) \times \boxed{}$

THE DISTRIBUTIVE PROPERTY

Place a number in each box to make the number sentence true.

Example

$(\boxed{5} \times 3) + (5 \times 7) = 50$

C–80

$7 \times (3 + \boxed{}) = 63$

C–81

$9 \times (\boxed{} + 3) = 45$

C–82

$(3 \times 5) + (3 \times \boxed{}) = 39$

C–83

$\boxed{} \times (3 + 7) = 50$

C–84

$(7 \times 3) + (7 \times \boxed{}) = 63$

C–85

$(2 \times \boxed{}) + (2 \times 7) = 16$

C–86

$2 \times (\boxed{} + 7) = 16$

C–87

$3 \times (5 + \boxed{}) = 39$

C–88

$(9 \times \boxed{}) + (9 \times 3) = 45$

WHOLE NUMBER DIVISION

In the division example on the right the <u>divisor</u> is 5,
the <u>dividend</u> is 17, the <u>quotient</u> is 3, and the <u>remainder</u> is 2.

The division can be checked by the following computation:

$$(5 \times 3) + 2 = 17.$$

$$\begin{array}{r} 3 \\ 5\overline{)17} \\ \underline{15} \\ 2 \end{array}$$

Fill in the blanks in the following exercises.

Example

Divisor = $\boxed{2}$

Dividend = 7

Quotient = 3

Remainder = 1

C–89

Divisor = 5

Dividend = 39

Quotient = $\boxed{}$

Remainder = $\boxed{}$

C–90

Divisor = 6

Dividend = $\boxed{}$

Quotient = 9

Remainder = 3

C–91

Divisor = $\boxed{}$

Dividend = 85

Quotient = 8

Remainder = 5

C–92

Divisor = $\boxed{}$

Dividend = 100

Quotient = 33

Remainder = 1

C–93

Divisor = $\boxed{}$

Dividend = 17

Quotient = $\boxed{}$

Remainder = 2

EXPANDED NOTATION

Place a single digit in each blank to make the computation match the set.
In the box, write the number in standard form.
Refer to the chart below.

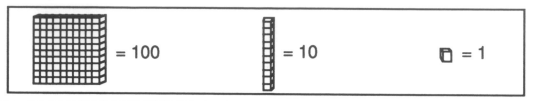

= 100   = 10   = 1

Example

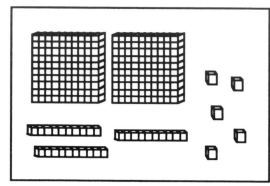

(_2_ × 100) + (_3_ × 10) + (_5_)

235

C–94

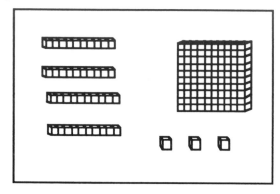

(___ × 100) + (___ × 10) + (___)

C–95

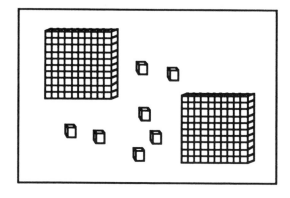

(___ × 100) + (___ × 10) + (___)

C–96

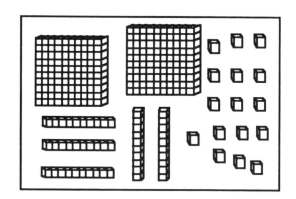

(___ × 100) + (___ × 10) + (___)

EXPANDED NOTATION

The following numbers are associated with the shapes pictured below.

$\bigcirc$ = 25 $\square$ = 10 $\triangle$ = 5

Circle the number represented by each computation.

---

		a.	b.	c.
Example	$(3 \times \bigcirc) + (2 \times \square) + (1 \times \triangle) + 2 =$	87	92	(102)
C–97	$(2 \times \bigcirc) + (4 \times \square) + (0 \times \triangle) + 4 =$	74	94	99
C–98	$(4 \times \square) + (4 \times \triangle) + 9 =$	69	119	129
C–99	$(0 \times \bigcirc) + (1 \times \triangle) + 1 =$	6	31	36
C–100	$(5 \times \bigcirc) + (5 \times \triangle) + 9 =$	144	159	184
C–101	$(8 \times \bigcirc) + (13 \times \square) + (4 \times \triangle) + 12 =$	242	317	362

EXPANDED NOTATION

Place a single digit in each blank to make the statement true.
Refer to the chart below.

$\bigcirc$ = 100 $\bigcirc$ = 25 $\square$ = 10 $\triangle$ = 5

Example

(_1_ × $\bigcirc$) + (_2_ × $\bigcirc$) + (_1_ × $\square$) + (_1_ × $\triangle$) + _3_ = 168

C–102

(__ × $\bigcirc$) + (__ × $\bigcirc$) + (__ × $\square$) + (__ × $\triangle$) + __ = 342

C–103

(__ × $\bigcirc$) + (__ × $\bigcirc$) + (__ × $\square$) + (__ × $\triangle$) + __ = 103

C–104

(__ × $\bigcirc$) + (__ × $\bigcirc$) + (__ × $\square$) + (__ × $\triangle$) + __ = 590

C–105

(__ × $\bigcirc$) + (__ × $\bigcirc$) + (__ × $\square$) + (__ × $\triangle$) + __ = 191

C–106

(__ × $\bigcirc$) + (__ × $\bigcirc$) + (__ × $\square$) + (__ × $\triangle$) + __ = 85

C–107

(__ × $\bigcirc$) + (__ × $\bigcirc$) + (__ × $\square$) + (__ × $\triangle$) + __ = 999

EXPANDED NOTATION

Circle the number represented by each computation.
Refer to the chart below.

$$10^3 = 1,000 \qquad 10^2 = 100 \qquad 10^1 = 10$$

Example

	a.	b.	c.
$(5 \times 10^3) + (0 \times 10^2) + (8 \times 10^1) + 2 =$	582	(5,082)	5,182

C–108

	a.	b.	c.
$(8 \times 10^3) + (7 \times 10^2) + (1 \times 10^1) + 9 =$	7,819	8,710	8,719

C–109

	a.	b.	c.
$(7 \times 10^3) + (4 \times 10^2) + (9 \times 10^1) + 0 =$	749	4,790	7,490

C–110

	a.	b.	c.
$(0 \times 10^3) + (7 \times 10^2) + (8 \times 10^1) + 9 =$	789	1,789	7,809

C–111

	a.	b.	c.
$(9 \times 10^3) + (2 \times 10^2) + (8 \times 10^1) + 12 =$	9,282	9,292	92,812

C–112

	a.	b.	c.
$(7 \times 10^3) + (9 \times 10^2) + (9 \times 10^1) + 10 =$	7,910	8,000	79,910

EXPANDED NOTATION

Place a single digit in each blank to make the statement true.
Refer to the chart below.

$$10^4 = 10,000 \qquad 10^3 = 1,000 \qquad 10^2 = 100 \qquad 10^1 = 10$$

Example

$(\underline{\ 1\ } \times 10^4) + (\underline{\ 2\ } \times 10^3) + (\underline{\ 0\ } \times 10^2) + (\underline{\ 9\ } \times 10^1) + \underline{\ 5\ } = 12,095$

C–113

$(\underline{\ \ \ } \times 10^4) + (\underline{\ \ \ } \times 10^3) + (\underline{\ \ \ } \times 10^2) + (\underline{\ \ \ } \times 10^1) + \underline{\ \ \ } = 9,880$

C–114

$(\underline{\ \ \ } \times 10^4) + (\underline{\ \ \ } \times 10^3) + (\underline{\ \ \ } \times 10^2) + (\underline{\ \ \ } \times 10^1) + \underline{\ \ \ } = 10,100$

C–115

$(\underline{\ \ \ } \times 10^4) + (\underline{\ \ \ } \times 10^3) + (\underline{\ \ \ } \times 10^2) + (\underline{\ \ \ } \times 10^1) + \underline{\ \ \ } = 798$

C–116

$(\underline{\ \ \ } \times 10^4) + (\underline{\ \ \ } \times 10^3) + (\underline{\ \ \ } \times 10^2) + (\underline{\ \ \ } \times 10^1) + \underline{\ \ \ } = 7,980$

C–117

$(\underline{\ \ \ } \times 10^4) + (\underline{\ \ \ } \times 10^3) + (\underline{\ \ \ } \times 10^2) + (\underline{\ \ \ } \times 10^1) + \underline{\ \ \ } = 1,010$

EXPANDED DECIMAL NOTATION

Place a single digit in each blank to make the computation match the set.
In the box, write the number in decimal form. Refer to the chart below.

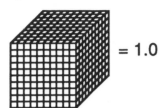 = 1.0   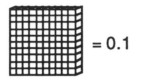 = 0.1   ❘ = 0.01   ▯ = 0.001

Example

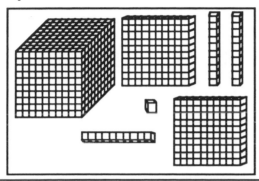

$(\underline{1} \times 1.0) + (\underline{2} \times 0.1) + (\underline{3} \times 0.01) + (\underline{1} \times 0.001)$

$$\boxed{1.231}$$

C–118

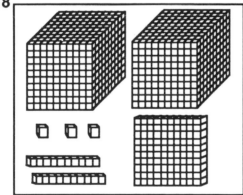

$(\underline{} \times 1.0) + (\underline{} \times 0.1) + (\underline{} \times 0.01) + (\underline{} \times 0.001)$

$$\boxed{}$$

C–119

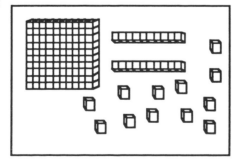

$(\underline{} \times 1.0) + (\underline{} \times 0.1) + (\underline{} \times 0.01) + (\underline{} \times 0.001)$

$$\boxed{}$$

EXPANDED DECIMAL NOTATION

Place a single digit in each blank to make the statement true.
Refer to the chart below.

| ⬭ = 1.00 | ◯ = 0.25 | ▯ = 0.10 | △ = 0.05 | ▮ = 0.01 |

Example

$(\underline{4} \times ⬭) + (\underline{3} \times ◯) + (\underline{2} \times ▯) + (\underline{0} \times △) + (\underline{2} \times ▮) = 4.97$

C–120

$(\underline{\hspace{1em}} \times ⬭) + (\underline{\hspace{1em}} \times ◯) + (\underline{\hspace{1em}} \times ▯) + (\underline{\hspace{1em}} \times △) + (\underline{\hspace{1em}} \times ▮) = 7.94$

C–121

$(\underline{\hspace{1em}} \times ⬭) + (\underline{\hspace{1em}} \times ◯) + (\underline{\hspace{1em}} \times ▯) + (\underline{\hspace{1em}} \times △) + (\underline{\hspace{1em}} \times ▮) = 9.98$

C–122

$(\underline{\hspace{1em}} \times ⬭) + (\underline{\hspace{1em}} \times ◯) + (\underline{\hspace{1em}} \times ▯) + (\underline{\hspace{1em}} \times △) + (\underline{\hspace{1em}} \times ▮) = 6.50$

C–123

$(\underline{\hspace{1em}} \times ⬭) + (\underline{\hspace{1em}} \times ◯) + (\underline{\hspace{1em}} \times ▯) + (\underline{\hspace{1em}} \times △) + (\underline{\hspace{1em}} \times ▮) = 1.10$

C–124

$(\underline{\hspace{1em}} \times ⬭) + (\underline{\hspace{1em}} \times ◯) + (\underline{\hspace{1em}} \times ▯) + (\underline{\hspace{1em}} \times △) + (\underline{\hspace{1em}} \times ▮) = 0.41$

C–125

$(\underline{\hspace{1em}} \times ⬭) + (\underline{\hspace{1em}} \times ◯) + (\underline{\hspace{1em}} \times ▯) + (\underline{\hspace{1em}} \times △) + (\underline{\hspace{1em}} \times ▮) = 0.87$

MAKING CHANGE

Each exercise states the cost of an item and the amount paid by the customer. Place a single digit in each box to indicate the customer's change.

Example

Cost = $2.85

Paid = $5.00

Dollars	Quarters	Dimes	Nickels	Pennies
2	0	1	1	0

C–126

Cost = $14.60

Paid = $20.00

Dollars	Quarters	Dimes	Nickels	Pennies

C–127

Cost = $0.63

Paid = $1.00

Dollars	Quarters	Dimes	Nickels	Pennies

C–128

Cost = $5.98

Paid = $10.00

Dollars	Quarters	Dimes	Nickels	Pennies

C–129

Cost = $2.25

Paid = $5.25

Dollars	Quarters	Dimes	Nickels	Pennies

C–130

Cost = $5.89

Paid = $6.04

Dollars	Quarters	Dimes	Nickels	Pennies

FRACTIONAL PARTS

A fractional part of each figure is shaded.
In the box, write the fraction that indicates the shaded part of the figure.
In the circle, write the fraction that indicates the unshaded part of the figure.
Write each fraction in lowest terms.

Example

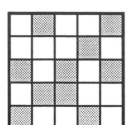

$$\boxed{\frac{2}{5}} + \left(\frac{3}{5}\right) = 1$$

C–131

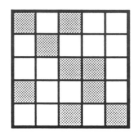

$$\square + \bigcirc = 1$$

C–132

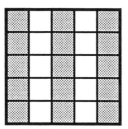

$$\square + \bigcirc = 1$$

C–133

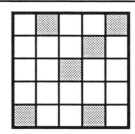

$$\square + \bigcirc = 1$$

C–134

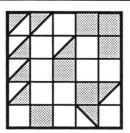

$$\square + \bigcirc = 1$$

C–135

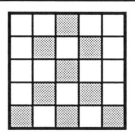

$$\square + \bigcirc = 1$$

MIXED NUMBERS

In the box, write a mixed number which estimates the number of shaded rectangles.
In the circle, write the number of unshaded rectangles.

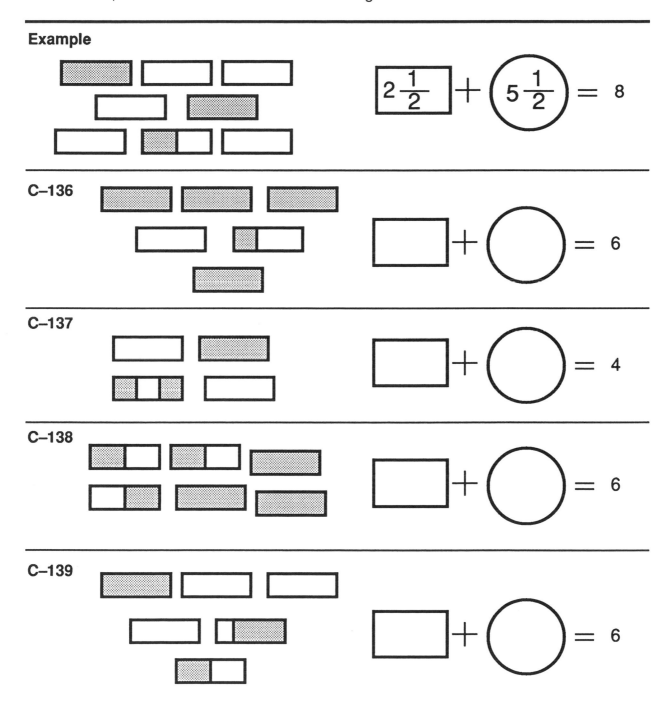

Example

$2\dfrac{1}{2}$ + $5\dfrac{1}{2}$ = 8

C–136

☐ + ◯ = 6

C–137

☐ + ◯ = 4

C–138

☐ + ◯ = 6

C–139

☐ + ◯ = 6

MISSING ADDENDS

In each box, write the fraction or mixed number that completes the number sentence. Reduce each fraction to lowest terms.

Example

$$2\frac{1}{4} + \boxed{6\frac{3}{4}} = 9$$

C–140

$$\boxed{} + \frac{3}{5} = 1$$

C–141

$$\boxed{} + 4\frac{5}{12} = 6$$

C–142

$$6\frac{7}{8} + \boxed{} = 9$$

C–143

$$2 = \frac{1}{8} + \boxed{} + \frac{1}{2}$$

C–144

$$\frac{2}{3} + \boxed{} + \frac{1}{9} = 1$$

C–145

$$3\frac{1}{5} + \boxed{} = 10\frac{4}{5}$$

C–146

$$2\frac{1}{2} = 2\frac{1}{4} + \boxed{}$$

C–147

$$\boxed{} + 2\frac{1}{2} = 4\frac{1}{4}$$

C–148

$$6\frac{3}{4} + \boxed{} = 8\frac{1}{4}$$

DECIMAL NUMBERS

Each grid below represents one unit.
In the box, write the decimal that indicates the shaded portion of the grid.
In the oval, write the decimal that indicates the unshaded portion.

Example

C–149

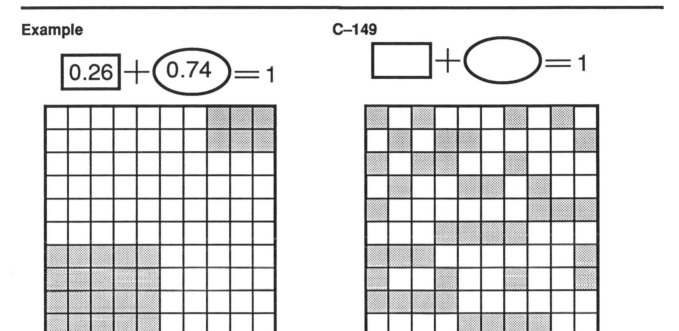

C–150

C–151

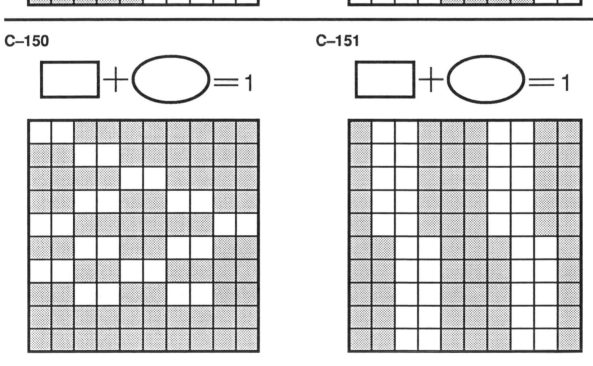

MISSING ADDENDS

In each box, write a decimal number that completes the number sentence.

Example

$0.81 + \boxed{0.19} = 1.0$

C–152

$\boxed{} + 0.7 = 1.0$

C–153

$1.0 = 0.36 + \boxed{}$

C–154

$0.07 + \boxed{} = 1.0$

C–155

$0.24 + \boxed{} + 0.15 = 1.0$

C–156

$0.64 + 0.36 = \boxed{}$

C–157

$\boxed{} + 0.36 = 2.0$

C–158

$0.15 + \boxed{} + 0.24 = 3.0$

C–159

$0.7 + \boxed{} = 3.9$

C–160

$\boxed{} + 0.68 = 2.04$

SUMMING DECIMAL NUMBERS

A number, N, is pictured on a Japanese Abacus.
The location of the decimal point is not shown.
Based upon the statement below the abacus, write two possible valules for N in the blanks.
Write the sum of these two values in the box.

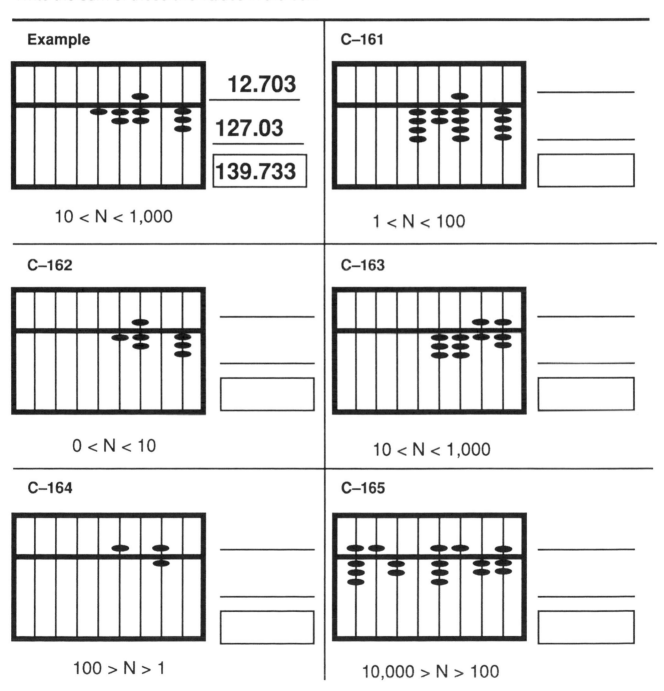

Example

12.703
127.03
139.733

10 < N < 1,000

C–161

1 < N < 100

C–162

0 < N < 10

C–163

10 < N < 1,000

C–164

100 > N > 1

C–165

10,000 > N > 100

SUMMING DECIMAL NUMBERS

Two numerals and a decimal point are written on 3 cards.
Write all the possible arrangements of these cards in the box.
Then write the sum of these decimal numbers.

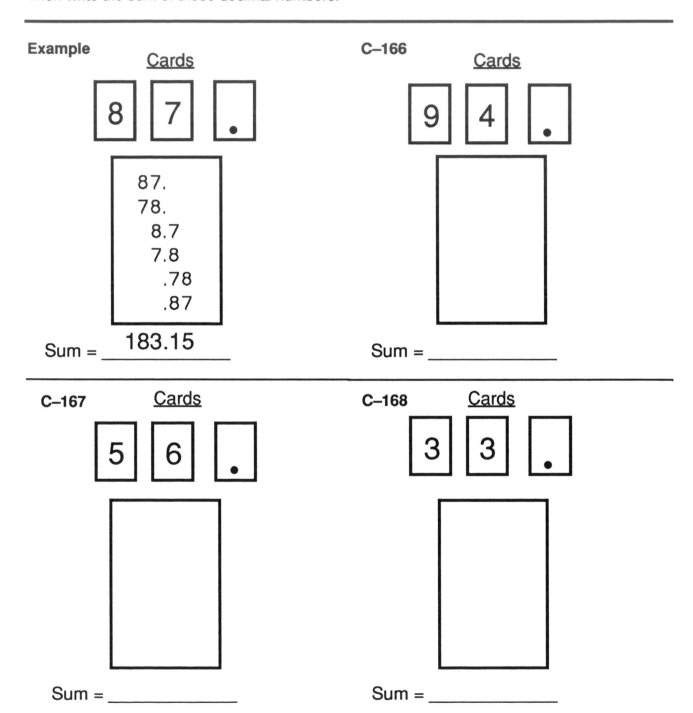

Example

Cards

8 7 .

87.
78.
8.7
7.8
.78
.87

Sum = __183.15__

C–166

Cards

9 4 .

Sum = _____

C–167

Cards

5 6 .

Sum = _____

C–168

Cards

3 3 .

Sum = _____

ILLUSTRATING NUMBER PROPERTIES

Using only whole numbers, write a numerical example to illustrate each statement below.

Example   A number times itself is greater than 5 times the number.

$$7 \times 7 > 5 \times 7$$

C–169   The sum of two different odd numbers is an even number.

C–170   The difference of two numbers is 18.

C–171   The product of two odd numbers is an odd number.

C–172   The sum of two prime numbers is a prime number.

C–173   The sum of two numbers is 12 and one of the numbers is twice as large as the other.

C–174   A number times itself is equal to the same number.

USING NUMBER PROPERTIES

N represents a whole number.
Find all possible values of N described in each exercise below.

Example

Properties of N
N is odd. N > 3. N < 12. 3 does not divide N. N does not divide 5.

Possible Values of N
7, 11

C–175

Properties of N
N < 10. 2 does not divide N. 3 does not divide N. N is not prime.

Possible Values of N
_____

C–176

Properties of N
N is a two-digit number. N < 40. 9 divides the sum of the two digits.

Possible Values of N
_____

C–177

Properties of N
N < 40. N is a multiple of 3. N is odd. 9 does not divide N.

Possible Values of N
_____

C–178

Properties of N
N > 10. N < 40. N is prime. The sum of the digits of N is less than 10.

Possible Values of N
_____

C–179

Properties of N
N is even. N < 50. N is a multiple of 3. 9 divides the sum of its digits.

Possible Values of N
_____

DISCOVERING NUMBER PROPERTIES

In each exercise below, N represents a whole number.
Check all the properties of N that are always true.

Example

If N is between 0 and 10,
then N – 1 is

_____even
_____odd
_____not zero
__✔__less than N
__✔__less than 10

C–180

If N > 5, then 2 × N is

_____even
_____odd
_____not zero
_____greater than N
_____greater than 10

C –181

If N is even, then N + N is

_____even
_____odd
_____not zero
_____greater than N

C–182

If N is odd, then N + 2 is

_____even
_____odd
_____not zero
_____greater than N
_____greater than 3

C–183

If N is even, then 3 × N is

_____even
_____odd
_____not zero
_____greater than N
_____divisible by 2
_____divisible by 3
_____divisible by 6

C–184

If N is odd, then 3 × N is

_____even
_____odd
_____not zero
_____greater than N
_____divisible by 2
_____divisible by 3
_____not a prime number

DIVISIBLITY OF NUMBERS

Put a box around all the numbers greater than 2 that are divisible by 2.
Circle all the numbers greater than 3 that are divisible by 3.

```
 1    2    3   [4]   5   (6)   7    8    9   10

11   12   13   14   15   16   17   18   19   20

21   22   23   24   25   26   27   28   29   30

31   32   33   34   35   36   37   38   39   40

41   42   43   44   45   46   47   48   49   50

51   52   53   54   55   56   57   58   59   60

61   62   63   64   65   66   67   68   69   70

71   72   73   74   75   76   77   78   79   80

81   82   83   84   85   86   87   88   89   90

91   92   93   94   95   96   97   98   99  100
```

C–185 What numbers in the list are divisible by 4? _____

_____

C–186 What numbers in the list can be divided by both 2 and 3? _____

_____

C–187 What numbers in the list are divisible by 9? _____

_____

DIVISIBLITY OF NUMBERS

Put a box around all the numbers greater than 5 that are divisible by 5.
Circle all the numbers greater than 7 that are divisible by 7.

1	2	3	4	5	6	7	8	9	10
11	12	13	14	15	16	17	18	19	20
21	22	23	24	25	26	27	28	29	30
31	32	33	34	35	36	37	38	39	40
41	42	43	44	45	46	47	48	49	50
51	52	53	54	55	56	57	58	59	60
61	62	63	64	65	66	67	68	69	70
71	72	73	74	75	76	77	78	79	80
81	82	83	84	85	86	87	88	89	90
91	92	93	94	95	96	97	98	99	100

C–188 What numbers in the list are divisible by 10?

C–189 What numbers in the list can be divided by both 5 and 7?

C–190 List all the prime numbers that are less than 100.

CONSTRUCTING RECTANGLES

Two different rectangles can be constructed with a set of 6 tiles.
The two models below show the possible arrangements of the tiles.

Example	Determine how many different rectangles can be constructed with 3 tiles. Then write the dimensions of the rectangles.

$$1 \times 3$$

C–191	Write the dimensions of the different rectangles that can be constructed with 4 tiles.

C–192	Write the dimensions of the different rectangles that can be constructed with 12 tiles.

C–193	Find the smallest set of tiles that would be needed to construct 4 different rectangles. Then write the dimensions of each rectangle.

C–194	Write the dimensions of the different rectangles that can be constructed using the number of tiles indicated.

a. 2 _____

b. 10 _____

c. 45 _____

d. 34 _____

e. 7 _____

f. 21 _____

g. 30 _____

h. 41 _____

CONSTRUCTING RECTANGLES

The numbers in the chart below have been sorted by the number of possible rectangles that can be constructed from a set of tiles.
Use the information in the chart to complete the exercises.

Number of Rectangles

ONE	TWO	THREE	FOUR	FIVE	SIX
2	4	16	24	48	60
3	6	20	30	80	72
5	8	28	42		
11	9	50	54		
17	14	68	56		
19	21	76	64		
37	25	81			
53	49				

Example   Write the dimensions of the rectangles that can be made with the following number of tiles.

$2 = $ 1×2 $11 = $ 1×11

$17 = $ 1×17 $37 = $ 1×37

C–195   Write the dimensions of the rectangles that can be constructed with the following number of tiles.

$4 = $ _____ $9 = $ _____

$25 = $ _____ $49 = $ _____

C–196   Write the dimensions of the rectangles that can be constructed with the following number of tiles.

$20 = $ _____ $50 = $ _____

$30 = $ _____ $42 = $ _____

$48 = $ _____ $60 = $ _____

C–197   List 3 numbers less than 100 which are not in the chart that can be used to construct two different rectangles.

_____

FACTOR TREES

A factor tree is suggested for the number in each exercise.
Use the tree to write the number as a product of prime numbers.

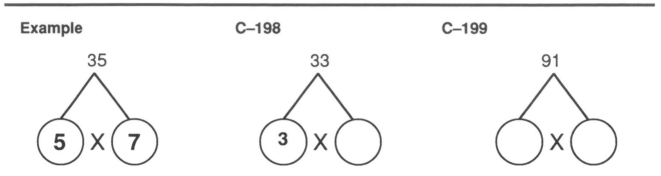

Example 35

C–198 33

C–199 91

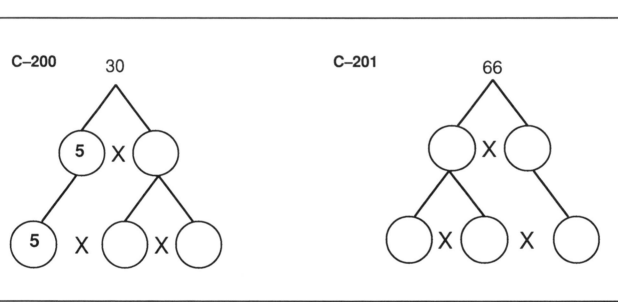

C–200 30

C–201 66

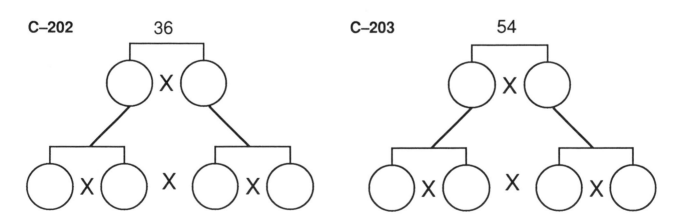

C–202 36

C–203 54

FOLLOWING A FLOWCHART

Using a pair of dice, follow the flowchart below.

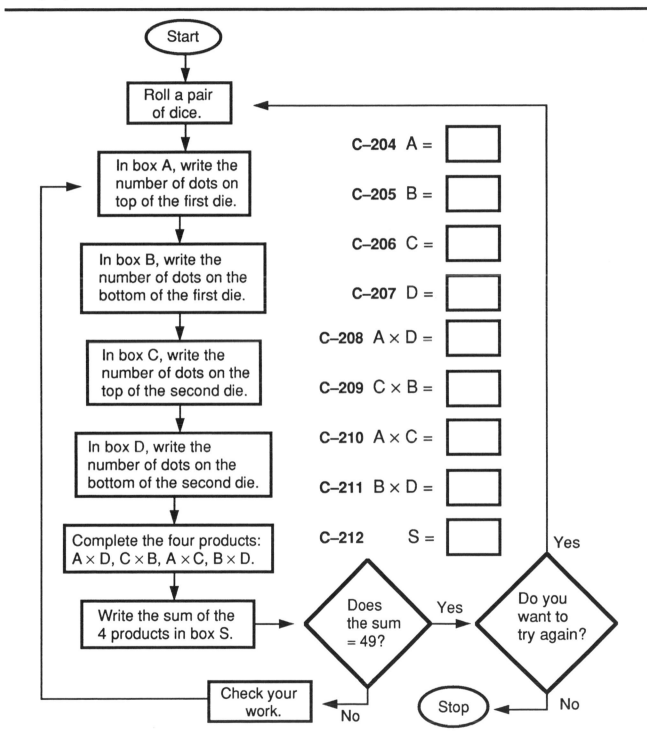

FOLLOWING A FLOWCHART

Follow the flowchart below using the fractions in the exercises.
Write the final answer in the circle.

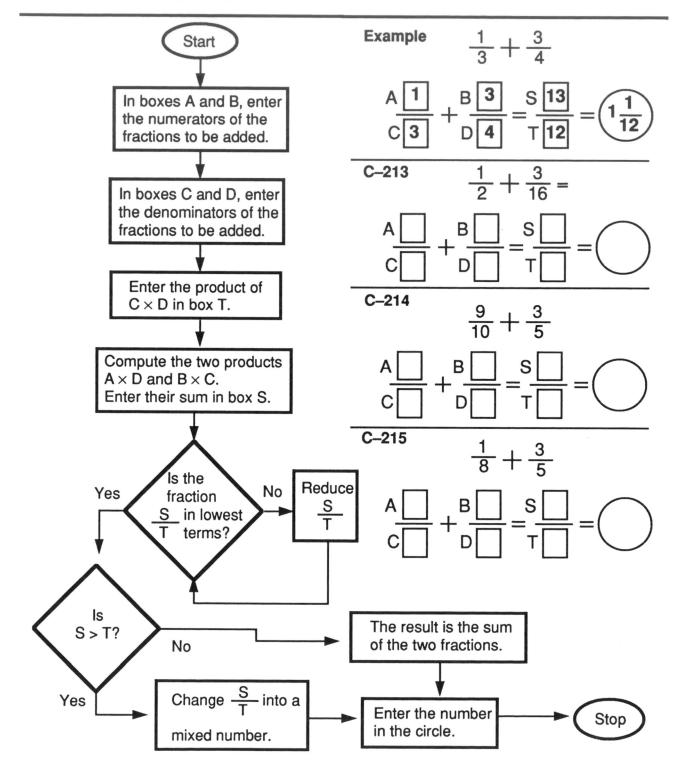

COMPLETING A FLOWCHART

You wish to divide two fractions.
Complete the flowchart below to accomplish this task.
Test the completed flowchart using the fractions in the exercises.

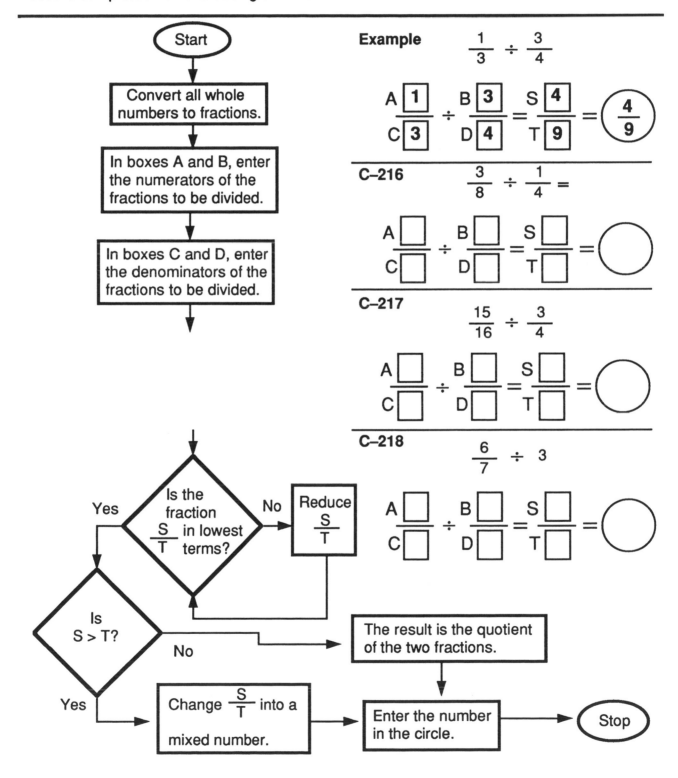

COMPLETING A FLOWCHART

You wish to average a list of whole numbers and express the answer to the nearest tenth.
Complete the flowchart to accomplish this task.
Then test your flowchart using the list of numbers in each exercise.

Example 4, 6, 3, 8

C–219 3, 2, 5, 7, 1, 0

C–220 5, 2, 2, 6, 4

C–221 9, 17, 5

C–222 100, 90, 88, 85, 80, 78, 60, 50, 15

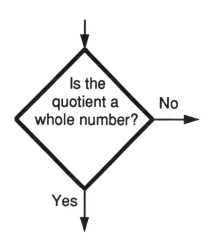

CONSTRUCTING A FLOWCHART

A well-known number game is described below.
Construct a flowchart for the game.
Then test your flowchart using the numbers in the exercises.

---

1. Write down a 3-digit number, making sure that the unit's digit and the hundred's digit differ by at least 2.

2. Reverse the digits and write down the resulting number.

3. Compute the difference of these two numbers and write it down.

4. Reverse the digits of this new number and add the result to the previous number.

5. The sum should always be 1089.

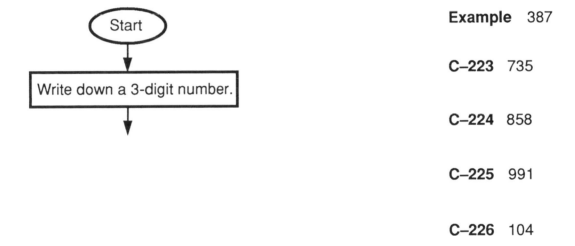

Example   387

C–223   735

C–224   858

C–225   991

C–226   104

C–227   657

CONSTRUCTING A FLOWCHART

The formula for the relationship between Fahrenheit and
Centigrade temperature is given below.
Construct a flowchart to convert Fahrenheit temperature to Centigrade temperature.
Then test your flowchart using the Fahrenheit temperatures in the exercises.

$$C = \frac{5}{9} \times (F - 32)$$

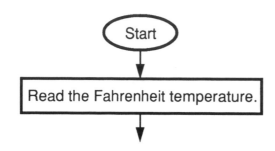

Example 212° F = <u>100°</u> C

C–228 32° F = _____ °C

C–229 98.6° F = _____ °C

C–230 68° F = _____ °C

C–231 90° F = _____ °C

PROBLEM SOLVING

A book store recently had a sale on used books. Books priced at $4.99 were reduced to $3.69, $6.99 books were reduced to $4.99, and $5.99 books were reduced to $4.99. Circle the computations that tell how much each person spent on books.

Example   Jim purchased 3 books that normally sell for $5.99.

$3 \times \$5.99$ 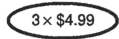 $3 \times \$4.99$ $3 \times \$3.69$

C–232

Sally purchased 4 books that normally sell for $4.99.

$4 \times \$4.99$ $4 \times \$5.99$ $4 \times \$3.69$

C–233

Hector purchased 3 books that normally sell for $5.99 and 4 books that normally sell for $4.99.

$(3 \times \$4.99) + (4 \times \$3.69)$ $(3 \times \$5.99) + (4 \times \$4.99)$

$7 \times \$4.99$ $(4 \times \$4.99) + (3 \times \$3.69)$

C–234

Sam bought 4 books that normally sell for $6.99 and 2 books that normally sell for $4.99.

$(4 \times \$4.99) + (2 \times \$4.99)$ $(4 \times \$5.99) + (2 \times \$3.69)$

$(4 \times \$4.99) + (2 \times \$3.69)$ $6 \times \$4.99$

C–235

Juanita bought 3 books that normally sell for $6.99, 2 books that normally sell for $5.99, and 1 book that normally sells for $4.99.

$(3 \times \$4.99) + (3 \times \$4.99)$ $(3 \times \$5.99) + (2 \times \$4.99) + \$3.69$

$(5 \times \$4.99) + \$3.69$ $(3 \times \$4.99) + (2 \times \$4.99) + \$3.69$

PROBLEM SOLVING

A book store recently had a sale on used books. Books priced at $4.99 were reduced to $3.69, $6.99 books were reduced to $4.99, and $5.99 books were reduced to $4.99.
Fill in the blanks in each computation and find the solution to the problem.

Example

Jim purchased 3 books that normally sell for $6.99.
How much money did he save?

$$3 \times (\underline{\$6.99} - \underline{\$4.99}) = \underline{\$6.00}$$

C–236

Hector purchased 2 books that normally sell for $5.99.
How much money did he spend?

$$\underline{\hspace{2cm}} \times (\$5.99 - \underline{\hspace{2cm}}) = \underline{\hspace{2cm}}$$

C–237

Juanita purchased 3 books that normally sell for $4.99, and
1 book that normally sells for $6.99.
How much money did she spend?

$$3 \times (\underline{\hspace{2cm}} - \underline{\hspace{2cm}}) + (\underline{\hspace{2cm}} - \underline{\hspace{2cm}}) = \underline{\hspace{2cm}}$$

C–238

Mary bought 2 books that normally sell for $6.99, and
3 books that normally sell for $5.99.
How much money did she save?

$$2 \times (\underline{\hspace{2cm}} - \$4.99) + \underline{\hspace{2cm}} \times (\underline{\hspace{2cm}} - \$4.99) = \underline{\hspace{2cm}}$$

$$2 \times (\underline{\hspace{2cm}}) + 3 \times (\underline{\hspace{2cm}}) = \underline{\hspace{2cm}}$$

C–239

Sally bought 3 books.
What is the most money that she could have saved on the books?

$$3 \times (\underline{\hspace{2cm}} - \underline{\hspace{2cm}}) = \underline{\hspace{2cm}}$$

PROBLEM SOLVING

Circle the letters of the expressions that describe the amount of money spent for each purchase. Then complete the computation to answer each question.

Example

The hardware store sells quarts of paint for $4.95 and gallon cans of paint for $16.95. Juanita purchased 2 quarts of white paint, 3 quarts of blue paint, and a gallon of red paint. How much did she pay for the paint?

    a. $(1 \times \$4.95) + (2 \times \$16.95)$ b. $(3 \times \$4.95) + (3 \times \$16.95)$

    (c.) $(5 \times \$4.95) + (1 \times \$16.95)$ d. $(5 \times \$16.95) + (1 \times \$4.95)$

                  ANSWER: <u>$ 41.70</u>

C–240

The supermarket is selling limes at 3/59¢ and lemons at 4/69¢. How much money does John need to buy 6 limes and a dozen lemons?

    a. $(6 \times 59¢) + (12 \times 69¢)$ b. $(2 \times 69¢) + (3 \times 69¢)$

    c. $(2 \times 59¢) + (4 \times 69¢)$ d. $(2 \times 59¢) + (3 \times 69¢)$

               ANSWER:_____

C–241

The supermarket sells cans of vegetables at 2/99¢ and cans of fruit at 3/99¢. Jim bought 2 cans of corn, 1 can of beans, 3 cans of peas, 2 cans of peaches, 1 can of pears, 2 cans of applesauce, and a can of plums. How much money did Jim spend?

    a. $12 \times 99¢$ b. $(6 \times 99¢) + (6 \times 99¢)$

    c. $(3 \times 99¢) + (2 \times 99¢)$ d. $5 \times 99¢$

               ANSWER:_____

C–242

The supermarket sells oranges at $1.09 per dozen. Sue purchased 1/2 dozen oranges on Wednesday and another 1/2 dozen oranges on Friday. How much did she pay for the dozen oranges?

    a. $(2 \times \$1.09)$ b. $(\$1.09 \div 2) + (\$1.09 \div 2)$

    c. $(1 \times \$1.09)$ d. $2 \times (\$1.09 \div 2)$

               ANSWER:_____

PROBLEM SOLVING

Circle the letter of the expression that describes the amount of money spent for each purchase. Then complete the computation to answer each question.

C–243

The sale price on socks in the department store was 2 pairs for $5.99. Jose decided to buy 5 pairs of socks. How much money did he spend?

    a. $5 \times \$5.99$

    b. $(2 \times \$5.99) + \$2.99$

    c. $(2 \times \$5.99) + (\$5.99 \div 2)$

    d. $(3 \times \$5.99)$

             ANSWER:_____

C–244

A garden and nursery center is selling 3 bags of lawn fertilizer for $23.89. Each bag will fertilize 5,000 square feet. Jill bought enough fertilizer for 24,354 square feet. How much did she pay for the fertilizer?

    a. $5 \times \$23.89$

    b. $(3 \times \$23.89) + (\$23.89 \div 3)$

    c. $3 \times \$23.89$

    d. $\$23.89 + 2 \times (\$23.89 \div 3)$

             ANSWER:_____

C–245

Jose found the same fertilizer on sale at 4 bags for $31.81. He needed fertilizer for 25,322 square feet. How much did Jose pay for his fertilizer?

    a. $6 \times \$31.81$

    b. $\$31.81 + (\$31.81 \div 2)$

    c. $\$31.81 + (\$31.81 \div 4)$

    d. $\$31.81 + 2 \times (\$31.81 \div 4)$

             ANSWER:_____

C–246

Taxi cab rates are $1.30 for the first 3/10 of a mile and 20¢ for each additional 1/10 of a mile. The distance from the train station to the nearest hotel is 1 3/4 miles. What is the cab fare for the journey?

    a. $17 \times 20¢$

    b. $\$1.30 + (17 \times 20¢)$

    c. $\$1.30 + (15 \times 20¢)$

    d. $\$1.30 + (14 \times 20¢)$

             ANSWER:_____

COMPARING LENGTHS

Pairs of lines are drawn on a grid.
Complete each statement by placing one of the symbols >, <, or = in the box.

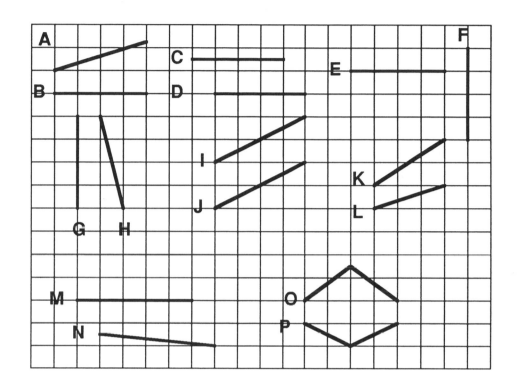

Example length of A $\boxed{>}$ length of B

D–1 length of C $\boxed{}$ length of D

D–2 length of E $\boxed{}$ length of F

D–3 length of G $\boxed{}$ length of H

D–4 length of I $\boxed{}$ length of J

D–5 length of K $\boxed{}$ length of L

D–6 length of M $\boxed{}$ length of N

D–7 length of O $\boxed{}$ length of P

COMPARING LENGTHS

Paths and lines are drawn on a grid.
Complete each statement by placing one of the symbols >, <, or = in the box.

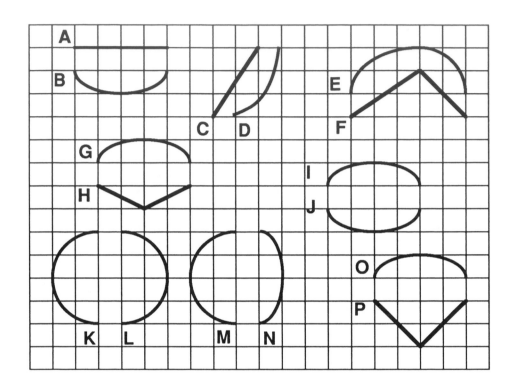

Example length of A | < | length of B

D–8 length of C | | length of D

D–9 length of E | | length of F

D–10 length of G | | length of H

D–11 length of I | | length of J

D–12 length of K | | length of L

D–13 length of M | | length of N

D–14 length of O | | length of P

COMPARING LENGTHS

Name the longest and the shortest line segments pictured in each figure.

Example

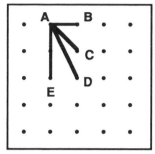

Longest: $\overline{AD}$

Shortest: $\overline{AB}$

D–15

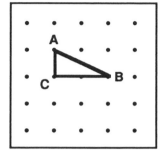

Longest: _____

Shortest: _____

D–16

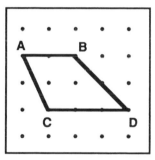

Longest: _____

Shortest: _____

D–17

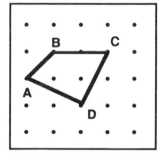

Longest: _____

Shortest: _____

D–18

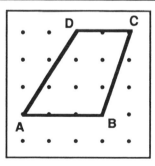

Longest: _____

Shortest: _____

D–19

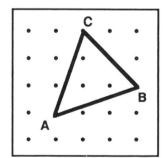

Longest: _____

Shortest: _____

COMPARING PATHS

Compare the length of path AB to the length of path XY.
Indicate the relationship by placing one of the symbols <, >, or = in the box.

Example

AB **>** XY

D–20

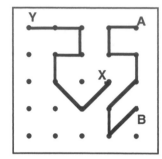

AB ☐ XY

D–21

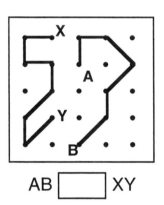

AB ☐ XY

D–22

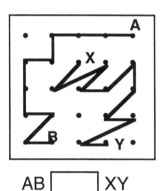

AB ☐ XY

D–23

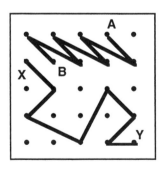

AB ☐ XY

D–24

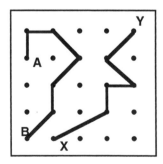

AB ☐ XY

COMPARING PERIMETERS

Circle the letter of the figure which has the largest perimeter.

Example

A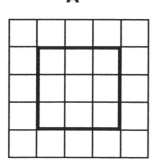

B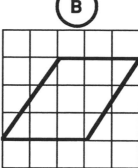

C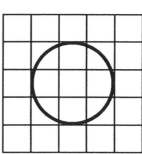

D–25

A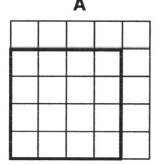

B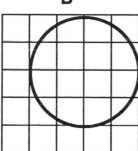

C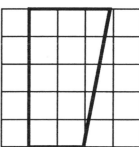

D–26

A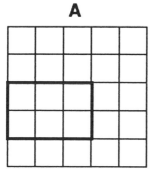

B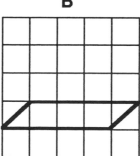

C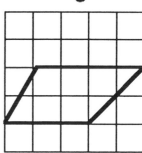

D–27

A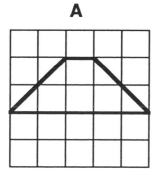

B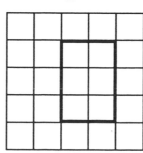

C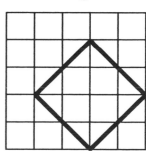

ESTIMATING PERIMETERS

For each figure, estimate the perimeter in grid units.
Circle the best estimate.

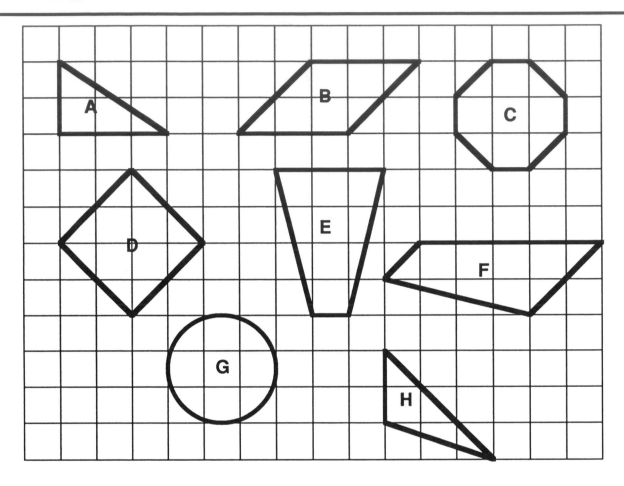

Example	Figure A :	3	7	⑨		**D–31**	Figure E :	8	12	14
D–28	Figure B :	6	10	12		**D–32**	Figure F :	7	10	13
D–29	Figure C :	7	9	12		**D–33**	Figure G :	7	9	12
D–30	Figure D :	8	11	14		**D–34**	Figure H :	3	7	9

COMPARING PERIMETERS

Complete each statement by placing one of the symbols >, <, or = in the box .
Assume one unit is the length of an edge of a square in the grid.

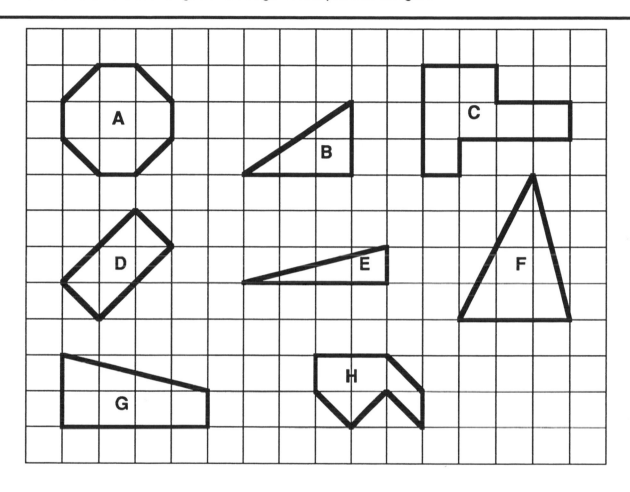

Example perimeter of A **>** 8 units

D–35 perimeter of B ☐ 8 units

D–36 perimeter of C ☐ 14 units

D–37 perimeter of D ☐ 6 units

D–38 10 units ☐ perimeter of E

D–39 11 units ☐ perimeter of F

D–40 12 units ☐ perimeter of G

D–41 8 units ☐ perimeter of H

COMPARING PERIMETERS

Complete each statement by placing one of the symbols >, <, or = in the box .
Assume one unit is the length of an edge of a square in the grid.

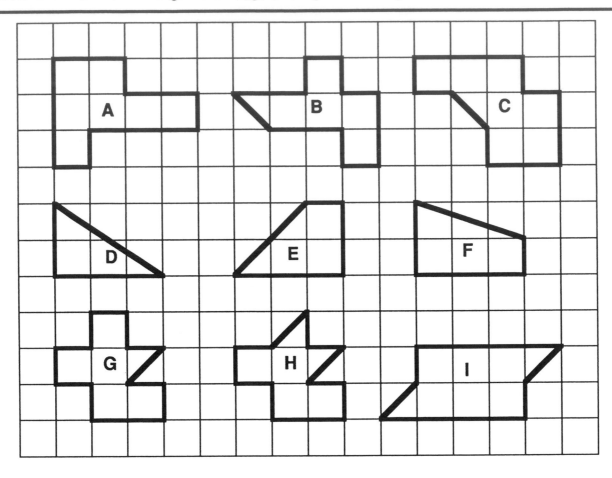

Example   perimeter of A **>** perimeter of B

D–42 perimeter of B ☐ perimeter of C

D–43 perimeter of A ☐ perimeter of C

D–44 perimeter of D ☐ perimeter of E

D–45 perimeter of E ☐ perimeter of F

D–46 perimeter of G ☐ perimeter of H

D–47 perimeter of H ☐ perimeter of I

D–48 perimeter of G ☐ perimeter of I

COMPUTING PERIMETERS

The lengths of some edges are marked on each figure.
Write the missing lengths in the circles and compute the perimeter of each figure.

Example

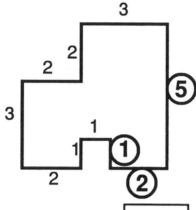

Perimeter = **22**

D–49

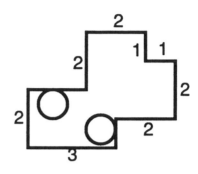

Perimeter = ☐

D–50

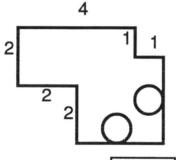

Perimeter = ☐

D–51

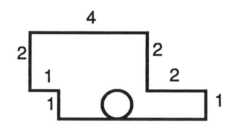

Perimeter = ☐

D–52

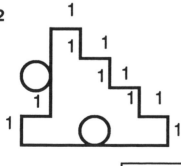

Perimeter = ☐

D–53

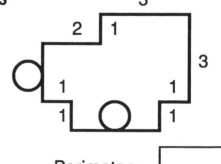

Perimeter = ☐

COMPUTING PERIMETERS

The lengths of some edges are marked on each figure.
Write the missing lengths in the circles, and compute the perimeter of each figure.

Example

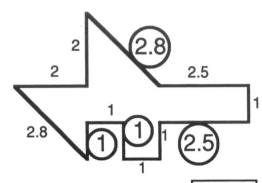

Perimeter = | 20.6 |

D–54

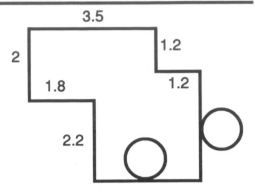

Perimeter = [ ]

D–55

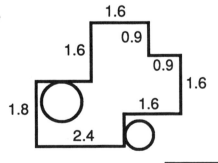

Perimeter = [ ]

D–56

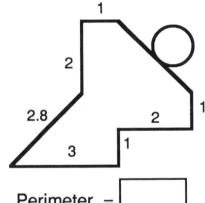

Perimeter = [ ]

D–57

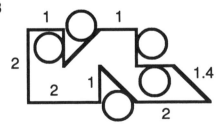

Perimeter = [ ]

D–58

Perimeter = [ ]

COMPUTING PERIMETERS

Each of the figures below have line symmetry.
Some lengths are marked on the figure.
Find the perimeter of each figure.

Example

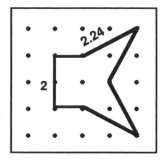

Perimeter = | 12.96 |

D–59

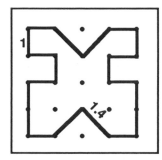

Perimeter =

D–60

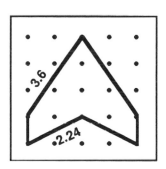

Perimeter =

D–61

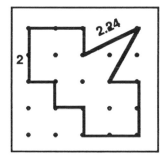

Perimeter =

D–62

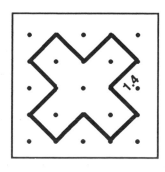

Perimeter =

D–63

Perimeter =

FINDING PERIMETERS OF POLYGONS

In each exercise a polygon is identified.
The lengths of some of the sides of the polygon are given.
Determine the perimeter of the polygon, if possible.
If you cannot determine the perimeter, place a "?" in the answer column.

	Polygon	Lengths	Perimeter
Example	Rhombus	4	16
D–64	Rectangle	3 7	
D–65	Isosceles Triangle	3 6	
D–66	Parallelogram	3 7	
D–67	Trapezoid	3 4 7	
D–68	Square	4	
D–69	Right Triangle	3 4	

COMPARING PERIMETERS

The figures in each exercise are similar.
Find the missing lengths, and compute the perimeter of each figure.

Example

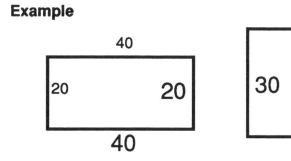

40
20   20
40

Perimeter = __120__

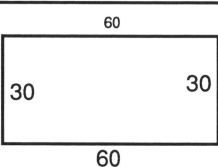

60
30   30
60

Perimeter = __180__

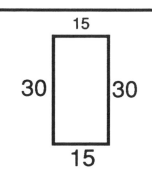

15
30   30
15

Perimeter = __90__

D–70

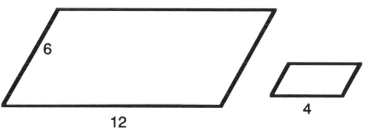

 6

12

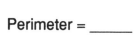

4

 5

Perimeter = _____

Perimeter = _____

Perimeter = _____

D–71

16   16

20

48

Perimeter = _____

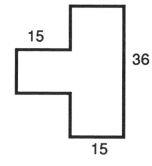

15

36

15

Perimeter = _____

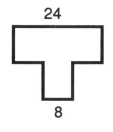

24

8

Perimeter = _____

COMPARING PERIMETERS

All figures below are similar and have line symmetry.
Find the perimeter of each figure.

Example

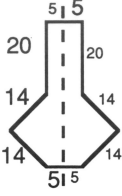

Perimeter = <u>116</u>

D–72

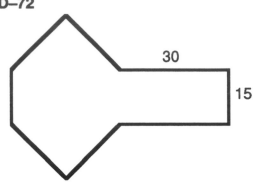

Perimeter = _____

D–73

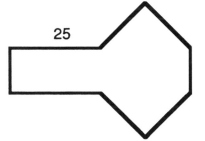

Perimeter = _____

D–74

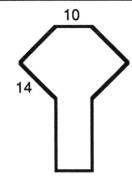

Perimeter = _____

D–75

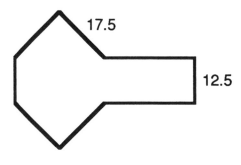

Perimeter = _____

D–76

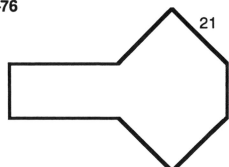

Perimeter = _____

USING SIMILARITY TO COMPUTE PERIMETERS

In each exercise the triangles pictured are similar.
The lengths of some sides are given.
Find the lengths of the indicated segments and the perimeter of triangle ABC.

Example

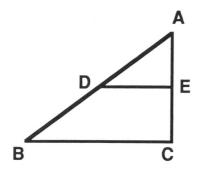

AE = 3   EC = 3   DE = 4

AD = 5   BC = __8__   BD = __5__

Perimeter △ ABC = __24__

D–77

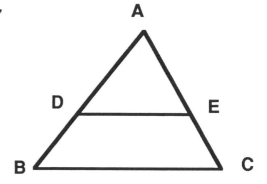

AE = 5   DB = 3   DE = 6

AD = 4   EC = ____   BC = _____

Perimeter △ ABC = _____

D–78

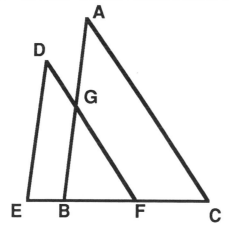

BG = 5   BF = 4   FC = 4

FG = 6   DG = 3   AC = _____

DE = _____   AG = _____

Perimeter △ ABC = _____

D–79

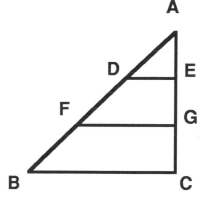

AE = 1   AC = 3   DE = 1

EG = 1   AF = 2.8   AD = _____

BF = _____   AB = _____   BC = _____

Perimeter △ ABC = _____

USING SIMILARITY TO COMPUTE PERIMETERS

The lengths of some sides are given for each polygon.
Find the lengths of the indicated segments and the perimeter of the indicated polygon.

Example

All triangles are similar.

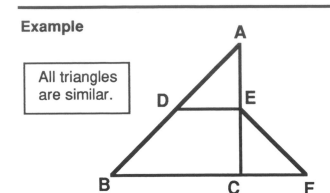

AE = 1   EC = 1   DE = 1

AD = 1.4   BC = 2   BD = 1.4

EF = 1.4   CF = 1

Perimeter ABFE = 8.2

D–80

All triangles are similar.

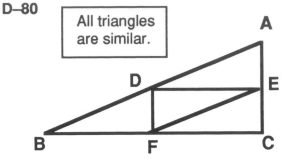

AE = 2.5   EC = 2.5   BD = 6.5

AD = 6.5   BC = 12   BF = _____

DF = _____   DE = _____   EF = _____

Perimeter △ EFC = _____

D–81   ABCD is a rectangle.
All right triangles are similar.

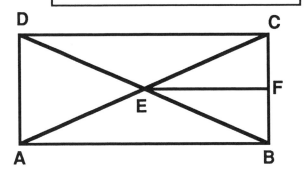

AB = 12   EC = 6.5   CF = 2.5

CB = 5   AE = _____   EF = _____

DA = _____ DB = _____

Perimeter △ BEF = _____

D–82   ABCD is a rhombus.
All triangles are similar.

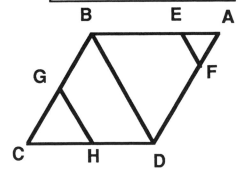

AB = 8   AF = 2   CG = 4

BD = 8   GH = _____   BE = _____

DF = _____ EF = _____   DH = _____

Perimeter EFDHGB = _____

PERIMETERS OF CONGRUENT AND SIMILAR FIGURES

The perimeter, rounded to the nearest tenth, of figure A = 9.2, figure B = 6.8, and figure C = 6.4.
Determine the perimeter of each figure below to the nearest tenth.

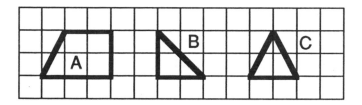

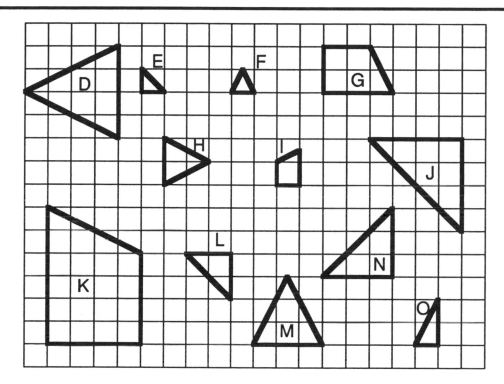

Example
perimeter of D = __12.8__

D–83
perimeter of E = _____

D–84
perimeter of F = _____

D–85
perimeter of G = _____

D–86
perimeter of H = _____

D–87
perimeter of I = _____

D–88
perimeter of J = _____

D–89
perimeter of K = _____

D–90
perimeter of L = _____

D–91
perimeter of M = _____

D–92
perimeter of N = _____

D–93
perimeter of O = _____

PERIMETERS OF CONGRUENT AND SIMILAR FIGURES

The perimeter, rounded to the nearest tenth, of figure A = 9.2, figure B = 6.8, and figure C = 6.4.
Determine the perimeter of each figure below to the nearest tenth.

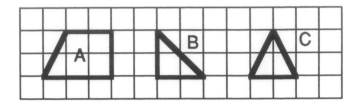

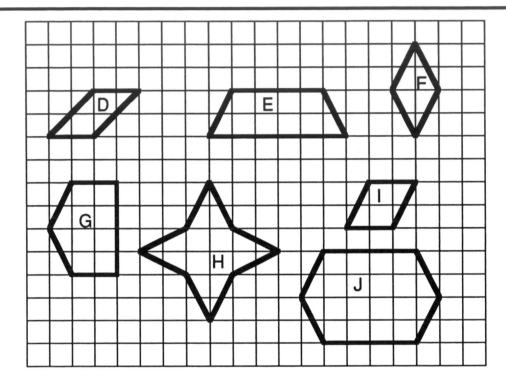

Example
perimeter of D = __9.6__

D–94
perimeter of E = _____

D–95
perimeter of F = _____

D–96
perimeter of G = _____

D–97
perimeter of H = _____

D–98
perimeter of I = _____

D–99
perimeter of J = _____

DRAWING POLYGONS

On the isometric geoboards below, draw each described polygon.

Example   A parallelogram with perimeter 10

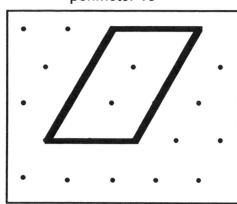

D–100   A parallelogram different from the Example with perimeter 10

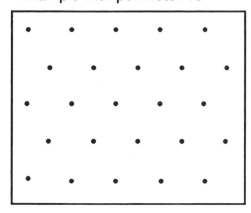

D–101   A triangle with perimeter 12

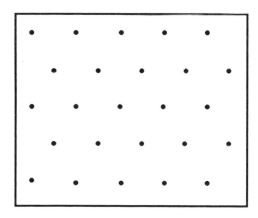

D–102   A trapezoid with perimeter 11

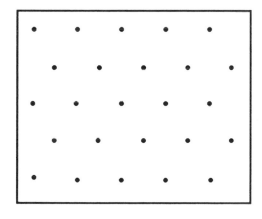

D–103   A hexagon with perimeter 10

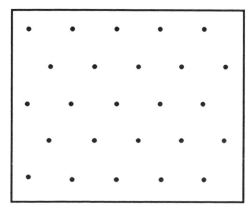

D–104   A pentagon with perimeter 9

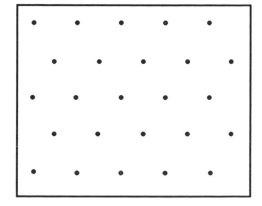

DRAWING POLYGONS

Draw a polygon similar to the given polygon.
Make your drawing as large as possible on the given grid.
Determine the perimeter of your drawing.

Example

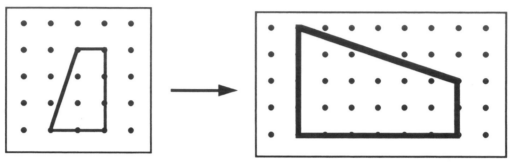

Perimeter = 9.16

Perimeter = **18.32**

D–105

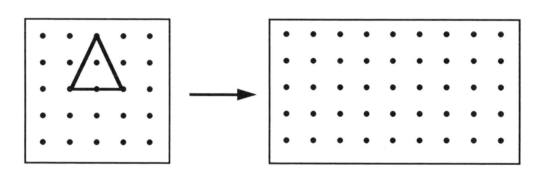

Perimeter = 6.47

Perimeter = _____

D–106

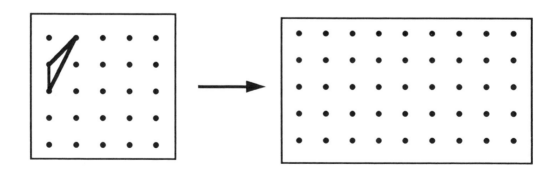

Perimeter = 4.65

Perimeter = _____

COMPARING PERIMETER AND CIRCUMFERENCE

The diameter of each circle is 4 centimeters.
Find the perimeter of each inscribed and circumscribed polygon.
Use each set of perimeters to approximate the circumference of the circle.

Example

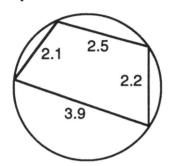

Approximate
Circumference

<u>13.8</u>

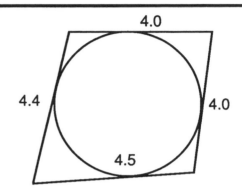

Perimeter = <u>10.7</u>

Perimeter = <u>16.9</u>

D–107

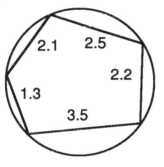

Approximate
Circumference

———

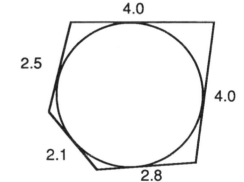

Perimeter = _____

Perimeter = _____

D–108

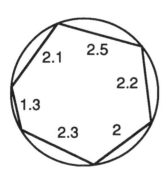

Approximate
Circumference

———

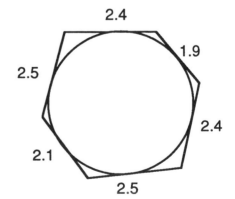

Perimeter = _____

Perimeter = _____

COMPARING PERIMETER AND CIRCUMFERENCE

The diameter of each circle is 4 centimeters.
Find the perimeter of each regular inscribed and circumscribed polygon.
Use each set of perimeters to approximate the circumference of the circle.

Example

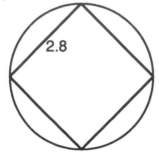

Approximate
Circumference

13.6

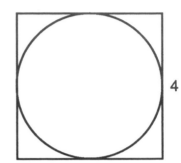

Perimeter = **11.2**

Perimeter = **16**

D–109

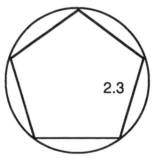

Approximate
Circumference

_____

Perimeter = _____

Perimeter = _____

D–110

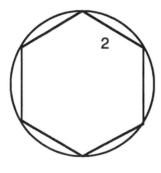

Approximate
Circumference

_____

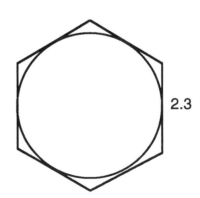

Perimeter = _____

Perimeter = _____

COMPARING AREAS

Compare each polygon with polygon A.
Separate the polygons into two sets, the first with figures having areas less than that of
A and the second with areas greater than figure A.

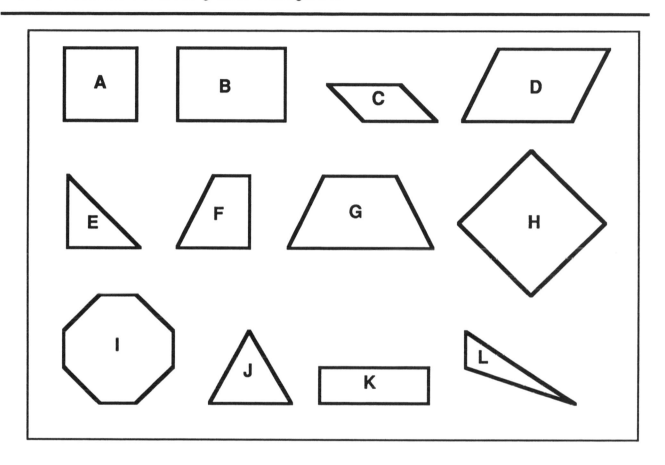

D–111 Polygons with area less than the area of polygon A

_____

D–112 Polygons with area greater than the area of polygon A

_____

COMPARING AREAS

Figure A has an area of 4 square centimeters.

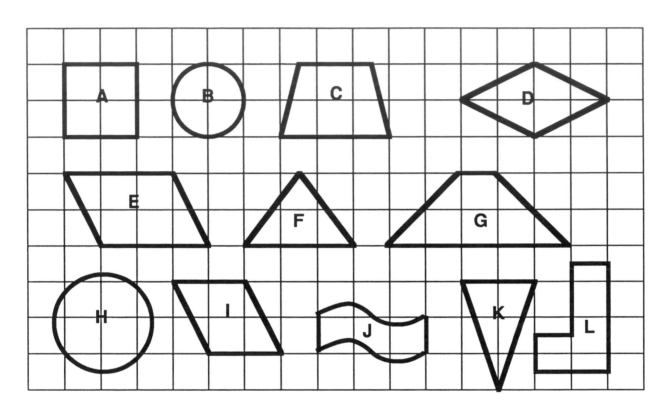

D–113 List the letters of all figures with areas less than 4 square centimeters.

_____

D–114 List the letters of all figures with areas greater than 4 square centimeters.

_____

D–115 List the letters of all figures with areas equal to 4 square centimeters.

_____

COMPARING AREAS

Polygon ABCDE is divided into 8 regions.
Compare the areas of the polygons formed by combining the regions listed. Place one of the symbols <, =, or > in the box.
If it is impossible to determine a solution, place a "?" in the box.

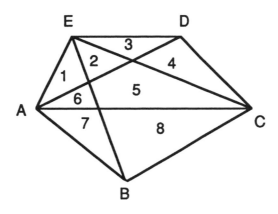

Example	Area of regions 1, 2, 3	**>**	Area of regions 1, 2, 6
D–116	Area of regions 2, 5		Area of regions 4, 5
D–117	Area of regions 2, 3, 5		Area of regions 2, 3, 4
D–118	Area of regions 3, 4		Area of regions 2, 5
D–119	Area of regions 1, 2, 3		Area of regions 3, 4
D–120	Area of regions 1, 6, 7		Area of regions 1, 2, 3

COMPUTING AREA BY COUNTING

Separate each figure into unit squares and half squares.
Write the area of each figure in the box.

Example

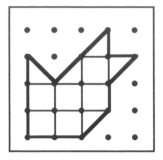

Area of figure = $8\frac{1}{2}$

D–121

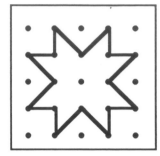

Area of figure =

D–122

Area of figure =

D–123

Area of figure =

D–124

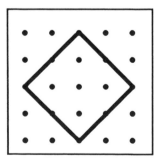

Area of figure =

D–125

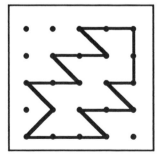

Area of figure =

COMPUTING AREA BY SUBTRACTION

Add one or more regions to each figure to form a rectangle with horizontal and vertical sides. Write the area of each figure in the appropriate box.

Example

D–126

D–127

AREA

Completed figure	9
Added regions	6
Original figure	3

AREA

Completed figure	
Added regions	
Original figure	

AREA

Completed figure	
Added regions	
Original figure	

D–128

D–129

D–130

AREA

Completed figure	
Added regions	
Original figure	

AREA

Completed figure	
Added regions	
Original figure	

AREA

Completed figure	
Added regions	
Original figure	

DRAWING FIGURES

One side of a polygon is drawn on a geoboard design.
Complete the figure described in each exercise.

Example   Parallelogram ABCD with area of 6 square units

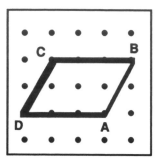

D–131   Rectangle ABCD with area of 6 square units

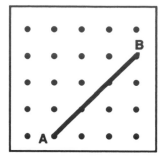

D–132   Triangle ABC with area of 8 square units

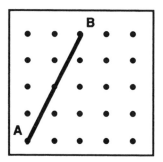

D–133   Square ABCD with area of 8 square units

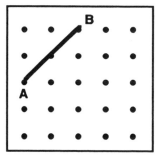

D–134   Trapezoid ABCD with area of 7 1/2 square units

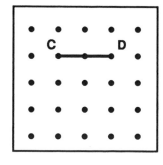

D–135   Isosceles triangle ABC with area of 6 square units

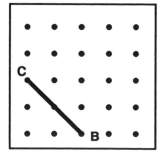

DRAWING FIGURES

One side of a polygon is drawn on a geoboard design.
Complete the figure described in each exercise.

Example   Triangle ABC with the
smallest possible area

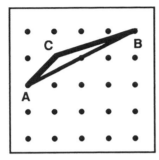

D–136   Rectangle ABCD with the
largest possible area

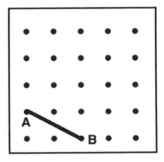

D–137   Quadrilateral ABCD with the
smallest possible area

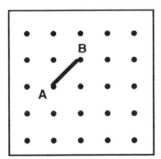

D–138   Triangle ABC with the
largest possible area

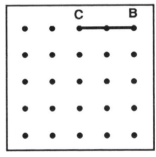

D–139   Triangle ABC with the
largest possible area

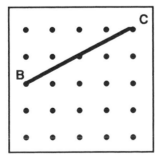

D–140   Quadrilateral ABCD with the
smallest possible area

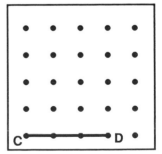

AREA IN TRIANGULAR UNITS

On the isometric grid to the right, figure A has an area of one triangular unit, and figure B has an area of 1/2 triangular unit.

Separate each figure in the exercises into triangular and 1/2 triangular units.

Write the area of the original figure in terms of triangular units.

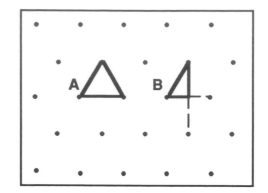

Example

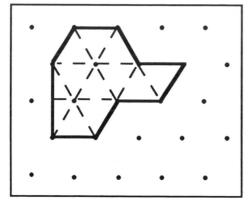

Area = 11

D–141

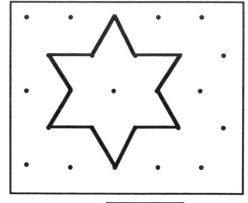

Area =

D–142

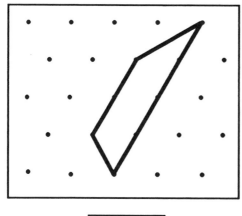

Area =

D–143

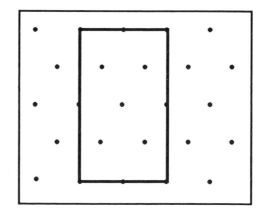

Area =

DRAWING FIGURES

One side of a polygon is drawn on an isomorphic grid.
The area of each polygon is given in triangular units.
Draw a polygon that satisfies the description.

Example

Triangle ABC with an area of 9

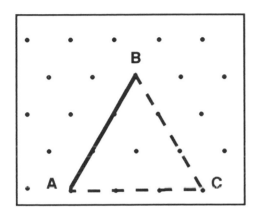

D–144

Parallelogram ABCD with an area of 12

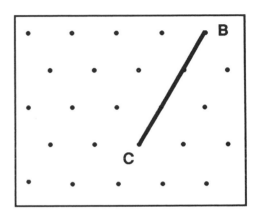

D–145

Rectangle ABCD with an area of 8

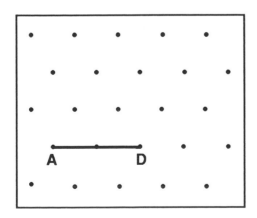

D–146

Right triangle ABC with an area of 8

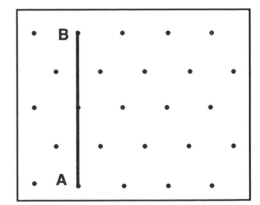

PERIMETER AND AREA

Find the perimeter and area of each rectangle.

Example

9

3 | Perimeter = __24__

Area = __27__

D–147

10

2

Perimeter = _____

Area = _____

D–148

6

6 | Perimeter = _____

Area = _____

D–149

8

4 | Perimeter = _____

Area = _____

D–150

5

7

Perimeter = _____

Area = _____

D–151

$7\frac{1}{2}$

$4\frac{1}{2}$ | Perimeter = _____

Area = _____

D–152

$8\frac{1}{2}$

$3\frac{1}{2}$ | Perimeter = _____

Area = _____

PERIMETER AND AREA

The length of each side of a rectangle is shown.
Find the perimeter and area of each rectangle.

Example

15

2

Perimeter = _34_

Area = _30_

D–153

12

$2\frac{1}{2}$

Perimeter = _____

Area = _____

D–154

3

10

Perimeter = _____

Area = _____

D–155

4

$7\frac{1}{2}$

Perimeter = _____

Area = _____

D–156

6

5

Perimeter = _____

Area = _____

PERIMETER AND AREA

Each figure below is a part of a rectangle which has an area of 36 square units.
Use the given information to shade in unit squares to complete each rectangle.
Find the perimeter of each rectangle.

Example   A rectangle with one side equal to 2 units

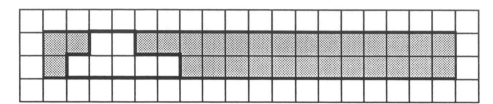

Perimeter = __40__

D–157

A rectangle with one side equal to 3 units

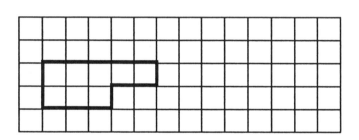

Perimeter = _____

D–158

A rectangle with one side equal to 6 units

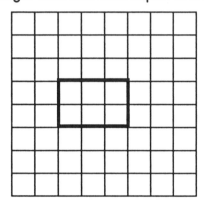

Perimeter = _____

D–159

A rectangle with one side equal to 8 units

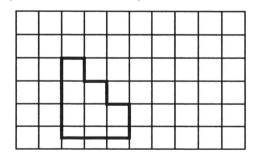

Perimeter = _____

D–160

A rectangle with one side equal to 9 units

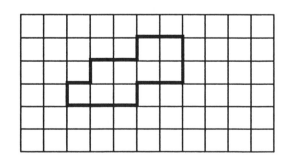

Perimeter = _____

PERIMETER AND AREA

Each figure below is part of a rectangle which has a perimeter of 20 units.
Use the given information to shade in unit squares to complete each rectangle.
Find the area of each rectangle.

Example   A rectangle with one side equal to 8 units

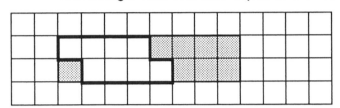

Area = ___16___

D–161

A rectangle with one side equal to 6 units

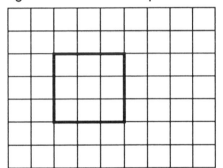

Area = _____

D–162

A rectangle with one side equal to 3 units

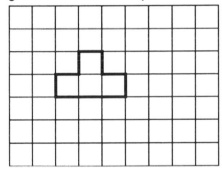

Area = _____

D–163

A rectangle with one side equal to 5 units

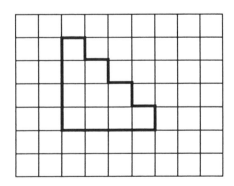

Area = _____

D–164

A rectangle with one side equal to 4 1/2 units

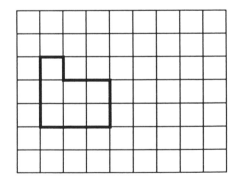

Area = _____

PERIMETER AND AREA

The perimeter of each parallelogram is 26 units.
Estimate the area of each parallelogram in square units.

Example

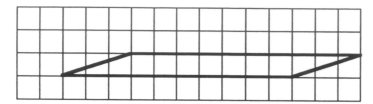

Area = <u>10</u>

D–165

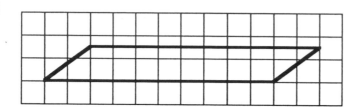

Area = _____

D–166

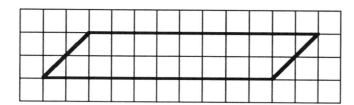

Area = _____

D–167

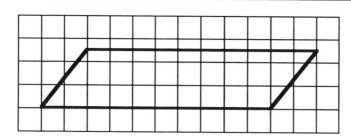

Area = _____

D–168

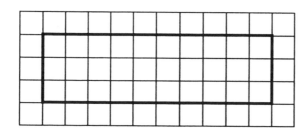

Area = _____

COMPUTING AREA

The lengths of some sides are given for each figure.
Divide each figure into rectangular regions.
Write the area of each region inside the rectangle.
Then compute the area of the given figure by adding the areas of the regions.

Example

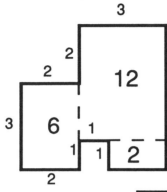

Area of figure = | 20 |

D–169

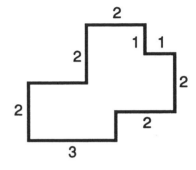

Area of figure = | |

D–170

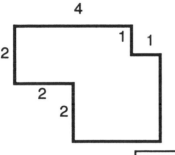

Area of figure = | |

D–171

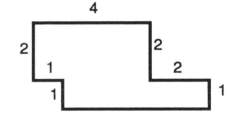

Area of figure = | |

D–172

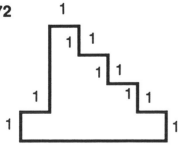

Area of figure = | |

D–173

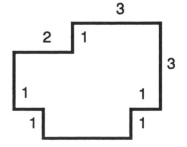

Area of figure = | |

COMPUTING AREA

The lengths of some sides are given for each figure.
Make each figure into a rectangle by adding regions to the figure.
Write the area within each added region.
Then fill in the boxes with the appropriate areas.

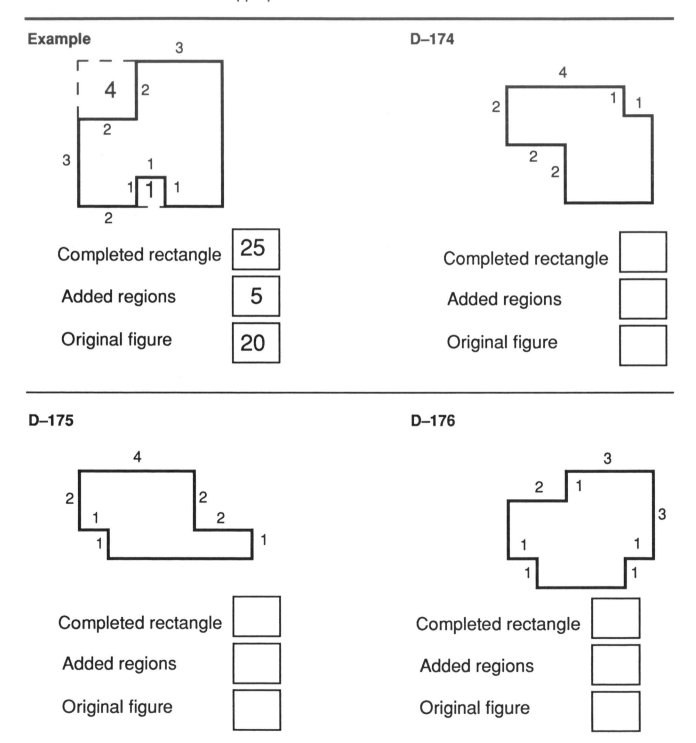

Example

Completed rectangle 25

Added regions 5

Original figure 20

D–174

Completed rectangle

Added regions

Original figure

D–175

Completed rectangle

Added regions

Original figure

D–176

Completed rectangle

Added regions

Original figure

COMPUTING AREA

The length of some sides are given for each figure.
Divide each figure into triangular or rectangular regions.
Write the area within each region.
Then compute the area of the original figure by adding areas.

Example

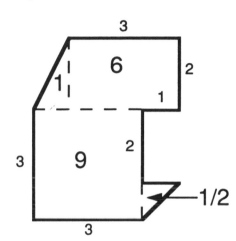

Area of figure = | 16 1/2 |

D–177

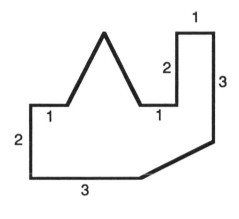

Area of figure = | |

D–178

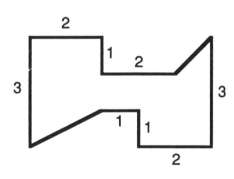

Area of figure = | |

D–179

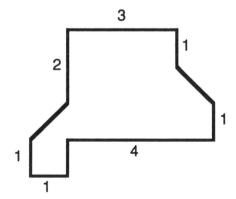

Area of figure = | |

213

FINDING AREA

Find the number of shaded squares in each exercise.
Circle the number in the box that is the best estimate of the area of the circle.

Example   Shaded squares = __4__   **D–180**   Shaded squares = _____

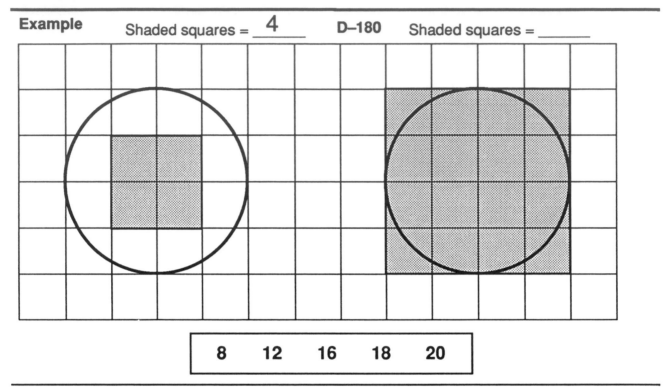

| 8 | 12 | 16 | 18 | 20 |

D–181   Shaded squares = _____   **D–182**   Shaded squares = _____

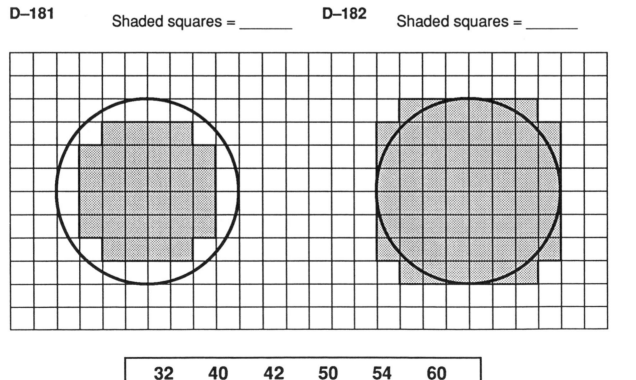

| 32 | 40 | 42 | 50 | 54 | 60 |

FINDING AREA

Find the number of shaded squares in each exercise.
Circle the number in the box that is the best estimate of the area of the circle.

Example   Shaded squares = __12__   **D–183**   Shaded squares = _____

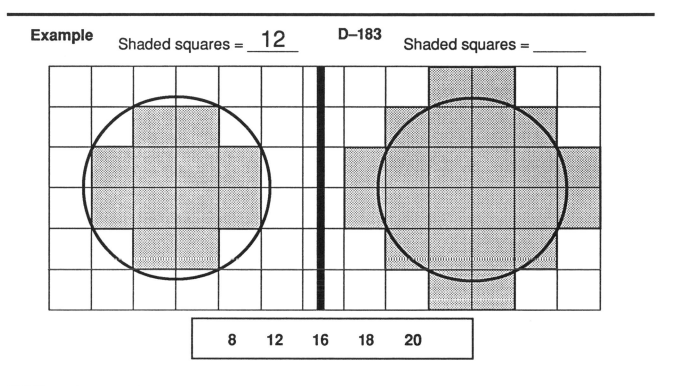

| 8 | 12 | 16 | 18 | 20 |

D–184   Shaded squares = _____   **D–185**   Shaded squares = _____

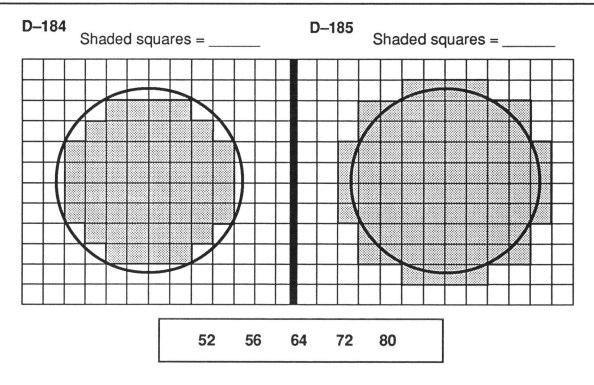

| 52 | 56 | 64 | 72 | 80 |

ESTIMATING AREA

Find the number of shaded squares in each exercise.
Circle the number in the box that is the best estimate of the area of the shape.

Example Shaded squares = __8__

D–186 Squares containing any part of the shape = _____

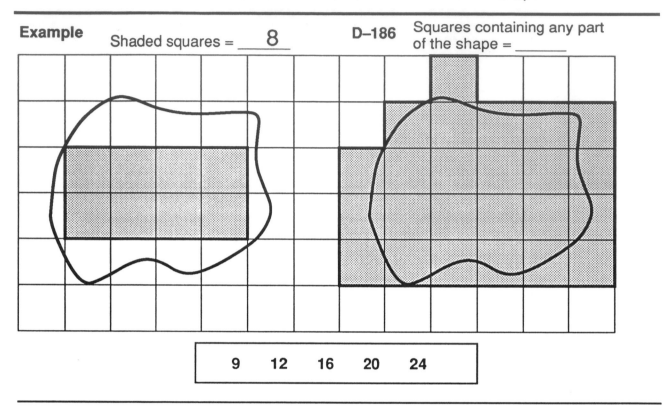

9	12	16	20	24

D–187 Squares contained entirely inside of the shape = _____

D–188 Squares containing any part of the shape = _____

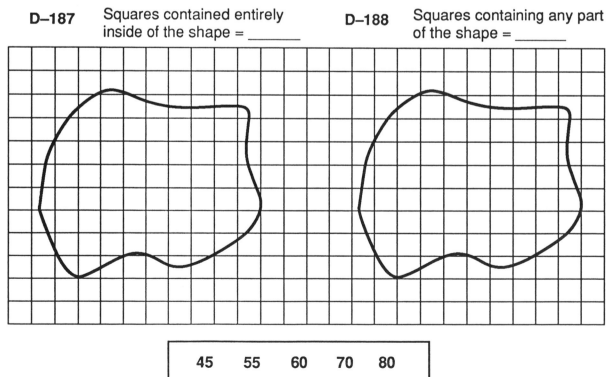

45	55	60	70	80

COMPARING CIRCLES

Each table lists information about the radius, diameter, circumference, or area for the two circles.
In each exercise complete the table.

Example

	r	d	C	A
A	0.5	1	3.14	0.79
B	1	2	6.28	3.14

D–189

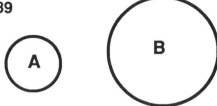

	r	d	C	A
A		1.5		
B	1.5			

D–190

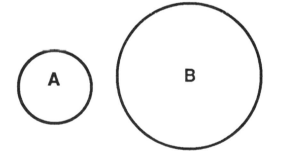

	r	d	C	A
A	1			
B			12.56	

D–191

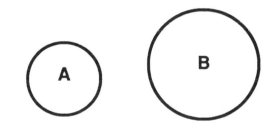

	r	d	C	A
A				3.14
B		3		

COMPUTING AREAS

In each exercise, the diameter of the larger circle is 4 units, and the smaller circle is 2 units in diameter. Find the area of the shaded regions.

Example

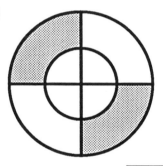

Area of shaded region = 9.42

D–192

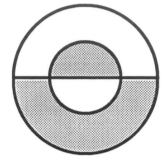

Area of shaded region =

D–193

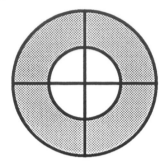

Area of shaded region =

D–194

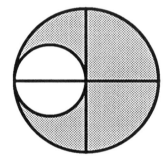

Area of shaded region =

D–195

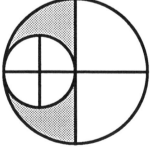

Area of shaded region =

D–196

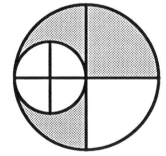

Area of shaded region =

RECTANGULAR SOLIDS

Rectangular solids are pictured on an isometric grid.
Indicate the number of unit cubes in each solid.

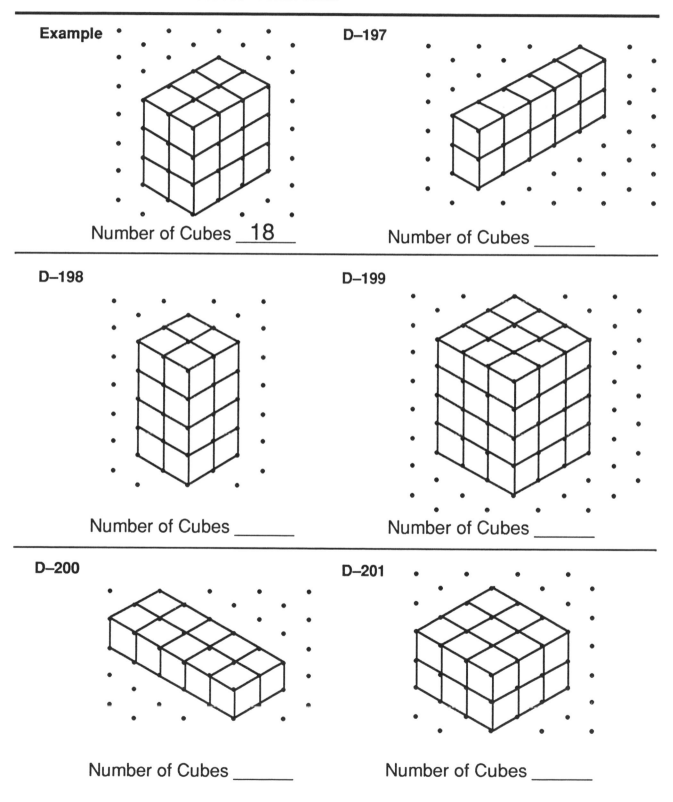

Example

Number of Cubes ___18___

D–197

Number of Cubes _____

D–198

Number of Cubes _____

D–199

Number of Cubes _____

D–200

Number of Cubes _____

D–201

Number of Cubes _____

RECTANGULAR SOLIDS

In each exercise below, 36 cubes are used to build a rectangular solid.
Each exercise pictures the base on which the solid is built.
Determine the height of each rectangular solid.

Example

Base ⟶

Height = ___9___

D–202

Base ⟶

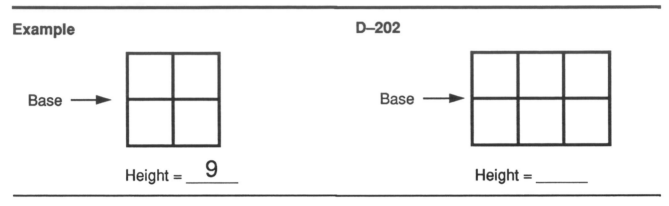

Height = _____

D–203

Base ⟶

Height = _____

D–204

Base ⟶

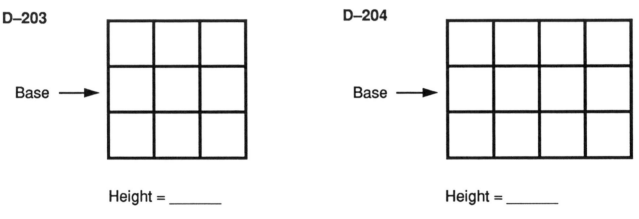

Height = _____

D–205

Base ⟶

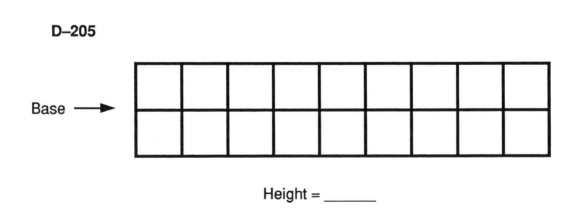

Height = _____

COUNTING CUBES IN SOLIDS

The following solids are built from cubes.
Indicate the number of cubes in each solid.
Assume that all nonvisible parts of the figures are solid.

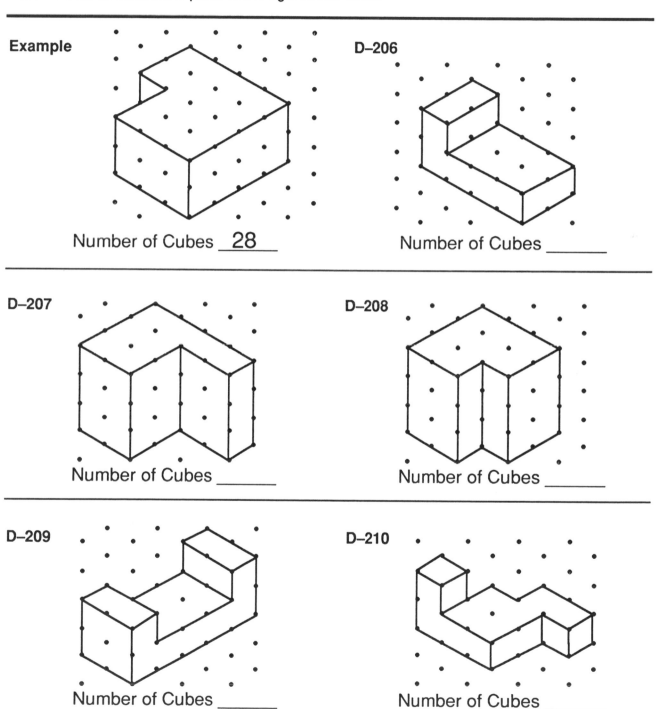

Example

Number of Cubes ___28___

D–206

Number of Cubes _____

D–207

Number of Cubes _____

D–208

Number of Cubes _____

D–209

Number of Cubes _____

D–210

Number of Cubes _____

VOLUME OF SOLIDS

Determine the number of cubes needed to build each figure.
Assume all nonvisible parts of the figures are solid.

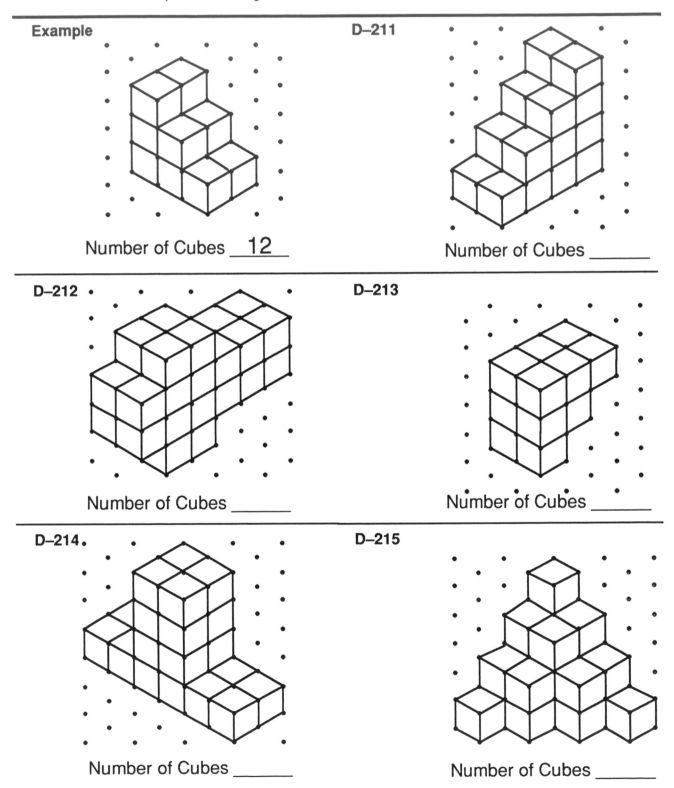

Example

Number of Cubes ___12___

D–211

Number of Cubes _____

D–212

Number of Cubes _____

D–213

Number of Cubes _____

D–214

Number of Cubes _____

D–215

Number of Cubes _____

MAKING SOLIDS BY FOLDING

When cut out and folded, each pattern forms one of the solids pictured.
Draw lines connecting each pattern to its corresponding solid.
Then determine the volume of the solid in unit cubes.

Example

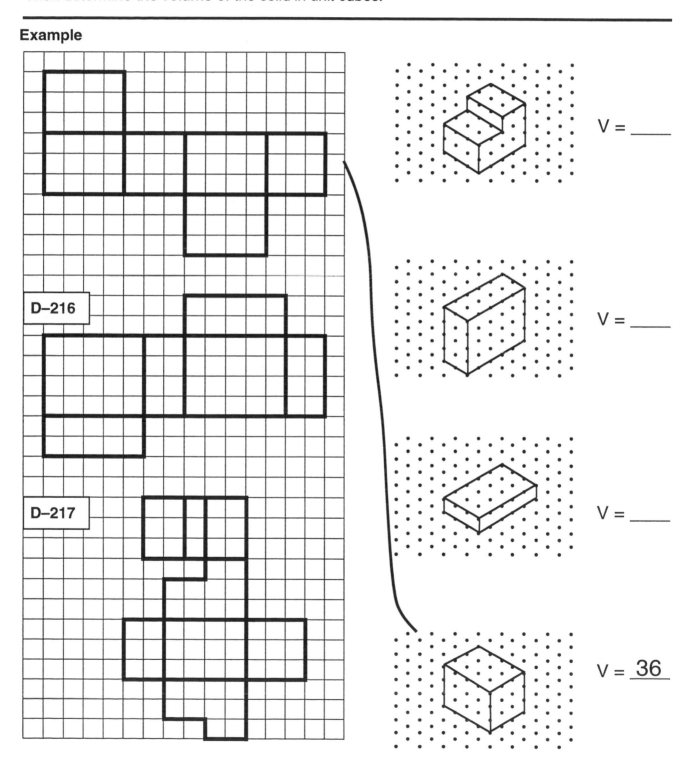

V = ____

V = ____

V = ____

V = 36

COUNTING CUBES IN SOLIDS

The solids below are constructed with cubes and half cubes.
In each exercise determine the number of cubes, the number of half cubes, and the volume.

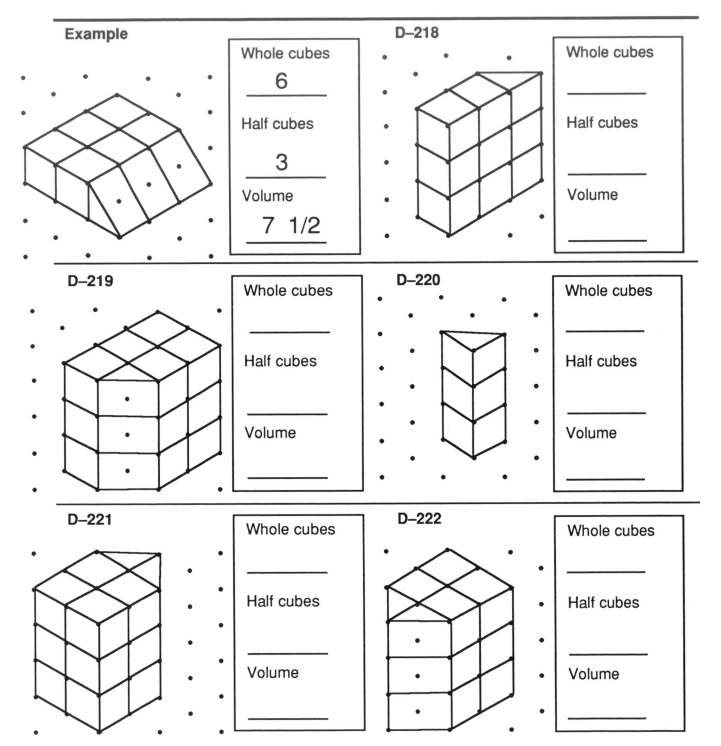

Example

Whole cubes

6

Half cubes

3

Volume

7 1/2

D–218

Whole cubes

_____

Half cubes

_____

Volume

_____

D–219

Whole cubes

_____

Half cubes

_____

Volume

_____

D–220

Whole cubes

_____

Half cubes

_____

Volume

_____

D–221

Whole cubes

_____

Half cubes

_____

Volume

_____

D–222

Whole cubes

_____

Half cubes

_____

Volume

_____

MAKING SOLIDS BY FOLDING

When cut out and folded, each pattern forms one of the solids pictured.
Draw lines connecting each pattern to its corresponding solid.
Then determine the volume of the solid in unit cubes.

Example

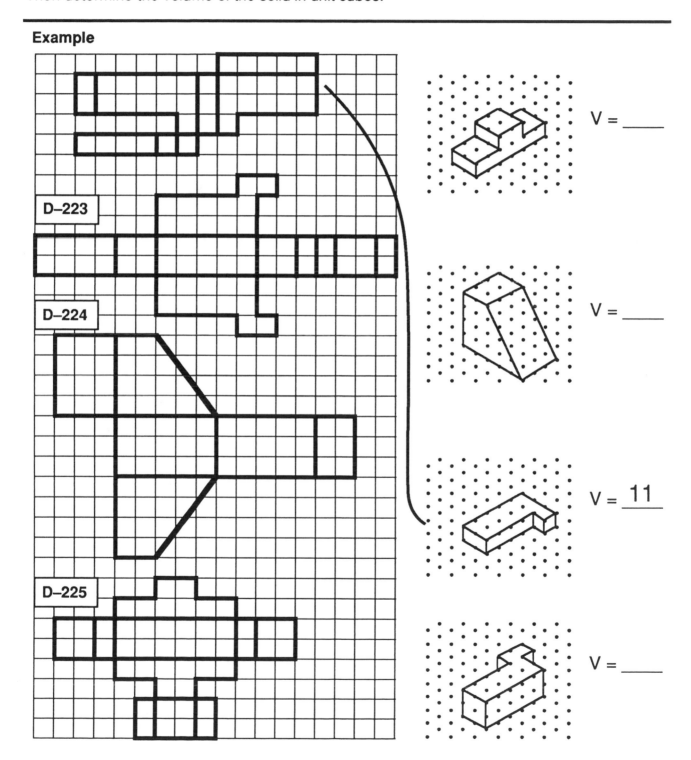

D–223

D–224

D–225

V = _____

V = _____

V = 11

V = _____

DRAWING SOLIDS

One surface of a solid is drawn on an isometric grid.
The volume of each solid is given in unit cubes.
Complete the drawing of the solid.

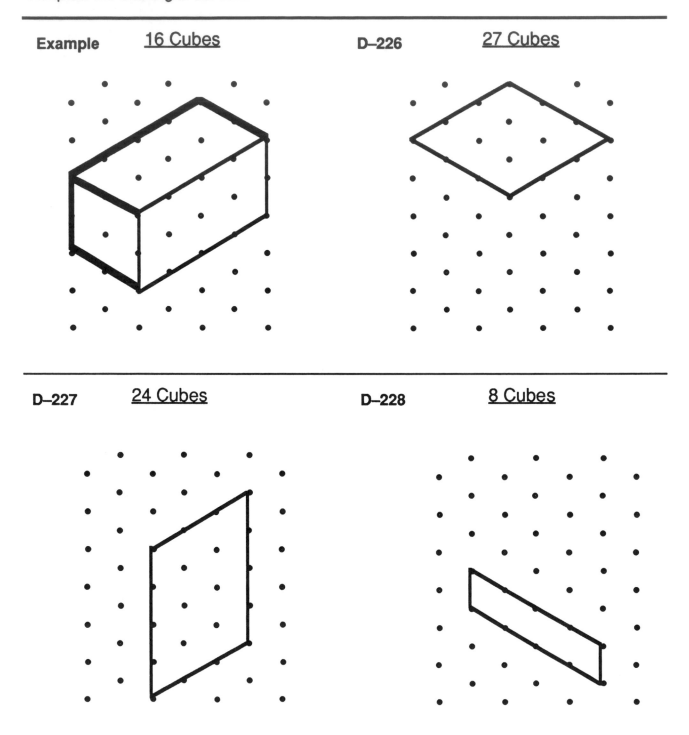

Example   16 Cubes   D–226   27 Cubes

D–227   24 Cubes   D–228   8 Cubes

COMPUTING VOLUME

The length of the diagonal line that indicates the depth of each solid is 4 units.
Compute the volume of each solid.

Example

D–229

D–230

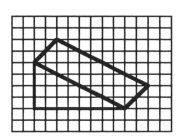
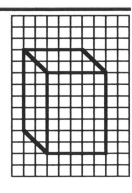

V = <u>100</u>

V = _____

V = _____

D–231

D–232

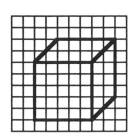
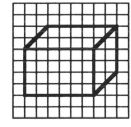

V = _____

V = _____

D–233

D–234

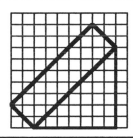
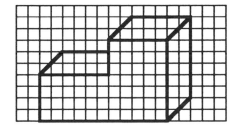

V = _____

V = _____

D–235

D–236

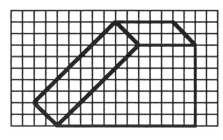
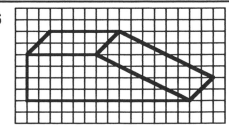

V = _____

V = _____

DECOMPOSING SOLIDS

The volumes of three solids are given.
Use the composition of these solids to compute the volumes of the other solids.

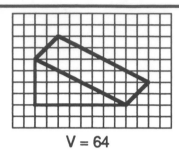

V = 64

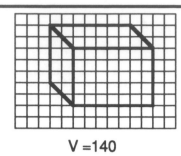

V =140

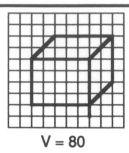

V = 80

Example

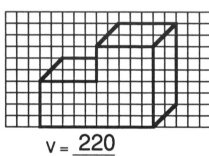

V = __220__

D–237

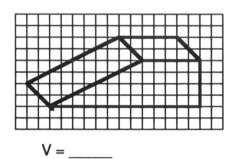

V = _____

D–238

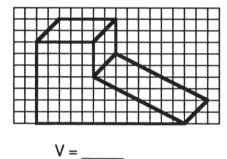

V = _____

D–239

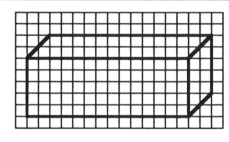

V = _____

D–240

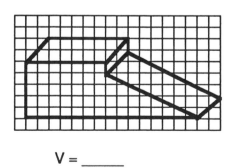

V = _____

D–241

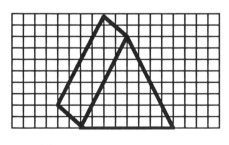

V = _____

FINDING THE DIMENSIONS OF A SOLID

The volume of each rectangular solid is given.
Select the letter that indicates the most likely dimensions of the solid.
Write the dimensions of each solid in the blanks.

a. 5, 5, 10	b. 3, 4, 6	c. 5, 6, 3	d. 3, 3, 10	e. 2, 8, 6
f. 3, 4, 8	g. 4, 6, 10	h. 3, 3, 8	i. 10, 12, 2	j. 5, 2, 25

Example

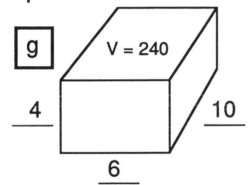

g   V = 240

4   10

6

D–242

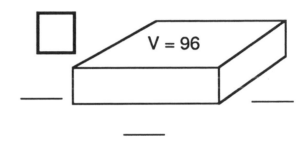

V = 96

D–243

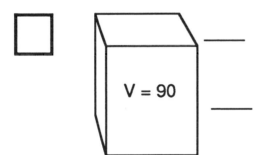

V = 90

D–244

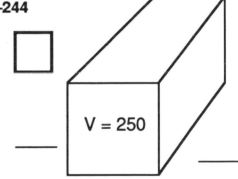

V = 250

D–245

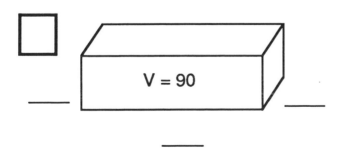

V = 90

D–246

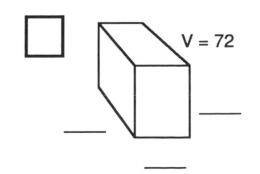

V = 72

ESTIMATING VOLUME

Some of the dimensions are given for each rectangular solid.
Circle the number in the box that is the best esimate of its volume.

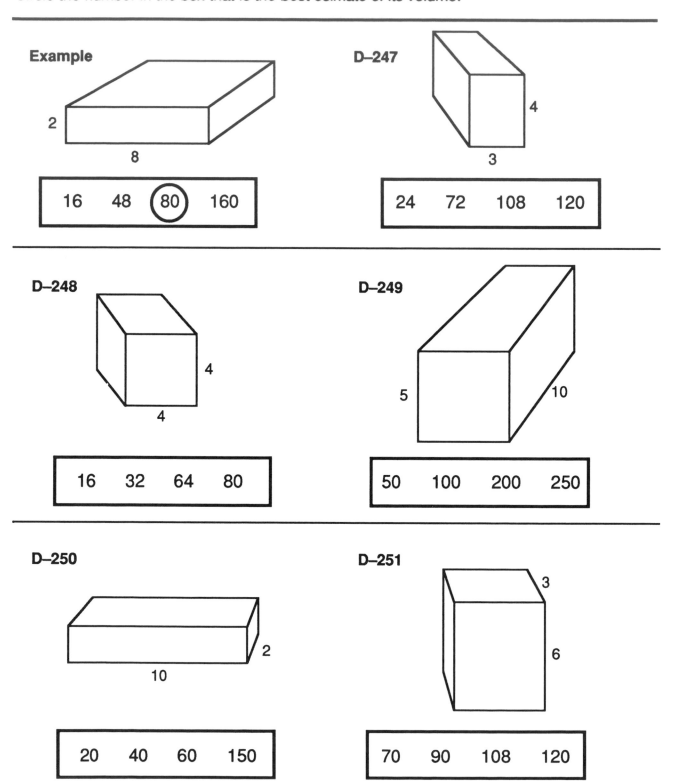

Example

2

8

| 16 | 48 | (80) | 160 |

D–247

4

3

| 24 | 72 | 108 | 120 |

D–248

4

4

| 16 | 32 | 64 | 80 |

D–249

5

10

| 50 | 100 | 200 | 250 |

D–250

2

10

| 20 | 40 | 60 | 150 |

D–251

3

6

| 70 | 90 | 108 | 120 |

COMPARING NUMBERS

Circle the largest number in each set.
Draw a box around the smallest number in each set.

Example

$$\frac{3}{4} \qquad \boxed{\frac{2}{8}} \qquad \frac{2}{5}$$

$$\enclose{circle}{\frac{8}{9}} \qquad \frac{3}{10} \qquad \frac{1}{2}$$

E–1

$$\frac{3}{12} \qquad \frac{1}{6} \qquad \frac{7}{10}$$

$$\frac{4}{8} \qquad \frac{3}{5} \qquad \frac{4}{6}$$

E–2

$$\frac{3}{8} \qquad \frac{1}{2} \qquad \frac{7}{16}$$

$$\frac{11}{16} \qquad \frac{3}{4} \qquad \frac{2}{8}$$

E–3

$$\frac{4}{10} \qquad \frac{3}{4} \qquad \frac{4}{9}$$

$$\frac{2}{3} \qquad \frac{3}{5} \qquad \frac{3}{8}$$

E–4

$$\frac{3}{8} \qquad \frac{7}{20} \qquad \frac{2}{5}$$

$$\frac{3}{10} \qquad \frac{1}{2} \qquad \frac{1}{4}$$

E–5

$$\frac{3}{5} \qquad \frac{5}{6} \qquad \frac{5}{8}$$

$$\frac{2}{3} \qquad \frac{3}{4} \qquad \frac{4}{9}$$

E–6 Which is the largest number in all the sets? _____

E–7 Which is the smallest number in all the sets? _____

COMPARING NUMBERS

Circle the largest number in each set.
Draw a box around the smallest number in each set.

Example

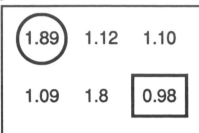

1.89   1.12   1.10

1.09   1.8   0.98

E–8

0.08   0.01   0.59

0.61   0.09   0.16

E–9

0.375   0.057   0.735

0.537   0.705   0.037

E–10

0.2   0.102   0.02

0.21   0.1   0.021

E–11

$\frac{3}{8}$ 1.8 $\frac{8}{9}$

0.62 $\frac{8}{5}$ 0.8

E–12

$2\frac{1}{4}$ 1.09 $\frac{4}{3}$

1.98 $\frac{7}{3}$ 2.05

E–13 Which is the largest number in all the sets? _____

E–14 Which is the smallest number in all the sets? _____

ORDERING NUMBERS

The symbols below are used to compare numbers.
Write the correct symbol in each box.

is greater than	is less than	is equal to
>	<	=

Example

$$1 \boxed{<} \frac{3}{8} + \frac{3}{4}$$

E–15

$$\frac{1}{2} \times \frac{3}{4} \ \square \ \frac{3}{4}$$

E–16

$$\frac{6}{7} \div \frac{6}{7} \ \square \ 1$$

E–17

$$\frac{1}{2} \ \square \ \frac{1}{2} \div 5$$

E–18

$$\frac{1}{4} - \frac{1}{12} \ \square \ \frac{1}{8}$$

E–19

$$3 \times \frac{1}{2} \ \square \ 3 \div \frac{1}{2}$$

E–20

$$\frac{7}{8} \div \frac{3}{5} \ \square \ \frac{5}{3} \times \frac{7}{8}$$

E–21

$$\frac{3}{5} \div \frac{1}{2} \ \square \ \frac{5}{3} \times \frac{2}{1}$$

FINDING COMMON MULTIPLES

Circle all the numbers that are common multiples of the two numbers above each box.
Then list 3 other numbers that are common multiples of the two numbers.

Example

6 and 9

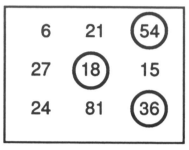

72, 90, 108

E–22

3 and 4

15	52	24
18	36	28
12	48	16

_____

E–23

8 and 12

64	24	36
4	32	96
48	60	56

_____

E–24

10 and 15

60	20	90
5	120	70
45	30	150

_____

What is the smallest number that is a common multiple of each of the
following pairs of numbers?

E–25
    6 and 9 _____

E–26
    3 and 4 _____

E–27
    8 and 12 _____

E–28
    10 and 15 _____

USING COMMON FACTORS

Circle the numbers in the box that are factors of each number.
Use these factors to reduce each fraction to lowest terms.

Example	72	(4)	5	(6)	7	(8)	(36)	48

E–29	80	4	6	7	8	12	16	24

E–30	256	4	8	12	14	16	32	48

E–31	144	4	7	9	32	48	72	81

E–32	81	3	6	9	12	15	27	31

E–33	360	7	8	9	14	36	72	108

E–34

$$\frac{72}{80} = \underline{\qquad}$$

E–35

$$\frac{256}{360} = \underline{\qquad}$$

E–36

$$\frac{81}{144} = \underline{\qquad}$$

E–37

$$\frac{80}{256} = \underline{\qquad}$$

E–38

$$\frac{144}{360} = \underline{\qquad}$$

E–39

$$\frac{81}{360} = \underline{\qquad}$$

USING ORDER RELATIONS

A number is missing from each sentence.
Circle all the numbers that will make a true statement.

Example

$$3\frac{3}{8} + \bigcirc < 4\frac{1}{2}$$

$$\boxed{\;\;\textcircled{\small$\frac{7}{8}$}\quad 1\frac{1}{8}\quad 2\frac{1}{8}\quad \textcircled{\small$\frac{3}{4}$}\;\;}$$

E–40

$$\bigcirc - 2\frac{2}{3} > 1\frac{2}{9}$$

$$\boxed{\;\;3\frac{1}{3}\quad 1\frac{4}{9}\quad 4\quad 3\frac{8}{9}\;\;}$$

E–41

$$2\frac{3}{4} \div \bigcirc < 3\frac{1}{4}$$

$$\boxed{\;\;1\frac{1}{2}\quad \frac{3}{4}\quad \frac{1}{2}\quad \frac{11}{13}\;\;}$$

E–42

$$\frac{2}{3} \times \bigcirc < \frac{7}{8} \times \frac{2}{3}$$

$$\boxed{\;\;\frac{9}{10}\quad \frac{7}{8}\quad \frac{3}{4}\quad \frac{4}{5}\;\;}$$

E–43

$$2\frac{2}{3} \times 1\frac{1}{2} > 1\frac{3}{8} \times \bigcirc$$

$$\boxed{\;\;2\frac{1}{2}\quad 3\frac{1}{8}\quad 2\frac{2}{3}\quad 1\frac{3}{8}\;\;}$$

E–44

$$5\frac{1}{2} + 3\frac{1}{4} < 10 - \bigcirc$$

$$\boxed{\;\;1\frac{1}{8}\quad \frac{7}{8}\quad 1\frac{1}{4}\quad 2\frac{1}{8}\;\;}$$

E–45

$$11\frac{2}{3} - 7\frac{1}{2} < 13\frac{2}{3} - \bigcirc$$

$$\boxed{\;\;10\frac{1}{4}\quad 9\frac{1}{2}\quad 8\frac{3}{8}\quad 11\frac{1}{3}\;\;}$$

E–46

$$7\frac{5}{8} \times 3\frac{1}{4} > 7\frac{5}{8} \div \bigcirc$$

$$\boxed{\;\;\frac{4}{13}\quad \frac{5}{13}\quad 3\frac{1}{8}\quad \frac{1}{12}\;\;}$$

USING ORDER RELATIONS

Two numbers are missing from each sentence.
Circle all the ordered pairs that will make a true statement.
The first number in each pair must go in the circle and the second number in the box.

Example $2.98 - \bigcirc > 1.4 + \boxed{}$

(2.05, 0.97)   (1.89, 0.08) $\boxed{(0.25, 1.32)}$ (1.89, 1.48)

E–47 $3.04 \times \bigcirc < 4.75 \times \boxed{}$

(4.8, 2.98)   (4.25, 3.15)   (4.75, 3.04)   (6.08, 9.50)

E–48 $19.25 - \bigcirc > \boxed{} - 7.75$

(7.75, 19.25)   (7.25, 19.50)   (8.25, 19.15)   (1.25, 20)

E–49 $135 \div \boxed{} < 135 \div \bigcirc$

(5, 6)   (6, 5)   (7, 7)   (5, 7)

USING ARITHMETIC OPERATIONS

In each box place one of the four operations (+, −, ×, ÷) to make a true statement.

Example $3 \boxed{+} (4 + 2) < 9 \boxed{\times} 2$

E–50 $(5 \boxed{} 7) \boxed{} 9 > 7 \boxed{} (9 \boxed{} 5)$

E–51 $3 \boxed{} (4 \boxed{} 5) = (3 \boxed{} 4) \boxed{} (3 \boxed{} 5)$

E–52 $1.85 \boxed{} 3.75 < 1.85 \boxed{} 3.75$

E–53 $\dfrac{7}{8} \div 1\dfrac{1}{2} < \dfrac{2}{3} \boxed{} \dfrac{7}{8}$

E–54 $3\dfrac{3}{4} \boxed{} 4\dfrac{1}{4} = 4\dfrac{1}{4} \boxed{} 3\dfrac{3}{4}$

USING OPERATIONS AND RELATIONS

In each box place one of the operations (+, −, ×, ÷) or
one of the relations (<, =, >) to make a true sentence.

Example   3 $\boxed{+}$ 2 $\boxed{<}$ 7 + 4

E–55 $9 \times 7 \ \Box \ 7 \ \Box \ 9$

E–56 $\dfrac{3}{8} + \dfrac{5}{8} \ \Box \ \dfrac{7}{8} \ \Box \ \dfrac{8}{7}$

E–57 $4.54 - 3.85 \ \Box \ 4.54 \ \Box \ 3.85$

E–58 $3 \ \Box \ 4 \ \Box \ 5 \ \Box \ 6$

E–59 $12.75 \ \Box \ 9.50 \ \Box \ 6.75 \ \Box \ 4.95$

E–60 $1 \ \Box \ 0 \ \Box \ 0 \ \Box \ 1$

CONTINUING THE SEQUENCE

Place numbers in the blank spaces to continue the sequence.

___

Example   1, 2, 4, 7, 11, __16__, __22__, __29__

E–61   5, 6, 8, 11, 15, _____, _____, _____

E–62   1, 2, 5, 10, 17, _____, _____, _____

E–63   1, 3, 6, 10, 15, _____, _____, _____

E–64   1, 4, 9, 16, 25, _____, _____, _____

E–65   9, 11, 12, 14, 15, _____, _____, _____

E–66   4, 7, 13, 22, 34, _____, _____, _____

E–67   1, 5, 12, 22, 35, 51, _____, _____, _____

E–68   3, 5, 8, 13, 20, 31, _____, _____, _____

SEQUENCES OF NUMBERS

The three dots mean that the sequence continues.
Circle all the numbers that belong to the sequence.

Example
2, 5, 8, 11, 14, . . .

a. (38)　b. 36

c. 24　d. (23)

E–69
9, 13, 17, 21, . . .

a. 32　b. 33

c. 40　d. 41

E–70
4, 9, 14, 19, 24, . . .

a. 27　b. 54

c. 39　d. 43

E–71
8, 10, 14, 20, 28, 38, . . .

a. 49　b. 98

c. 51　d. 48

E–72
8, 12, 16, 20, 24, . . .

a. 48　b. 62

c. 254　d. 96

E–73
8, 10, 13, 18, 25, 36, . . .

a. 85　b. 64

c. 75　d. 108

SEQUENCES OF NUMBERS

Each exercise below begins a sequence.
Circle the row that continues the sequence.

Example

1, 2, 4, 5, 7, 8, 10, . . .

a. 21, 22, 24, 25

b. 17, 18, 19, 20

c. 22, 23, 25, 26

E–74

1, 2, 3, 5, 6, 7, 9, 10, 11, . . .

a. 28, 29, 30, 32

b. 31, 32, 33, 35

c. 21, 22, 23, 25

E–75

1, 2, 4, 5, 6, 8, 9, 10, 12, 13, . . .

a. 19, 20, 21, 23

b. 24, 25, 26, 28

c. 25, 26, 27, 29

E–76

3, 5, 6, 8, 9, 11, 12, 14, 15, 17, . . .

a. 33, 34, 36, 37

b. 33, 35, 36, 38

c. 47, 48, 50, 51

E–77

3, 5, 6, 8, 10, 11, 13, 15, . . .

a. 63, 65, 66, 68

b. 65, 67, 69, 70

c. 45, 46, 48, 50

PAIRING NUMBERS

The arrows show how numbers are paired.
Fill in the circles with the missing numbers.

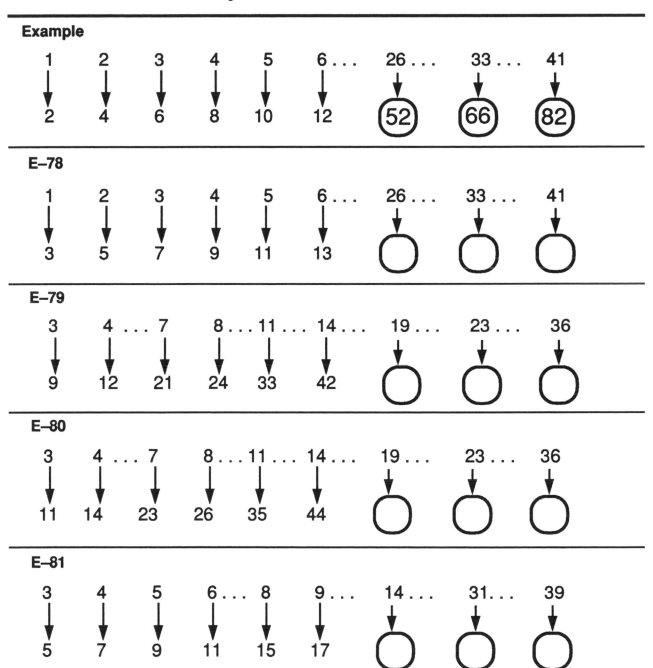

Example

1	2	3	4	5	6...	26...	33...	41
2	4	6	8	10	12	(52)	(66)	(82)

E–78

1	2	3	4	5	6...	26...	33...	41
3	5	7	9	11	13	◯	◯	◯

E–79

3	4...7	8...11...14...	19...	23...	36
9	12 21	24 33 42	◯	◯	◯

E–80

3	4...7	8...11...14...	19...	23...	36
11	14 23	26 35 44	◯	◯	◯

E–81

3	4	5	6...8	9...	14...	31...	39
5	7	9	11 15	17	◯	◯	◯

PAIRING NUMBERS

The arrows show how numbers are paired.
Fill in the circles with the missing numbers.

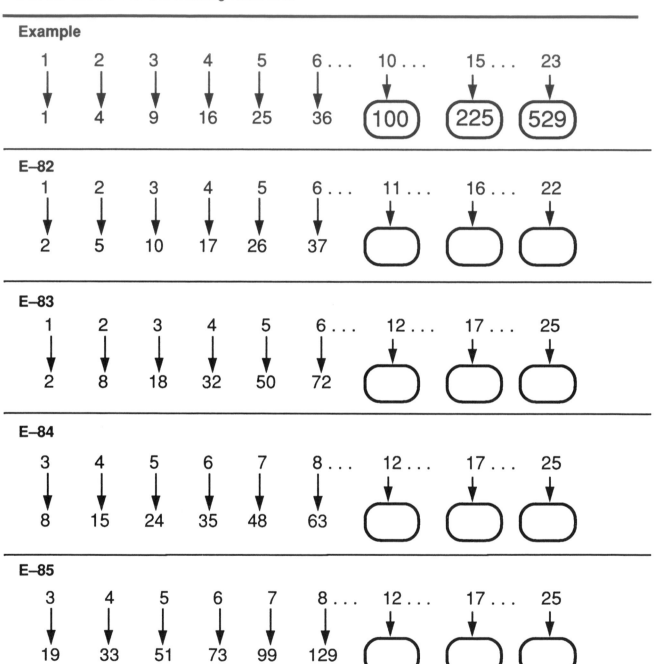

Example

1	2	3	4	5	6 . . .	10 . . .	15 . . .	23
1	4	9	16	25	36	(100)	(225)	(529)

E–82

1	2	3	4	5	6 . . .	11 . . .	16 . . .	22
2	5	10	17	26	37	◯	◯	◯

E–83

1	2	3	4	5	6 . . .	12 . . .	17 . . .	25
2	8	18	32	50	72	◯	◯	◯

E–84

3	4	5	6	7	8 . . .	12 . . .	17 . . .	25
8	15	24	35	48	63	◯	◯	◯

E–85

3	4	5	6	7	8 . . .	12 . . .	17 . . .	25
19	33	51	73	99	129	◯	◯	◯

PAIRING NUMBERS

The arrows show how numbers are paired.
Fill in the circles with the missing numbers.

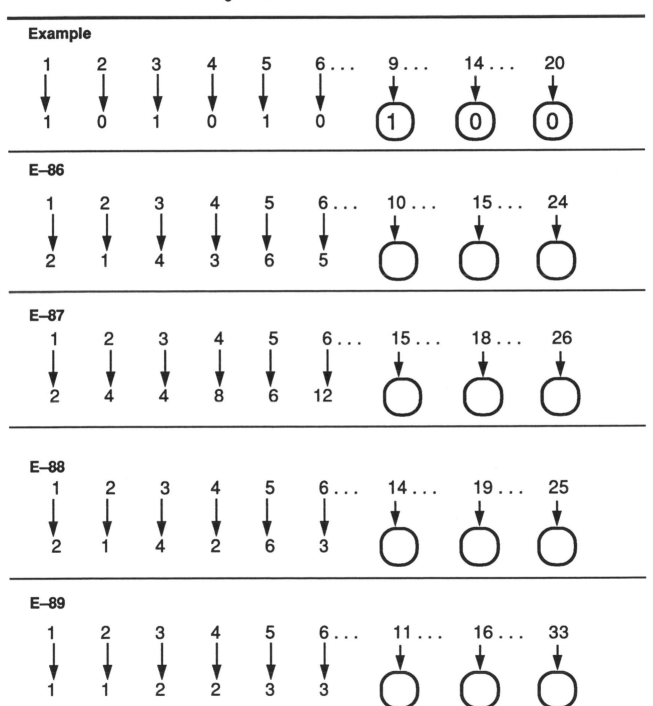

Example

1	2	3	4	5	6 . . .	9 . . .	14 . . .	20
1	0	1	0	1	0	(1)	(0)	(0)

E–86

1	2	3	4	5	6 . . .	10 . . .	15 . . .	24
2	1	4	3	6	5	◯	◯	◯

E–87

1	2	3	4	5	6 . . .	15 . . .	18 . . .	26
2	4	4	8	6	12	◯	◯	◯

E–88

1	2	3	4	5	6 . . .	14 . . .	19 . . .	25
2	1	4	2	6	3	◯	◯	◯

E–89

1	2	3	4	5	6 . . .	11 . . .	16 . . .	33
1	1	2	2	3	3	◯	◯	◯

MATCHING A TABLE TO A RULE

Each table contains a set of values for A and B.
Match each table with the rule which tells the relationship between A and B.

Example

Table

A	B
1	4
2	7
3	10
4	13
5	16

Rule

a. $B = (5 \times A) - 1$

b. $A = 1 + (3 \times B)$

(c.) $B = (3 \times A) + 1$

d. $4 \times A = B$

E–90

Table

A	B
1	1
2	3
3	5
4	7
5	9

Rule

a. $A = (2 \times B) - 1$

b. $B = A + 1$

c. $A = B$

d. $B = (2 \times A) - 1$

E–91

Table

A	B
1	3
2	6
3	9
4	12
5	15

Rule

a. $B = 3 \times A$

b. $B = A + 2$

c. $A = 3 \times B$

d. $B - A = 2$

E–92

Table

A	B
1	14
2	13
3	12
4	11
5	10

Rule

a. $B = 14 - A$

b. $A + B = 15$

c. $B = A + 13$

d. $B = 2 \times A$

E–93

Table

A	B
4	16
7	13
11	9
17	3
20	0

Rule

a. $A = B + 20$

b. $B = A \times 4$

c. $B = 20 - A$

d. $B = 3 \times A$

E–94

Table

A	B
0	0
2	3
4	6
10	15
12	18

Rule

a. $3 \times B = 2 \times A$

b. $B = (2 \times A) + 1$

c. $B = 3 \times A$

d. $2 \times B = 3 \times A$

COMPLETING A TABLE FROM A RULE

Each rule tells the relationship between numbers represented by A and B.
Use the rule to complete the table.

Example

Rule

$B = 2 \times A$

Table

A	B
0	0
2	4
3	6
5	10
8	16

E–95

Rule

$B = A - 3$

Table

A	B
7	—
9	—
10	—
—	14
—	30

E–96

Rule

$\dfrac{A}{B} = \dfrac{1}{2}$

Table

A	B
6	—
8	—
1	—
—	6
—	8

E–97

Rule

$B = (2 \times A) - 1$

Table

A	B
1	—
3	—
4	—
7	—
—	9

E–98

Rule

$A < B + 2$

Table

A	B
0	—
1	—
3	—
4	—
—	12

E–99

Rule

$B = A^2$

Table

A	B
0	—
—	1
3	—
—	49
10	—

SEQUENCES OF ORDERED PAIRS

Fill in the missing numbers in the following sequences of ordered pairs.

Example (1, 4) (2, 7) (3, 10) (4, _13_) (5, 16) (6, _19_)

E–100 (3, 5) (4, ___) (5, 7) (6, 8) (7, 9) (8, ___)

E–101 (1, 3) (2, 6) (3, ___) (4, 12) (5, ___) (6, 18)

E–102 (2, 1) (3, 1.5) (4, 2) (5, ___) (6, 3) (7, ___)

E–103 (3, ___) (4, ___) (5, 17) (6, 20) (7, 23) (8, 26)

E–104 (1, 1) (2, 4) (3, ___) (4, ___) (5, 25) (6, 36)

E–105 (3, 1) (___, 2) (9, 3) (___, 4) (15, 5) (18, ___)

E–106 (1, 4) (2, ___) (3, ___) (4, 16) (___, 20) (6, 24)

SEQUENCES OF ORDERED PAIRS

Fill in the missing numbers in the following sequences of ordered pairs.
The three dots indicate that the sequence continues.

Example   (4, 1)   (5, 1.25)   (6, 1.5)   (7, 1.75)   (8, _2_) • • •   (15, _3.75_)

E–107   (2, 7)   (3, 8)   (4, ___)   (5, 10)   (6, 11) • • •   (12, ___)

E–108   (1, ___)   (2, 10)   (3, ___)   (4, 20)   (5, 25) • • •   (19, ___)

E–109   (3, 7)   (4, 9)   (5, 11)   (6, 13)   (7, ___) • • •   (10, ___)

E–110   (1, 4)   (2, ___)   (3, 10)   (4, 13)   (5, 16) • • •   (11, ___)

E–111   (4, 2)   (9, 3)   (16, 4)   (___, 5)   (36, 6) • • •   (___, 12)

E–112   (2, 3)   (4, 6)   (6, 9)   (8, 12)   (___, 15) • • •   (___, 36)

E–113   (5, 1)   (___, 1.2)   (7, 1.4)   (8, ___)   (___, 1.8) • • •   (___, 2.4)

MATCHING ORDERED PAIRS TO A RULE

In each ordered pair, the first number is the "A" value and
the second number is the "B" value.
Circle the ordered pairs that satisfy the rule.

Example

Rule

$A + B < 10$

Ordered Pairs

$(3, 5)$ $(7, 4)$ $(5, 5)$ $(5, 3)$

$(10, 0)$ $(4, 10)$ $(1, 6)$ $(4, 7)$

E–114

Rule

$B = A^2$

Ordered Pairs

$(6, 12)$ $(1, 1)$ $(25, 5)$ $(3, 9)$

$(9, 3)$ $(0, 0)$ $(12, 144)$ $(4, 4)$

E–115

Rule

$B = (2 \times A) + 1$

Ordered Pairs

$(3, 1)$ $(5, 11)$ $(3, 7)$ $(9, 17)$

$(1, 3)$ $(1, 0)$ $(11, 5)$ $(0, 1)$

E–116

Rule

$\dfrac{A}{B} = \dfrac{1}{3}$

Ordered Pairs

$(3, 1)$ $(2, 6)$ $(1, 3)$ $(1, 6)$

$(6, 2)$ $(12, 36)$ $(3, 9)$ $(5, 7)$

E–117

Rule

$A = 2 \times B$

Ordered Pairs

$(1, 2)$ $(3, 6)$ $(6, 3)$ $(7, 5)$

$(5, 10)$ $(10, 12)$ $(2, 1)$ $(10, 5)$

MATCHING A RULE TO ORDERED PAIRS

In each ordered pair, the first number is the "A" value and
the second number is the "B" value.
Identify the rule that each of the six ordered pairs satisfies.

Example	Ordered Pairs		Rule
(2, 7)	(5, 16)	(3, 10)	a. $A = (3 \times B) + 1$
			b. $B > A + 3$
(0, 1)	(10, 31)	(1, 4)	ⓒ $(3 \times A) + 1 = B$
			d. $B = A + 5$

E–118	Ordered Pairs		Rule
(1, 5)	(3, 11)	(4, 16)	a. $B = (3 \times A) + 2$
			b. $B > (3 \times A) + 1$
(5, 19)	(0, 2)	(10, 33)	c. $A > (3 \times B) + 1$
			d. $A + B > 5$

E–119	Ordered Pairs		Rule
(7, 35)	(4, 20)	(0, 0)	a. $5 \times B = A$
			b. $A + B > 5$
(1, 5)	(3, 15)	(10, 50)	c. $B = A + 28$
			d. $B = 5 \times A$

E–120	Ordered Pairs		Rule
(0, 1)	(1, 2)	(4, 17)	a. $B = A + 1$
			b. $B = (A \times A) + 1$
(2, 5)	(5, 26)	(10, 101)	c. $A = (B \times B) + 1$
			d. $6 \times A > B$

E–121	Ordered Pairs		Rule
(2, 3)	(3, 4)	(0, 1)	a. $B = A + 1$
			b. $2 \times A > B$
(5, 6)	(7, 8)	(10, 18)	c. $B < A + 9$
			d. $B - A = 1$

SATISFYING NUMBER PROPERTIES

Circle all the pairs of numbers that satisfy the given properties.

Example The product of the numbers is less than 24 and their sum is 10.

5 and 5	(8 and 2)	
4 and 6	(0 and 10)	
(1 and 9)	5 and 4	

E–122 Both numbers are multiples of 3 and their difference is greater than 6.

9 and 12	12 and 3
15 and 25	18 and 6
36 and 30	0 and 15

E–123 One number is 2 more than the other and their product is an odd number.

7 and 5	4 and 6
2 and 3	5 and 9
13 and 11	0 and 2

E–124 Both numbers are prime numbers and their product is less than 20.

7 and 5	4 and 2
3 and 5	5 and 9
13 and 11	2 and 7

E–125 The sum of the two numbers is less than 9 and one number is twice the other.

3 and 6	4 and 2
4 and 8	2 and 6
3 and 5	2 and 1

SATISFYING NUMBER PROPERTIES

Find 3 pairs of whole numbers that satisfy the given properties.

Example One number is greater than the square of the other number.	10 and 3	
	24 and 4	
	30 and 5	

E–126 Three times the sum of the two numbers is less than the product of the numbers.

_____

_____

_____

E–127 One number plus 3 is greater than 2 times the other number.

_____

_____

_____

E–128 The square of one number equals twice the other number.

_____

_____

_____

E–129 The sum of the squares of the two numbers is less than 13.

_____

_____

_____

INFERENCES

The two sentences below give information about two numbers, **m** and **n**.

m and **n** are both whole numbers.
(**m** + **n**) is an even number.

Decide whether the following statements are always true, always false, or cannot be determined (CBD).

Example	**m** and **n** are even numbers.	**CBD** _____
E–130	(**m** + **n**) is divisible by 2.	_____
E–131	(**m** + **n**) is divisible by 4.	_____
E–132	Suppose **n** is an even number. Then **m** is an odd number.	_____
E–133	**m** and **n** are different numbers.	_____
E–134	If **m** = 2 × **n** then **m** is an even number.	_____
E–135	Suppose **m** = 2 × **n**. Then **n** is an odd number.	_____
E–136	(**m** + **n**) is not a prime number.	_____
E–137	If **n** is greater than 2, then (**m** + **n**) is not a prime number.	_____
E–138	Suppose **n** is an odd number. Then **m** is an odd number.	_____

INFERENCES

The two sentences below give information about two numbers, **m** and **n**.

m and **n** are both whole numbers.
m is equal to (**n** + 1).

Decide whether the following statements are always true, always false, or cannot be determined (CBD).

Example	(**m** + **n**) is an even number.	<u>False</u>
E–139	(**m** × **n**) is an even number.	_____
E–140	**m** is an odd number.	_____
E–141	(**m** + **m**) is an odd number.	_____
E–142	(**n** + 1) is not divisible by 2.	_____
E–143	**m** could be equal to **n**.	_____
E–144	When **n** is an even number, (**m** + **n**) is an even number.	_____
E–145	(**n** + **n**) is an odd number.	_____
E–146	(**m** + **m**) is an even number.	_____
E–147	When **n** is an odd number, (**m** + **n**) is an odd number.	_____

MATCHING GRAPHS WITH LABELS

Select the bar graph that fits the given description.

Example Daily high temperatures in degrees Fahrenheit for June 1–7   C

F–1 Average number of hours of homework done for a math class for one week   _____

F–2 Number of absences for a school of 1100 for one week   _____

F–3 Number of tickets sold in one week for a 500 ticket raffle   _____

F–4 Number of hours worked per day for one week in a summer job   _____

a.

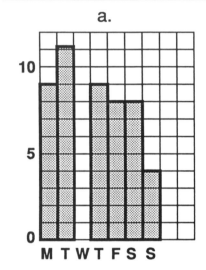

b.

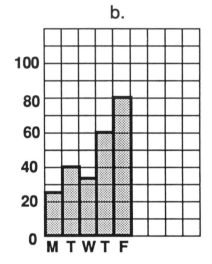

c.

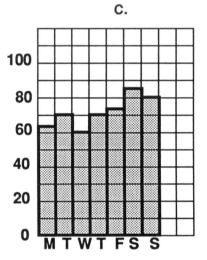

d.

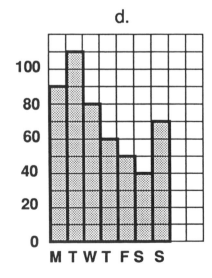

e.

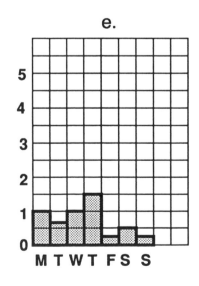

f.

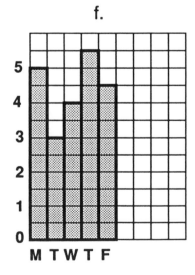

INTERPRETING A BAR GRAPH

Use the graph to answer the questions below.

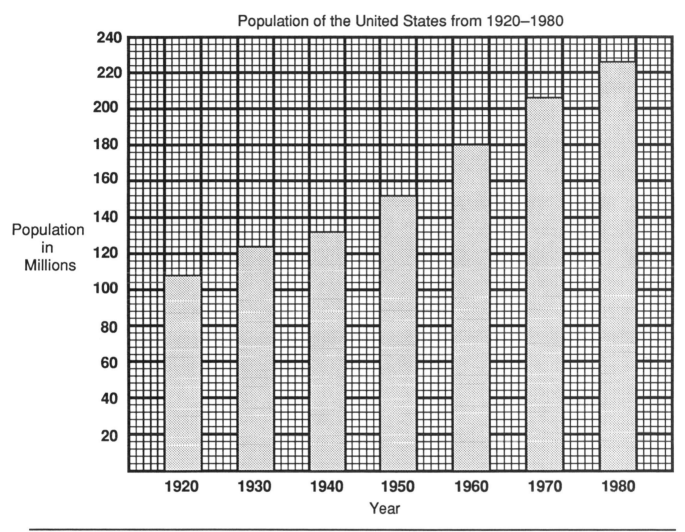

Population of the United States from 1920–1980

Example In what year was the population about 150 million? _____1950_____

F–5 What was the increase in population during the 1940s? _____

F–6 During which decade was the population increase the greatest? _____

F–7 During which decade was the population increase the smallest? _____

F–8 What do you think the population was in 1990? _____

F–9 What do you think the population was in 1910? _____

SUMS OF WHOLE NUMBERS

Write the area of the rectangle in the circle.
Count the number of squares with Xs in each row of the rectangle.
Use the information to complete the table in F–13.

Example

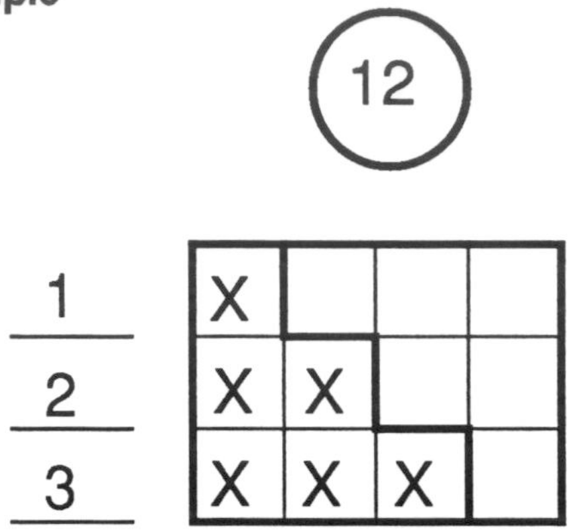

(12)

$\dfrac{1}{}$
$\dfrac{2}{}$
$\dfrac{3}{}$

F–10

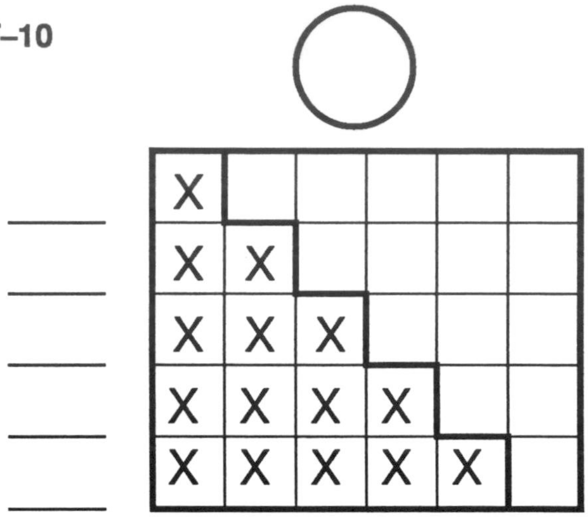

( )

F–11

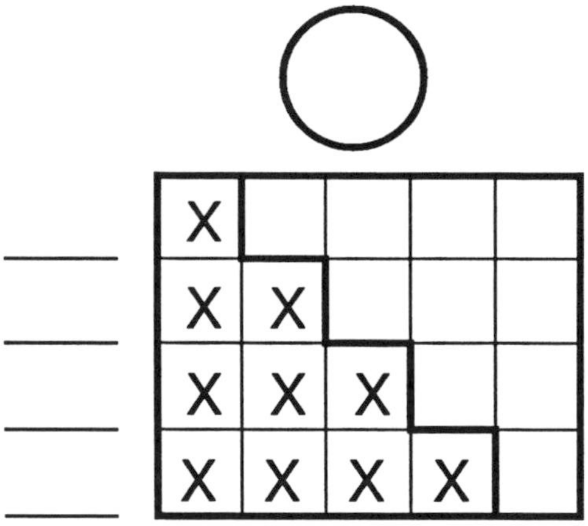

( )

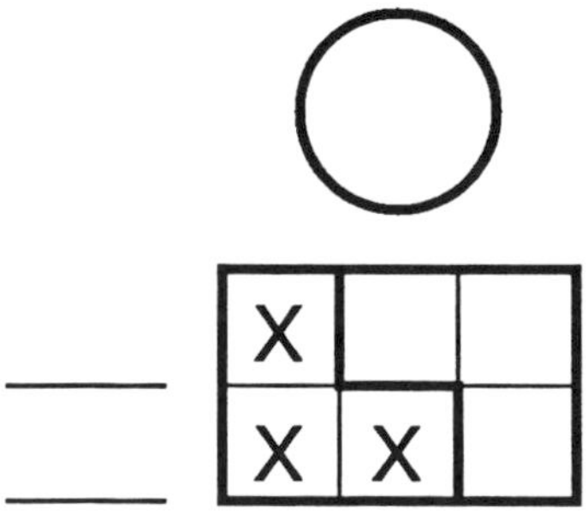

F–13

1 + 2 =	
1 + 2 + 3 =	6
1 + 2 + 3 + 4 =	
1 + 2 + . . . + 5 =	
1 + 2 + . . . + 6 =	
1 + 2 + . . . + 7 =	

F–12

( )

COUNTING CHORDS

Draw chords connecting point A with each of the other points on the circle.
In the table, write the number of chords drawn.
Draw additional chords that connect point B with the other points on the circle.
In the table, write the number of additional chords drawn.
Continue until each pair of points is connected and the table is completed.

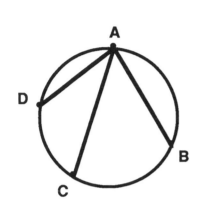

Example How many chords are drawn from point A?

3

F–14 How many additional chords can be drawn from point B?

F–15 How many additional chords can be drawn from point C?

F–16

POINT	A	B	C
NUMBER OF CHORDS	3		

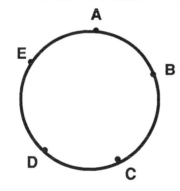

F–17

POINT	A	B	C	D
NUMBER OF CHORDS				

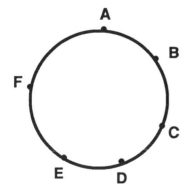

F–18

POINT	A	B	C	D	E
NUMBER OF CHORDS					

SURFACE AREA

A 3 × 3 × 3 cube is constructed with 27 unit cubes.
An X is placed on the outside surface of each of the unit cubes.

Example

How many Xs are on the front of the cube?

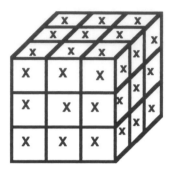

_____9_____

F–19 How many Xs are on the top of the cube?

_____

F–20 How many Xs are on the bottom of the cube?

_____

F–21 How many Xs are on the back of the cube?

_____

F–22 Complete the table.

SURFACE	# OF X'S
FRONT	9
BOTTOM	
BACK	
LEFT SIDE	
RIGHT SIDE	
TOP	
TOTAL	

SURFACE AREA

The $3 \times 3 \times 3$ cube from the previous activity has been enlarged to form a $4 \times 4 \times 4$ cube.

Example
How many unit cubes were needed to make the $3 \times 3 \times 3$ cube?   **27**

F–23
What is the total number of unit cubes in the $4 \times 4 \times 4$ cube? _____

F–24
How many cubes were added to the $3 \times 3 \times 3$ cube to make the $4 \times 4 \times 4$ cube? _____

Suppose Xs are placed on the OUTSIDE surfaces of each of the NEW unit cubes.

F–25 How many Xs are on the front of the $4 \times 4 \times 4$ cube?

_____

F–26 How many Xs are on the bottom of the $4 \times 4 \times 4$ cube?

_____

F–27 Complete the Table.

SURFACE	# OF X'S
FRONT	16
BOTTOM	
BACK	
LEFT SIDE	
RIGHT SIDE	
TOP	
TOTAL	

SURFACE AREA

Xs were placed on the outside surface of each of the unit cubes in the figure below.
Then the $3 \times 3 \times 3$ cube is disassembled.
The unit cubes are sorted according to the number of Xs on each.

Example

What is the GREATEST number of Xs
appearing on a unit cube?

<u>   3   </u>

Describe the location of the unit cubes that have three Xs.

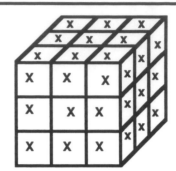

<u>   each of the 8 corners of the cube   </u>

F–28 How many unit cubes have three Xs? _____

F–29 How many unit cubes have only two Xs? _____

F–30 How many unit cubes have only one X? _____

F–31 Are there any unit cubes that do not have any Xs? _____

F–32 How many unit cubes have no Xs? _____

F–33 Complete the Table.

NUMBER OF X'S	NUMBER OF CUBES
3	
2	
1	
0	

USING TABLES TO COMPUTE PARKING FEES

The hourly parking fees for the Metroplex Parking System are shown in the table.
Compute the parking fee for each ticket.

PARKING RATES   METROPLEX PARKING SYSTEM

ARRIVE BEFORE 8:00 a.m.

SAVE $1.00

First 1/2 hour	$1.00
Next 1/2 hour to 2 hours total	additional 50¢ per 1/2 hour
Next 2 hours to 4 hours total	additional 25¢ per 1/2 hour
each additional hour over 4 hours	25¢ per hour
Maximum charge per 24 hours	$8.00

PARK FREE ON HOLIDAYS

Example The first 1/2 hour costs $1.00, the next three 1/2 hours cost 3 X .50 = 1.50, and the final 1/2 hour costs .25.

dep:	02/16/92	12:46 a.m.
arr:	02/16/92	10:16 a.m.

time __2 1/2 hrs__   fee __$2.75__

F–34

dep:	06/06/89	11:05 a.m.
arr:	06/06/89	8:35 a.m.

time _____   fee _____

F–35

dep:	10/11/90	11:45 a.m.
arr:	10/11/90	7:45 a.m.

time _____   fee _____

F–36

dep:	04/29/88	4:56 p.m.
arr:	04/29/88	9:56 a.m.

time _____   fee _____

F–37

dep:	07/04/89	1:42 p.m.
arr:	07/04/89	11:12 a.m.

time _____   fee _____

F–38

dep:	09/16/91	6:39 a.m.
arr:	09/15/91	7:39 p.m.

time _____   fee _____

USING TABLES TO COMPUTE PARKING FEES

The hourly parking fees for the Metroplex Parking System are shown in the table.
Compute the parking fee for each ticket.

PARKING RATES   METROPLEX PARKING SYSTEM

ARRIVE BEFORE 8:00 a.m.

SAVE $1.00

First 1/2 hour	$1.00
Next 1/2 hour to 2 hours total	additional 50¢ per 1/2 hour
Next 2 hours to 4 hours total	additional 25¢ per 1/2 hour
each additional hour over 4 hours	25¢ per hour
Maximum charge per 24 hours	$8.00

PARK FREE ON HOLIDAYS

Example

dep:	07/30/91	1:37 a.m.
arr:	07/29/91	4:15 p.m.

time __9 hrs 22 min__ fee __$5.00__

F–39

dep:	09/10/89	9:52 a.m.
arr:	09/10/89	7:39 a.m.

time _____ fee _____

F–40

dep:	10/18/88	4:03 p.m.
arr:	10/17/88	2:39 p.m.

time _____ fee _____

F–41

dep:	02/01/89	6:51 a.m.
arr:	01/31/89	4:52 p.m.

time _____ fee _____

F–42

dep:	01/01/90	2:51 p.m.
arr:	12/31/89	9:08 p.m.

time _____ fee _____

F–43

dep:	03/01/88	5:56 p.m.
arr:	02/28/88	3:27 p.m.

time _____ fee _____

USING TABLES TO COMPUTE COST

The price charts below show the cost of purchasing books.
Use the two charts to complete each sales slip and compute the total cost of each purchase.

Book Prices

BOOK	1 BOOK	2 BOOKS
A	$3.99	$7.79
B	$4.59	$8.98
C	$5.95	$10.67
D	$6.83	$13.39
E	$7.49	$14.49
F	$8.25	$15.95

Quantity Discount

TOTAL PURCHASE	SAVE
$10.00–19.99	$2.00
$20.00–29.99	$3.00
$30.00–34.99	$4.50
$35.00–39.99	$5.00
over $40.00	$6.00

**Buy 8 or more books
save an additional $2.00.**

Example

2 A books	7.79
3 D books	20.22
1 E book	7.49
Subtotal	35.50
Discount	5.00
Total	30.50

F–44

2 F books	
1 D book	
3 C books	
Subtotal	
Discount	
Total	

F–45

3 A books	
3 C books	
2 E books	
Subtotal	
Discount	
Total	

USING TABLES TO COMPUTE COST

Use the price charts on the previous page to complete each sales slip for books.
Compute the total cost of each purchase.

F–46

3 A books _____

3 B books _____

1 F book _____

Subtotal _____

Discount _____

Total _____

F–47

3 A books _____

4 B books _____

1 F book _____

Subtotal _____

Discount _____

Total _____

F–48

4 A books _____

3 B books _____

1 F book _____

Subtotal _____

Discount _____

Total _____

F–49

3 D books _____

1 C book _____

1 A book _____

2 B books _____

Subtotal _____

Discount _____

Total _____

F–50

3 C books _____

2 F books _____

3 A books _____

2 B books _____

Subtotal _____

Discount _____

Total _____

F–51

3 F books _____

2 D books _____

1 C book _____

1 A book _____

Subtotal _____

Discount _____

Total _____

USING TABLES TO COMPUTE AIRCRAFT FUEL

Commerical airlines calculate the amount of aviation fuel needed for aircraft in pounds.
Each 1000 pounds of fuel will allow an aircraft to fly a given amount of time.
In addition each take off or landing requires an extra 1450 pounds of fuel.
Use the charts below to calculate the amount of fuel needed for each flight.
Round each flight time up to the next half hour and the answer to the nearest one hundred pounds.

	Atlanta	Boston	Chicago	Dallas	Detroit	New York	San Diego
Atlanta	X	2:46	1:10	1:39	1:24	2:23	4:28
Boston	2:46	X	1:58	3:12	1:19	0:55	5:58
Chicago	1:10	1:58	X	2:09	0:40	1:46	4:00
Dallas	1:39	3:12	2:09	X	2:13	2:53	2:49
Detroit	1:24	1:19	0:40	2:13	X	1:24	4:37
New York	2:23	0:55	1:46	2:53	1:24	X	5:40
San Diego	4:28	5:58	4:00	2:49	4:37	5:40	X

Minutes per 1000 lbs.

M–80	45
727	35
737	40
757	40
DC–9	30
DC–10	35

Example A flight from New York to San Diego through Dallas—
New York to Dallas, M–80; Dallas to San Diego, 737

_____14,300_____

F–52 A flight from Boston to Chicago through Detroit—
Boston to Detroit, DC–9; Detroit to Chicago, 727

_____

F–53 A flight from Dallas to Detroit through Atlanta—
Dallas to Atlanta, DC–10; Atlanta to Detroit, M–80

_____

F–54 A flight from San Diego to Chicago through Dallas—
San Diego to Dallas, 737; Dallas to Chicago, 757

_____

F–55 A flight from from Boston to San Diego through Chicago—
Boston to Chicago, DC–10; Chicago to San Diego, M–80

_____

F–56 A flight from San Diego to New York through Dallas and Chicago—
San Diego to Dallas, 737; Dallas to Chicago, 757;
Chicago to New York, DC–9

_____

SUMS OF ORDERED PAIRS

The points on the grid represent all ordered pairs that could result when two dice are rolled.

Example

Which ordered pairs are on the diagonal line in the figure?

(1, 2) and (2, 1)

What is the sum of the two numbers in each of these ordered pairs?

3

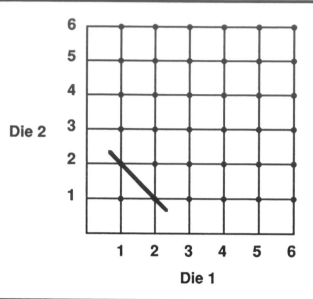

Die 2

Die 1

F–57 Draw the diagonal line that connects the ordered pairs that have a sum of 6.

F–58 List the ordered pairs that have a sum of 6.

_____

F–59 How many ordered pairs have a sum of 6? _____

F–60 Use other diagonal lines to complete the table.

SUM	2	3	4	5	6	7	8	9	10	11	12
NUMBER OF PAIRS	1	2									

F–61 How many different ordered pairs are possible? _____

F–62 Which sum has the greatest number of ordered pairs? _____

SUMS OF ORDERED PAIRS

The points on the grid represent all ordered pairs that could result when an octahedron (numbered 1–8) and a die (numbered 1–6) are rolled.

Example

Which ordered pairs are on the diagonal line in the figure?

$$(1, 2) \text{ and } (2, 1)$$

What is the sum of the two numbers in each of these ordered pairs?

$$3$$

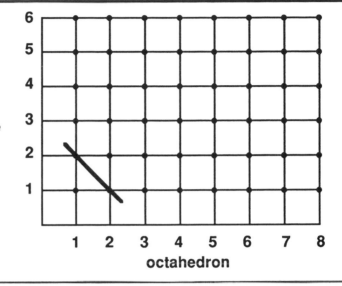

die

octahedron

F–63 Draw the diagonal line that connects the ordered pairs that have a sum of 11.

F–64 List the ordered pairs that have a sum of 11.

_____

F–65 How many ordered pairs have a sum of 11? _____

F–66 Use other diagonal lines to complete the table.

SUM	2	3	4	5	6	7	8	9	10	11	12	13	14
NUMBER OF PAIRS	1	2											

F–67 How many different ordered pairs are possible? _____

F–68 Which sum has the greatest number of ordered pairs? _____

SUMS OF ORDERED PAIRS

One person has two dice and another person has a die and an octahedron.
Use the completed tables in the last two activities to answer the questions below.

F–69   How many different ordered pairs are possible with the two dice? _____

F–70   How many different ordered pairs are possible with the die and octahedron? _____

The left column gives the sums that result from rolling two dice or a die and an octahedron.
The right column gives the chances of rolling a particular sum.
Match the statements in the left column with those in the right column.

Example 2 dice: sum of 2   a. 6 out of 36

F–71   die and octahedron: sum of 2   b. 1 out of 36

F–72 2 dice: sum of 7   c. 1 out of 12

F–73   die and octahedron: sum of 7   d. 1 out of 48

F–74   die and octahedron: sum of 5   e. 6 out of 48

F–75 2 dice: sum of 5   f. 1 out of 4

F–76 die and octahedron: sum of 5 or 11   g. 1 out of 9

F–77 2 dice: sum of 8 or 9   h. 8 out of 48

SUMS OF ORDERED PAIRS

Two octahedra are rolled and
the data is recorded on the grid.

Example

Which ordered pairs have a sum of 14?

$(6, 8), (7, 7), (8, 6)$

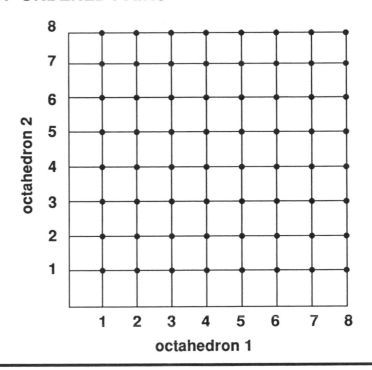

F–78 Which ordered pairs have a sum of 12? _____

F–79 What is the largest possible sum? _____

F–80 How many ordered pairs have a sum of 15? _____

F–81 How many ordered pairs have a sum of 10? _____

F–82 Complete the table.

SUM	2	3	4	5	6	7	8	9	10	11	12	13	14	15	16
NUMBER OF PAIRS															

GRAPHING SEQUENCES OF ORDERED PAIRS

Graph each ordered pair in the given sequence.
If A is the first number in each pair and B is the second number,
select the correct rule for the sequence.

Example

(0, 0), (1, 2), (2, 4), (3, 6), (4, 8)

RULE: a. A = B + 2

             b. A = 2 × B

             c. B = A + 2

             d. B = 2 × A

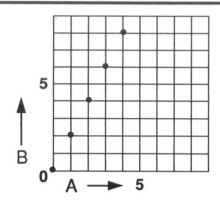

F–83

(0, 1), (1, 4), (2, 7), (3, 10), (4, 13)

RULE: a. A = (3 × B) + 1

             b. A = 3 × B

             c. B = (3 × A) + 1

             d. B = A + 3

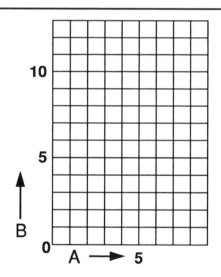

F–84

(0, 3), (1, 5), (2, 7), (3, 9), (4, 11)

RULE: a. B = (2 × A) + 3

             b. B = (3 × A) + 2

             c. A = (2 × B) + 3

             d. B = A + 4

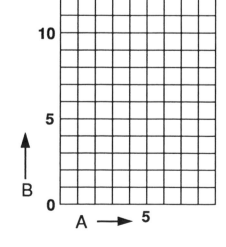

GRAPHING SEQUENCES OF ORDERED PAIRS

Graph each ordered pair in the given sequence.
If A is the first number in each pair and B is the second number,
select the correct rule for the sequence.

F–85

(0, 0), (1, 3), (2, 6), (3, 9), (4, 12)

RULE: a. B = A + 2

b. A = B − 3

c. B = 3 × A

d. A = 3 × B

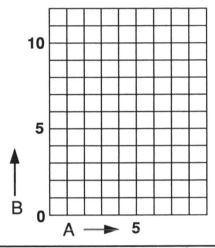

F–86

(0, 7), (1, 6), (2, 5), (3, 4), (4, 3)

RULE: a. B = A + 7

b. B = 6 × A

c. A = 7 − B

d. B = 7 − A

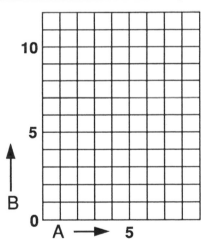

F–87

(0, 9), (1, 7), (2, 5), (3, 3), (4, 1)

RULE: a. A = 9 − (2 × B)

b. A + B = 9

c. B = 9 − (2 × A)

d. B = (2 × A) + 5

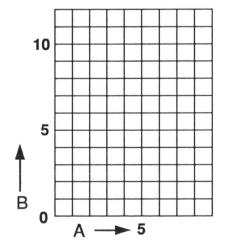

GRAPHING ORDERED PAIRS

A and B represent numbers in a given relationship.
Complete the table, and graph the resulting ordered pairs of numbers.

Example

$B = (2 \times A) + 1$

A	B
0	1
1	3
2	5
3	7
4	9

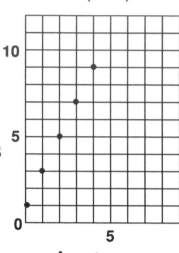

F–88

$B = (2 \times A) + 2$

A	B
0	
1	
2	
3	
4	

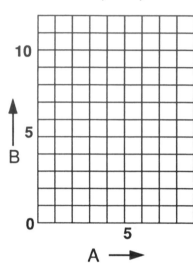

F–89

$A + B = 10$

A	B
0	
1	
2	
3	
4	

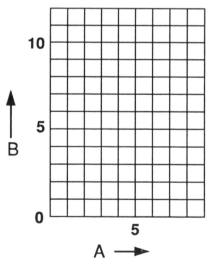

F–90

$B = 2 \times A$

A	B
0	
1	
2	
3	
4	

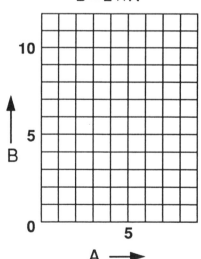

READING ORDERED PAIRS

Use the graph to complete the table.
Then select the correct rule.

Example

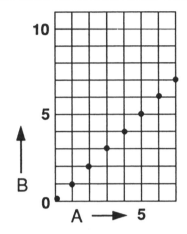

A	B
0	0
1	1
2	2
3	3
4	4
5	5
6	6
7	7

RULE:

a. B = A + 1

b. A + B = 2

c. B = A   *(circled)*

d. A = B + 1

F–91

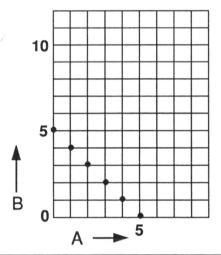

A	B
0	
1	
2	
3	
4	
5	

RULE:

a. B = A + 3

b. B = A − 5

c. B − A = 3

d. B = 5 − A

F–92

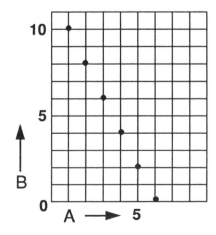

A	B
1	
2	
3	
4	
5	
6	

RULE:

a. B + A = 11

b. A = 12 − (2 × B)

c. B = 12 − (2 × A)

d. 7 = A + B

READING ORDERED PAIRS

Use the graph to complete the table.
Then select the correct rule.

F–93

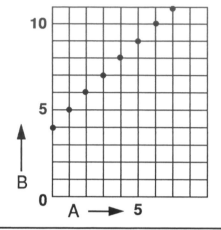

A	B
0	
1	
2	
3	
4	
5	
6	
7	

RULE:

a. $A = B$

b. $B - A = 5$

c. $B - A = 4$

d. $A = B + 4$

F–94

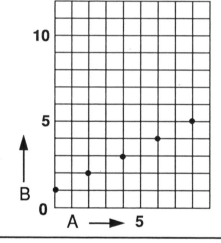

A	B
0	
2	
4	
6	
8	

RULE:

a. $B = A$

b. $2 \times B = A + 2$

c. $A = (1/2 \times B) + 1$

d. $B + 2 = 2 \times A$

F–95

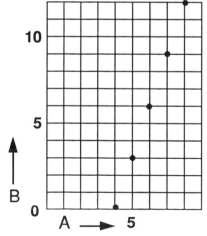

A	B
4	
5	
6	
7	
8	

RULE:

a. $B = (2 \times A) - 8$

b. $A = (3 \times B) - 12$

c. $B = (3 \times A) + 12$

d. $B = (3 \times A) - 12$

MATCHING RULES WITH GRAPHS

Match each rule with the correct graph.

Example	$3 \times A = 2 \times B$	GRAPH	C
F–96	$A + B = 10$	GRAPH	___
F–97	$2 \times B = A + 3$	GRAPH	___
F–98	$B = 12 - (3 \times A)$	GRAPH	___

a.

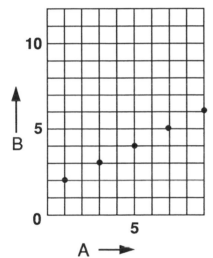

b.

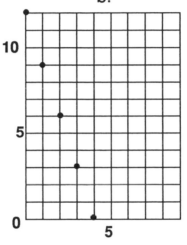

c.

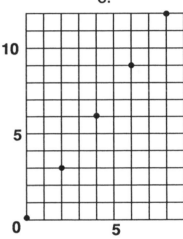

d.

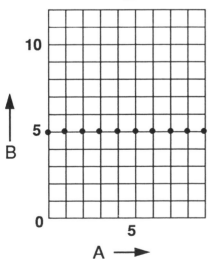

e.

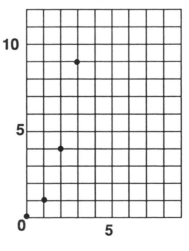

f.

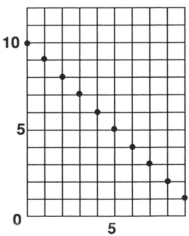

USING A GRAPH FOR CONVERSION

The graph below relates distances in miles to distances in kilometers.
Use the graph to answer the questions below.

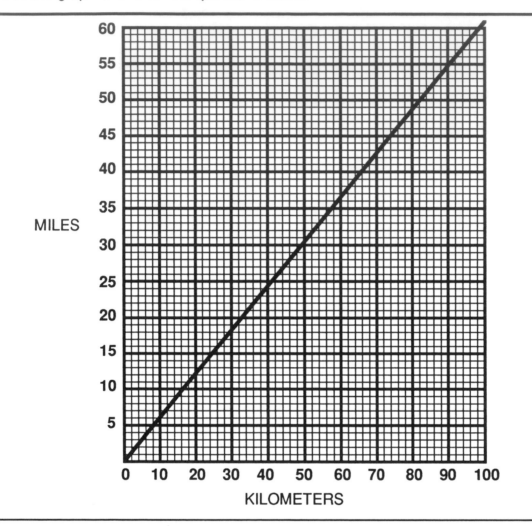

Example A distance of 50 kilometers is about _____31_____ miles.

F–99 A distance of 50 miles is about _____ kilometers.

F–100 Which is longer, a kilometer or a mile? _____

F–101 One kilometer is about _____ miles.

F–102 A speed of 55 miles per hour is about _____ kilometers per hour.

F–103 A car that travels 60 km on a gallon of gas will travel _____ miles per gallon.

USING A GRAPH FOR CONVERSION

On the grid below, plot the two well-known Centigrade/Fahrenheit equivalents:
0° C = 32° F and 100° C equals 212° F.
Connect these two points with a straight line.
Use the resulting graph to estimate the temperature equivalents.

F–104 50° F = _____ ° C.

F–105 20° C = _____ ° F.

F–106 100° F = _____ ° C.

F–107 50° C = _____ ° F.

F–108 98.6° F = _____ ° C.

F–109 70° C = _____ ° F.

F–110 At what value does the temperature have the same Centigrade and Fahrenheit temperature?

_____

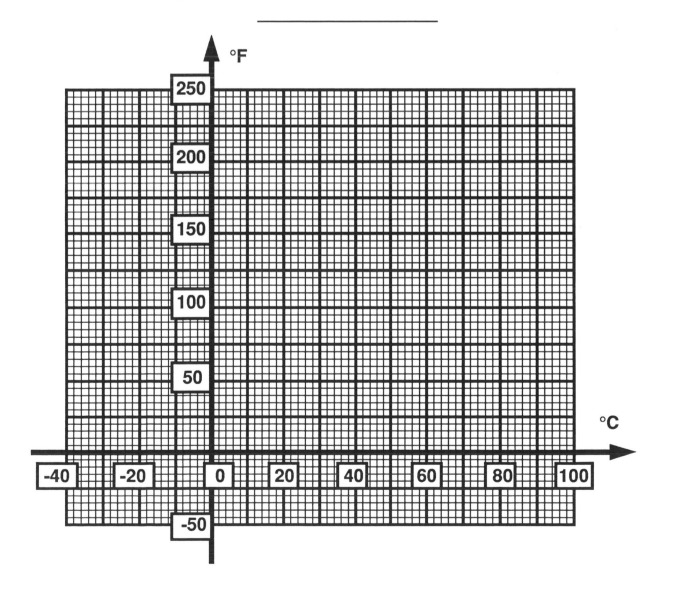

USING TWO GRAPHS FOR CONVERSION

Use the two conversion graphs to answer the questions below.

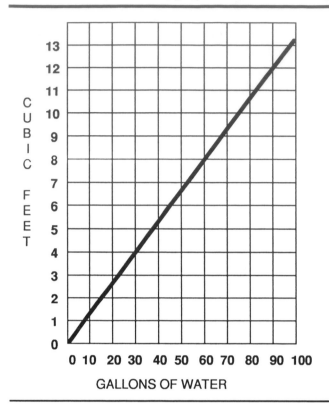

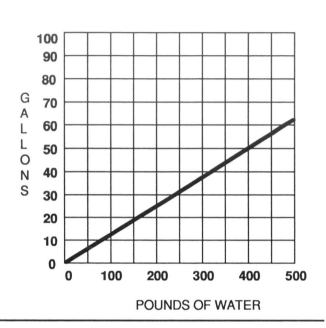

Example A 5 cubic foot water tank holds about _____38_____ gallons.

F–111 When full, a 5 cubic foot water tank holds about _____ pounds of water.

F–112 By weighing, it is determined that a water truck is carrying 475 pounds of water.

It is carrying about _____ gallons of water.

F–113 350 pounds of water is about _____ cubic feet.

F–114 130 gallons of water is about _____ cubic feet.

F–115 1000 pounds of water is about _____ gallons.

F–116 1000 pounds of water is about _____ cubic feet.

INTERPRETING A GRAPH

The graph below relates time measured in hours to the total distance traveled.
Use the graph to answer the questions.

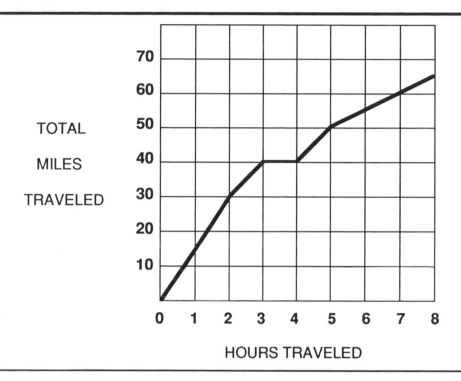

TOTAL

MILES

TRAVELED

HOURS TRAVELED

Example How many miles were traveled in the first 4 hours? **40 miles**

F–117 What do you think happened between the 3rd and 4th hour? _____

F–118 How many miles were traveled in 8 hours? _____

F–119 Was the traveler going faster in the first 3 hours or the last 3 hours? _____

F–120 What was the average rate of speed during the first 3 hours? _____

F–121 What was the average rate of speed during the last 3 hours? _____

F–122 What are two likely modes of travel? _____

INTERPRETING GRAPHS

The Kim and Jones families are traveling 220 miles from Westville to Center Port by car.
On the trip they must travel 40 miles by ferry.
The Kim family leaves at 2 p.m. on Friday and the Jones family at 4 p.m.
The graph below shows their travel progress.
Use the graphs to answer the questions about their trips.

Kim Family

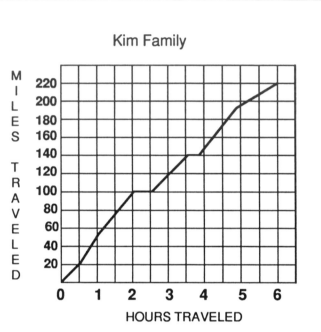

HOURS TRAVELED

Jones Family

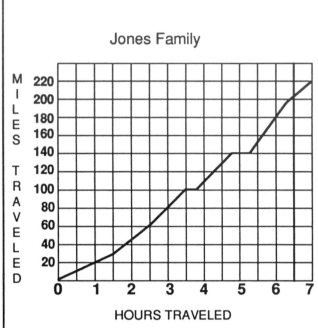

HOURS TRAVELED

Example

At what time did each family arrive in Center Port? **Kim 8 p.m., Jones 11 p.m.**

F–123 Explain the two horizontal lines in each graph. _____

F–124 How far do you think the ferry is from Westville? _____

F–125 How long did the ferry trip take? _____

F–126 Which family drove faster to the ferry? _____

F–127 Which family drove faster from the ferry to Center Port? _____

F–128 What was the speed of the ferry? _____

MATCHING GRAPHS WITH LABELS

Select the graph that best illustrates the stated relationship.

Example Conversion of inches to centimeters	GRAPH		d
F–129 Radius of a circle and the area of the circle	GRAPH		
F–130 Hours traveled and miles traveled on a bus trip	GRAPH		
F–131 Conversion of meters to centimeters	GRAPH		
F–132 Weeks of growth and height of a plant (in cm)	GRAPH		

a.
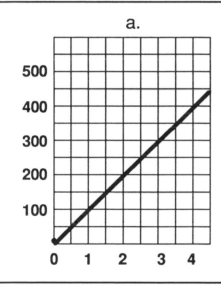

b.
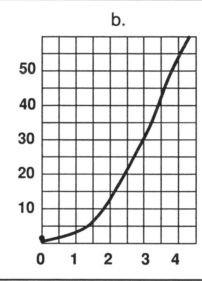

c.
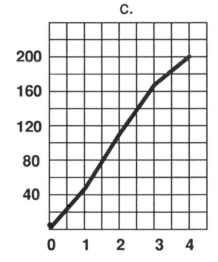

d.
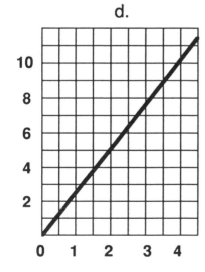

e.
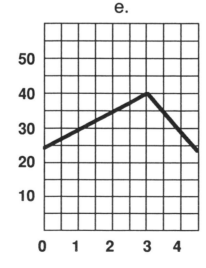

f.
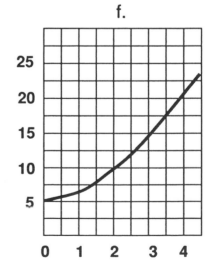

Answers

Page 1
A-1: 14
A-2: 14
A-3: 15

A-4: 16
A-5: 10

Page 2
A-6: 12
A-7: 9
A-8: 20

A-9: 10
A-10: 26

Page 3
A-11: 10, 6, 6
A-12: 16, 12, 33
A-13: 15, 5, 10

A-14: 20, 4, 16
A-15: 9, 6, 16

Page 4
A-16: 41
A-17: 130
A-18: 205

A-19: 130
A-20: 72

Page 5
A-21: 539
A-22: 4,605
A-23: 1,503,517

A-24: 1,000
A-25: 95,208,527

Page 6

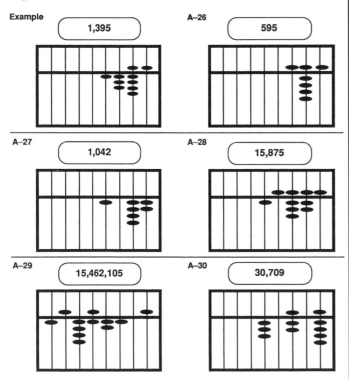

Page 7
A-31: 23, 26, 29, 32
A-32: 65, 72, 79, 86
A-33: 38, 35, 32, 29
A-34: 45, 52, 59, 66

A-35: 37, 40, 43, 46
A-36: 89, 87, 85, 83
A-37: 80, 73, 66, 59

Page 8

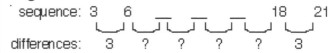

A-38: 16, 22, 29, 37
A-39: 20, 26, 33, 41
A-40: 26, 37, 50, 65
A-41: 21, 28, 36, 45

A-42: 39, 51, 65, 81
A-43: 30, 41, 54, 69
A-44: 36, 49, 64, 81
A-45: 64, 128, 256, 512

Page 9

sequence: 3   6   __   __   __   18   21
differences: 3   ?   ?   ?   ?   3

A-46: 9, 12, 15
A-47: 30, 28, 26
A-48: 28, 24, 16
A-49: 69, 63, 57, 51

A-50: 5, 15, 25, 35
A-51: 100, 80, 70, 50, 40
A-52: 136, 131, 121

Page 10
A-53: 24, 38, 45
A-54: 6, 12, 18, 24
A-55: 14, 19, 29, 34
A-56: 87, 83, 75, 71

A-57: 38, 24, 10
A-58: 8, 13, 23, 33, 38
A-59: 80, 77, 71, 65
A-60: 62, 60, 58, 54

Page 11
A-61: b. 33, d. 41
A-62: c. 28

A-63: c. 33
A-64: a. 42, d. 30

Page 12
A-65: c. 21, 22, 23
A-66: a. 25, 26, 29, 30

A-67: c. 31, 32, 36, 37
A-68: b. 19, 22, 23, 26

Page 13
A-69: 24
A-70: 84
A-71: 36, 54, 42

A-72: 18
A-73: 68

Page 14
A-74: 39
A-75: 30, 36
A-76: 35, 28, 20

A-77: 35
A-78: 4 (maybe) 6, 8

Page 15

A-79: 80, 888
A-80: 18, 36, 108
A-81: 41, 0, 8

A-82: 18, 14, 6
A-83: no solution
A-84: 29, 53

Page 16

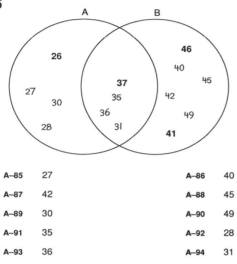

A–85	27		A–86	40
A–87	42		A–88	45
A–89	30		A–90	49
A–91	35		A–92	28
A–93	36		A–94	31

A–95   What numbers are in both circle A and circle B? 31, 35, 36, 37

A–96   What other numbers between 25 and 50 could be placed in both circle A and circle B? 32, 33, 34, 38, 39

Page 17

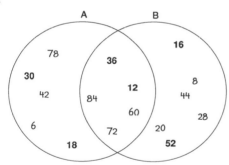

A–97	8		A–98	60
A–99	42		A–100	6
A–101	72		A–102	78
A–103	44		A–104	84
A–105	28		A–106	20

A–107   What numbers are in both circle A and circle B? 12, 36, 60, 72, 84

A–108   List two other numbers between 1 and 100 that could be placed in both circle A and circle B. 24, 48 (or 96)

Page 18

A-109: $\frac{6}{8}$

A-110: $\frac{6}{16}$

A-111: $\frac{9}{30}$

A-112: $\frac{10}{16}$

A-113: $\frac{2}{45}$

Page 19

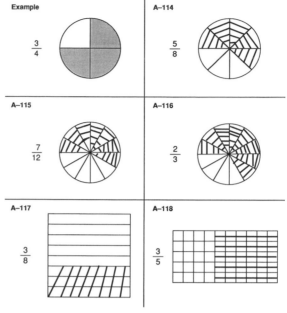

Page 20

A-119: d. $\frac{2}{5}$

A-120: d. $\frac{1}{5}$

A-121: b. $\frac{3}{4}$

A-122: a. $\frac{1}{3}$

Page 21

A-123: b.
A-124: a.

A-125: b.
A-126: a

Page 22

A-127: $\frac{5}{10}$, $\frac{5}{11}$, decreasing

A-128: $\frac{3}{10}$, $\frac{1}{10}$, decreasing

A-129: $\frac{4}{6}$, $\frac{8}{10}$, increasing

A-130: $\frac{3}{4}$, $\frac{5}{6}$, $\frac{6}{7}$, increasing

A-131: $\frac{1}{2}$, $\frac{2}{4}$, equivalent

A-132: $\frac{2}{6}$, $\frac{4}{12}$, $\frac{6}{18}$, equivalent

A-133: $\frac{5}{10}$, $\frac{10}{15}$, increasing

Page 23

Example

$\frac{1}{2}$	$\frac{1}{4}$	$\frac{1}{6}$	$\frac{1}{8}$	$\frac{1}{10}$
$\frac{2}{4}$	$\frac{2}{8}$	$\frac{2}{12}$	$\frac{2}{16}$	$\frac{2}{20}$

A–134

$\frac{1}{3}$	$\frac{1}{4}$	$\frac{1}{5}$	$\frac{1}{6}$	$\frac{1}{7}$
$\frac{3}{9}$	$\frac{3}{12}$	$\frac{3}{15}$	$\frac{3}{18}$	$\frac{3}{21}$

A–135

$\frac{2}{5}$	$\frac{3}{6}$	$\frac{4}{7}$	$\frac{5}{8}$	$\frac{6}{9}$
$\frac{4}{10}$	$\frac{6}{12}$	$\frac{8}{14}$	$\frac{10}{16}$	$\frac{12}{18}$

A–136

$\frac{1}{2}$	$\frac{2}{3}$	$\frac{3}{4}$
$\frac{2}{4}$	$\frac{4}{6}$	$\frac{6}{8}$
$\frac{3}{6}$	$\frac{6}{9}$	$\frac{9}{12}$

A–137

$\frac{1}{3}$	$\frac{1}{6}$	$\frac{1}{9}$
$\frac{2}{6}$	$\frac{2}{12}$	$\frac{2}{18}$
$\frac{3}{9}$	$\frac{3}{18}$	$\frac{3}{27}$

Page 24

A-138: 42.84
A-139: 16.120
A-140: 3.367

A-141: 5.06
A-142: 12.703

Page 25

A-143: 162.31
A-144: 1.623
A-145: 1.62

A-146: 16.23
A-147: 162.3

Page 26

A-148: 671.5
A-149: 6.75
A-150: 6.715

A-151: 67.105
A-152: 671.05

Page 27

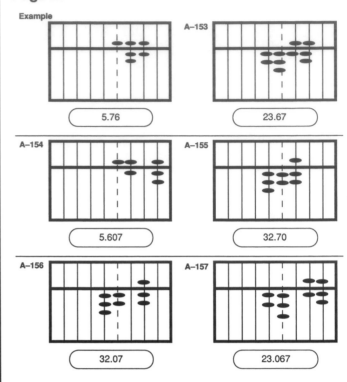

A-153

5.76   23.67

A–154   A–155

5.607   32.70

A–156   A–157

32.07   23.067

Page 28

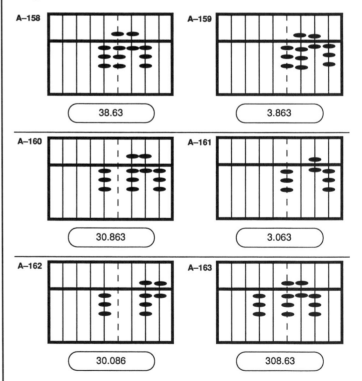

A–158   A–159

38.63   3.863

A–160   A–161

30.863   3.063

A–162   A–163

30.086   308.63

Page 29:

A-164: 6, 12, 14, 18
A-165: 40, 42, 44, 54

A-166: 113, 115, 117, 121

Page 30
A-167: b. 201, d. 108   A-170: c. 2109, d. 1890
A-168: a. 350, c. 318   A-171: a. 4899, c. 4000
A-169: a. 950, b. 902

Page 31
A-172: $\frac{2}{10}$ A-174: $\frac{2}{4}$

A-173: $\frac{4}{5}$ A-175: $\frac{5}{3}$

Page 32
A-176: c. $\frac{7}{10}$ A-179: b. $1\frac{3}{6}$

A-177: d. $\frac{2}{4}$ A-180: c. $2\frac{7}{8}$

A-178: a. $\frac{1}{3}$

Page 33
A-181: 2.2, 2.7, 2.9, 3.2   A-183: 6.0, 6.2, 6.4, 6.8
A-182: 0.4, 0.6, 1.1, 1.8

Page 34
A-184: c. 10.4   A-187: d. 0.25
A-185: d. 23.5   A-188: a. 45.05
A-186: a. 99.7

Page 35
A-189: 3,542   A-193: 398
A-190: 7,942   A-194: 2,909
A-191: 3,960   A-195: 90,000
A-192: 99,740

Page 36
A-196: 0.097   A-200: 4.09
A-197: 3.1405   A-201: 1.975
A-198: 2.90   A-202: 10,888.088
A-199: 610.08

Page 37
A-203: 2,080,705   A-206: 26,000.62
A-204: 118.34   A-207: 26,062
A-205 1.005   A-208: 555.055

Page 38
A-209: two thousand, eighty-four and thirty-five
        hundredths
A-210: twenty-five thousand, twenty-five and
        twenty-five thousandths
A-211: one and eight thousandths
A-212: two hundred eight thousand, seven
        hundred fifty
A-213: nine and ninety-nine hundredths
A-214: three and seven hundred fifty ten
        thousandths

Page 39
A-215: $\frac{4}{8}, \frac{5}{8}, \frac{7}{8}$ A-218: $\frac{3}{10}, \frac{2}{10}$

A-216: $\frac{2}{5}, \frac{2}{3}, \frac{2}{4}$ A-219: $\frac{1}{6}, \frac{3}{12}$

A-217: $\frac{9}{10}, \frac{15}{16}$

Page 40:
A-220: 8   A-224: 5, 4, 3, 2, 1
A-221: 6, 7, . . .   A-225: 4
A-222: 4, 3, 2, 1, 0   A-multiple solutions;
A-223: 5, 6, . . .   one pair is 8, 6

Page 41

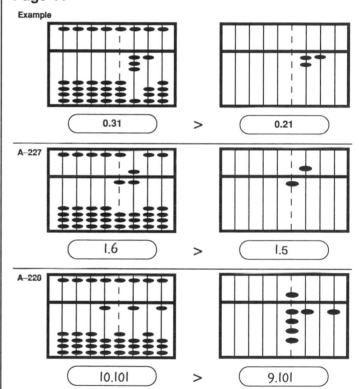

Page 42

Example	3.819	3. _9_ 19	3.8 _2_ 0	_4_ .819

A–229	0.222	0.2 _3_ 2	0.22 _3_	0. _2_ 3 _1_

A–230	5.869	5. _8_ 89	5.8 _7_ 9	5. _9_ 89

A–231	1.31	1. _2_ 1	_0_ .31	1.3 _0_

A–232	13.09	1 _2_ .09	13.0 _8_	1 _1_ . _8_ 9

A–233	3.22	3. _1_ 4	3.2 _1_	3. _0_ 4

Page 43

A-234: $\frac{3}{9}, \frac{4}{9}, \frac{5}{9}$

A-235: $\frac{2}{6}, \frac{3}{6}, \frac{4}{6}$, or $\frac{3}{12}, \ldots, \frac{9}{12}$

A-236: $\frac{3}{8}, \frac{4}{8}, \frac{5}{8}$

A-237: $\frac{3}{10}, \ldots, \frac{7}{10}$

A-238: $\frac{7}{12}, \frac{8}{12}, \frac{9}{12}$

A-239: $\frac{5}{16}, \frac{6}{16}, \frac{7}{16}$

Page 44

A-240: 9.99, . . ., 10.05
A-241: 0.50, . . ., 0.54
A-242: 1.5, . . ., 1.8
A-243: 2.109, 2.110, 2.111
A-244: 0.41, . . ., 0.48
A-245: 1.51, . . ., 1.69

Page 45

A-246: 3   A-249: 1
A-247: 1   A-250: 7
A-248: 10   A-251: 20

Page 46

A-252: 4.8   A-255: 1.1
A-253: 9.1   A-256: 1.1
A-254: 8.9   A-257: 19.4

Page 47

A-258: $\frac{4}{10}$ A-261: $\frac{8}{10}$

A-259: $\frac{7}{10}$ A-262: $\frac{1}{10}$

A-260: $\frac{8}{10}$

Page 48

A-263: 0.250   A-266: 0.875
A-264: 0.250   A-267: 0.750
A-265: 0.375

Page 49

A-268: 2.8   A-270: 5.5
A-269: 3.0   A-271: 1.2

Page 50

A-272: $7\frac{7}{8}$ A-274: $\frac{7}{2}$

A-273: 1   A-275: $\frac{3}{4}$

Page 51

A-276: $\frac{5}{10}$ A-278: $\frac{11}{20}$

A-277: $\frac{1}{3}$ A-279: $\frac{1}{3}$

Page 52

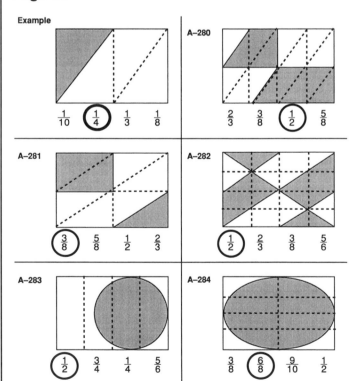

Page 53

A-285: b. $\frac{1}{3}$, c. $\frac{2}{6}$

A-286: b. $\frac{5}{25}$, d. $\frac{1}{5}$

A-287: b. $\frac{6}{25}$

A-288: a. $\frac{3}{5}$, d. $\frac{15}{25}$

A-289: b. $\frac{10}{25}$, c. $\frac{2}{5}$, d. $\frac{40}{100}$

Page 54

A-290: $\frac{6}{9}$, $\frac{4}{6}$

A-291: $\frac{10}{12}$

A-292: $\frac{9}{12}$, $\frac{3}{4}$, $\frac{12}{16}$

A-293: $\frac{1}{5}$, $\frac{5}{25}$

A-294: $\frac{9}{30}$, $\frac{30}{100}$

Page 55

A-295: b. $\frac{8}{20}$, c. $\frac{15}{20}$

A-296: b. $\frac{25}{64}$, c. $\frac{5}{16}$

A-297: b. $\frac{4}{10}$

A-298: a. $\frac{3}{4}$, c. $\frac{10}{15}$

Page 56

A-299: a. 0.4

A-300: d. 0.3

A-301: c. 0.4

A-302: c. 0.40

A-303: c. 0.36

Page 57

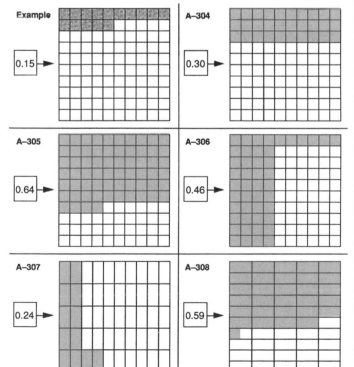

Page 58

A-309: a. $\frac{1}{2}$, c. $\frac{5}{10}$, d. 0.5

A-310: a. $\frac{4}{10}$, b. 0.4, c. $\frac{2}{5}$

A-311: b. 0.5, d. $\frac{1}{2}$

A-312: b. 0.75, c. $\frac{6}{8}$, d. $\frac{3}{4}$

A-313: b. $\frac{9}{12}$, c. 0.75, d. $\frac{3}{4}$

Page 59

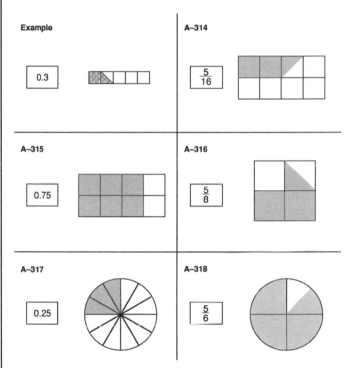

Page 60

A-319: 0.625   A-322: 2.2
A-320: 1.5   A-323: 0.75
A-321: 0.25

Page 61

A-324: $\frac{3}{4}$, $\frac{6}{8}$, $\frac{75}{100}$

A-325: $\frac{35}{100}$, $\frac{14}{40}$, $\frac{7}{20}$

A-326: $\frac{7}{8}$, $\frac{875}{1,000}$

A-327: $\frac{32}{10}$, $3\frac{1}{5}$, $\frac{320}{100}$, $3\frac{2}{10}$

A-328: $1\frac{1}{4}$, $\frac{125}{100}$, $1\frac{25}{100}$, $\frac{5}{4}$

Page 62

A-329: 0.625

A-330: $\frac{9}{20}$, $\frac{45}{100}$

A-331: $\frac{46}{10}$, 4.60, $4\frac{6}{10}$

A-332: $1\frac{4}{5}$, $1\frac{8}{10}$, 1.8

A-333: $\frac{375}{1000}$, $\frac{3}{8}$, 0.3750

A-334: $\frac{43}{20}$, 2.15

A-335: 1.95, $1\frac{95}{100}$

Page 63

Example $\overline{GI}$, $\overline{IC}$, $\overline{BC}$, $\overline{GB}$

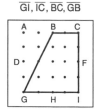

B–1 $\overline{BC}$, $\overline{GH}$, $\overline{BG}$, $\overline{HC}$

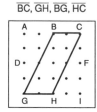

B–2 $\overline{HC}$, $\overline{CA}$, $\overline{HG}$, $\overline{GA}$

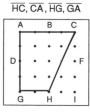

B–3 $\overline{HC}$, $\overline{IH}$, $\overline{CI}$

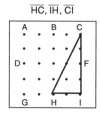

B–4 $\overline{GI}$, $\overline{BC}$, $\overline{GB}$, $\overline{HC}$, $\overline{CI}$

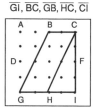

B–5 $\overline{AC}$, $\overline{CI}$, $\overline{IG}$, $\overline{AG}$, $\overline{BG}$, $\overline{CH}$

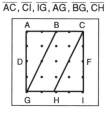

Page 64

Example

Figure 1: triangle GHB

Figure 2: triangle CIH

Figure 3: quadrilateral BCIH

Name the triangles: __Triangle CBH__

B–6

Figure 1: quadrilateral GICB

Figure 2: triangle GIC

Figure 3: triangle GHC

Name the triangles: BCG, HIC

B–7

Figure 1: triangle ACI

Figure 2: triangle GAE

Figure 3: triangle ACE

Name the triangles: ACG, CEI

B–8

Figure 1: triangle GAC

Figure 2: triangle IAC

Figure 3: triangle GIA

Name the triangles: GIC, ACE, GIE, AGE, CEI

Page 66

B-9: a., d., f.   B-10: b., c., d.

Example

B–11

B–12

B–13

B–14

B–15

B–16

B–17

Page 67

B-18: b., c., f.

B-19: b., d.

B-20: c., d., f.

Page 68:

B-21: a., e.

B-22: a., b.

B-23: d., e.

Page 69

B-24: $\overline{CB}$ or $\overline{CD}$

B-25: $\overline{BE}$

B-26: $\overline{OB}$ and $\overline{OE}$

B-27: $\overline{CD}$

B-28: $\overline{BF}$ or $\overline{BD}$

B-29: $\overline{BC}$ or $\overline{CD}$ or $\overline{BD}$ or $\overline{BF}$ or $\overline{AE}$

B-30: F to B to E, A to E to B, E to B to D., etc.

Page 70

Example
A diameter containing point A

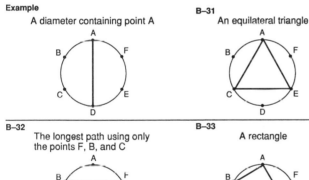

B-31
An equilateral triangle

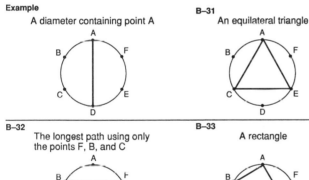

B-32
The longest path using only the points F, B, and C

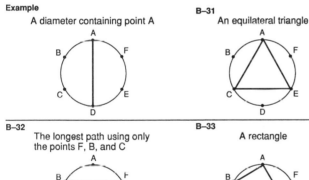

B-33
A rectangle

B-34
The longest path using only the points B, C, D, and F

B-35
A scalene triangle

Page 71

B-36: a., c., d.   B-37: b., d., e.

Page 72

B-38: b., c.   B-40: a., c., d.

B-39: a., c., d.

Page 73

Example   An equilateral triangle

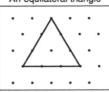

B-41   A right triangle

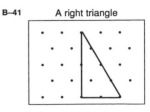

B-42   A regular hexagon

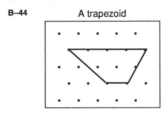

B-43   A rectangle

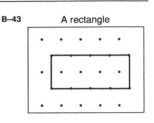

B-44   A trapezoid

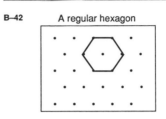

B-45   A parallelogram

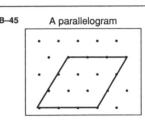

Page 74

B-46: circle both

B-47: circle ∠YRT

B-48: circle both

B-49: ∠XYZ

B-50: ∠GEI

Page 75

Example   ∠RST, which is the same size as ∠DAB

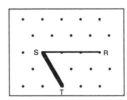

B-51   ∠PQR, which is twice the size of ∠BAD

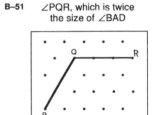

B-52   ∠KLM, which is the same size as ∠ABC

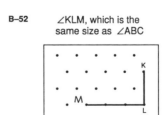

B-53   ∠FGH, which is half the size of ∠BAD

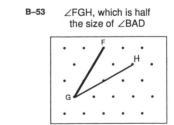

Page 76

Example A trapezoid with $\overline{XY}$ as one of the parallel sides

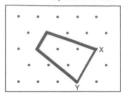

B–54 An equilateral triangle with $\overline{PQ}$ as a side

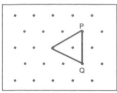

B–55 An isosceles triangle with $\overline{RS}$ as the shortest side

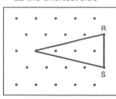

B–56 An equilateral triangle with $\overline{AB}$ as one side

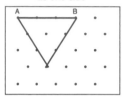

B–57 A scalene triangle with $\overline{MN}$ as one side

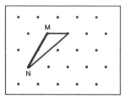

B–58 A right triangle with $\overline{CD}$ as one leg

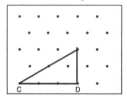

Page 77

Example Triangle RST so that the measure of ∠R is twice that of ∠A

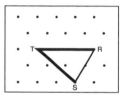

B–59 Triange DEF, which is the same size and shape as triangle ABC

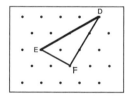

B–60 Triangle LMN so that the measure of ∠L is four times greater than that of ∠A

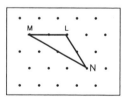

B–61 Isosceles triangle PQR so that the measure of ∠Q is the same as ∠B

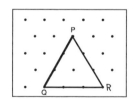

Page 78

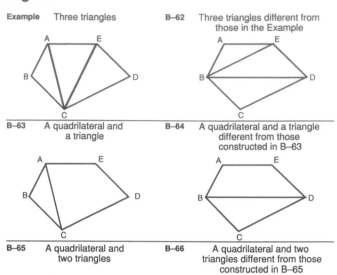

Example Three triangles

B–62 Three triangles different from those in the Example

B–63 A quadrilateral and a triangle

B–64 A quadrilateral and a triangle different from those constructed in B–63

B–65 A quadrilateral and two triangles

B–66 A quadrilateral and two triangles different from those constructed in B–65

Page 79

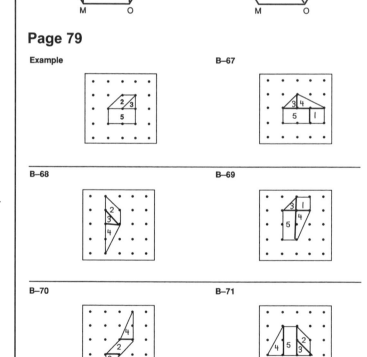

Example

B–67

B–68

B–69

B–70

B–71

Page 80

B-72: triangle, quadrilateral, quadrilateral, triangle, quadrilateral

B-73: triangle, quadrilateral, quadrilateral, quadrilateral, triangle

Page 81

B-74: 6 and 7, 6 and 7 and 8, 1 and 2 and 7 and 8,
1 and 2 and 6 and 7 and 8

B-75: 1 and 2, 1 and 2 and 3, 2 and 3 and 4 and 5,
1 and 2 and 3 and 4 and 5

Page 82

B-76: c.   B-78: b. or c.
B-77: c.   B-79: a.

Page 83

B-80: △ PQR   B-83: SVPR
B-81: △TUR   B-84: TRPV
B-82: UR

Page 84

Example

A polygon with four congruent sides or four congruent angles.

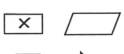

B–85

A polygon that is not a quadrilateral and has at least one right angle.

B–86

A polygon that has all sides congruent or all angles congruent.

B–87

A polygon that is a parallelogram and is not a rectangle.

Page 85

B-88: a., e.   B-91: a.
B-89: c.   B-92: c.
B-90: a., d.

Page 86

B-93: 2, 5, 8   B-96: 3, 5, 6, 8
B-94: 2, 4, 5, 6, 7   B-97: 1, 2, 4, 5, 9
B-95: 2, 5, 6, 9

Page 87

Example

A polygon that is a parallelogram and has a right angle

B–98

A polygon that is a quadrilateral and has two parallel sides

B–99

A polygon that is a right triangle and has two congruent sides

B–100

A polygon that is a parallelogram and has four congruent sides

B–101

A polygon that is a quadrilateral and has two sets of parallel sides

B–102

A polygon that is a triangle and has exactly two congruent sides

Page 88

B-103: a., c., e.   B-105: a., i.
B-104: a., c., f.

Page 89

B-106: 5   B109: 1
B-107: 4   B-110: 3
B-108: 7   B-111: 2

Page 90

B-112: 3, 4   B-114: 13
B-113: 2, 4, 6, 11, 12, 14   B-115: 3, 4, 7, 8

Page 91

B-116: triangles with at least two congruent sides,
or isosceles triangles

B-117: polygons with at least one right angle

B-118: hexagons with all angles congruent

B-119: quadrilaterals with all sides congruent, and
two pairs of parallel sides, or rhombuses

Page 92

(based on parallelism)

B-120: no two sides parallel, 5, 6, 9, 13, 14

B-121: exactly one pair of parallel sides, 7, 8

B-122: two or more pairs of parallel sides, 1, 2, 3,
4, 10, 11, 12, 15

Page 93

All rectangles
are parallelograms.

Example
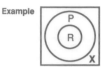
A polygon that is not
a parallelogram

B–123

A parallelogram that
is not a rectangle

B–124
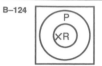
A parallelogram that
is a rectangle

B–125

A polygon that is
not a rectangle

B–126

A polygon that is
a parallelolgram

All squares
are rhombuses.

B–127

A rhombus that is
a square

B–128

A polygon that is
not a rhombus

B–129

A rhombus that is
not a square

B–130

A polygon that is
a rhombus

B–131

A polygon that is
not a square

Page 94

B-132: a. 4, b. 1, c. 3, d. 2, e. 3, f. 4
B-133: a. 2, b. 4, c. 2, d. 1, e. 3, f. 1 or 2

Page 95

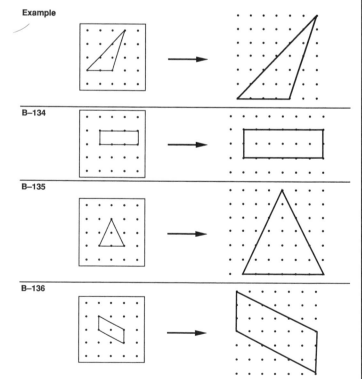

Page 96

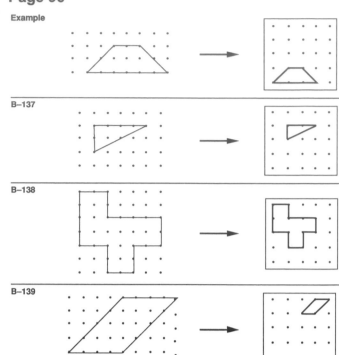

Page 97

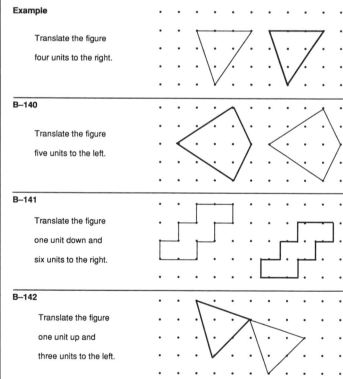

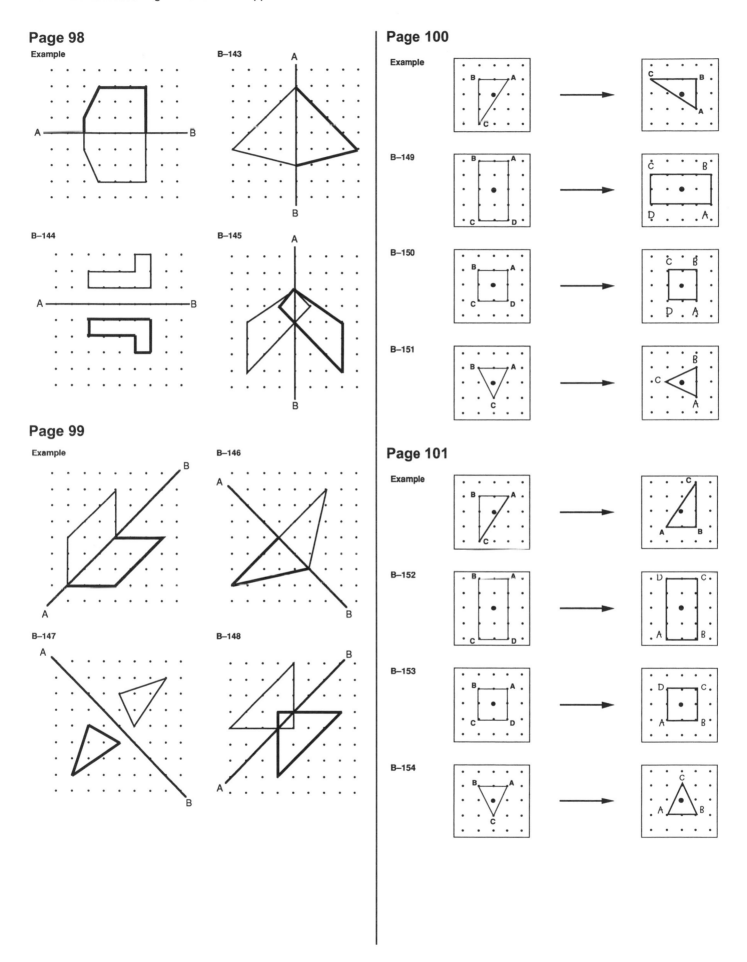

Page 98

Example

B–143

B–144

B–145

Page 99

Example

B–146

B–147

B–148

Page 100

Example

B–149

B–150

B–151

Page 101

Example

B–152

B–153

B–154

Page 102

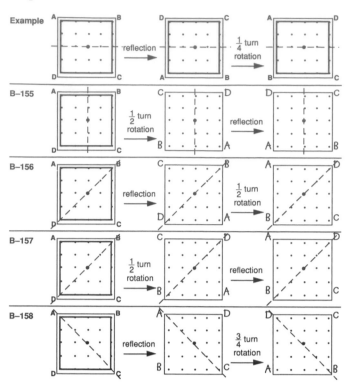

Page 103

B-159: rotation, one-half turn
B-160: reflection, diagonal $\overline{AC}$
B-161: rotation, one-quarter turn
B-162: reflection, vertical line

Page 104

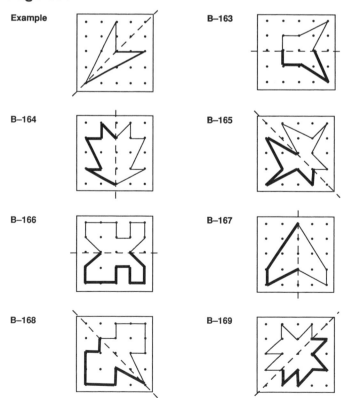

Page 105

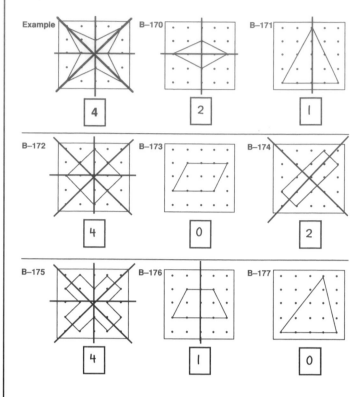

Page 106

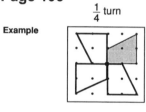

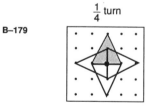

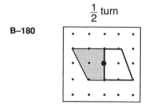

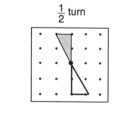

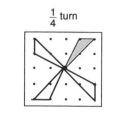

Page 107

B-183: $\frac{1}{2}$ turn

B-187: $\frac{1}{4}$ turn

B-184: $\frac{1}{2}$ turn

B-188: $\frac{1}{2}$ turn

B-185: $\frac{1}{2}$ turn

B-189: full turn

B-186: $\frac{1}{4}$ turn

Page 108

Example

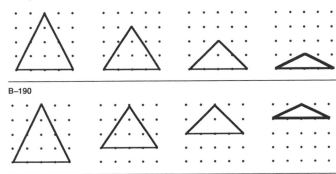

B–190

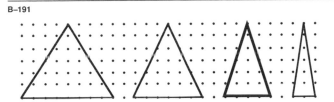

B–191

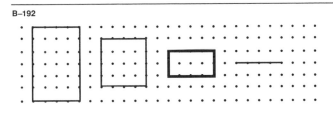

B–192

Page 109

Example

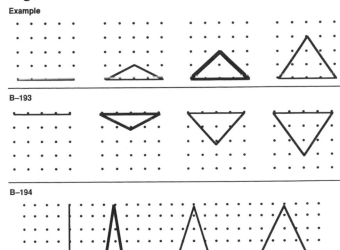

B–193

B–194

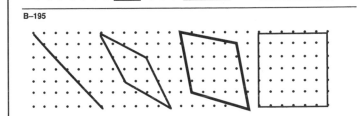

B–195

Page 110

Example

B–196

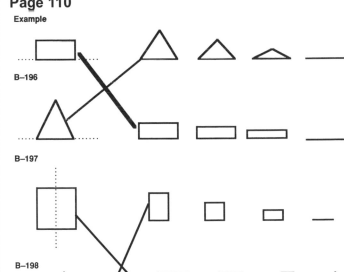

B–197

B–198

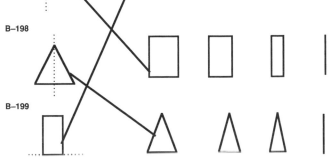

B–199

Page 111

Example

B–200

B–201

B–202

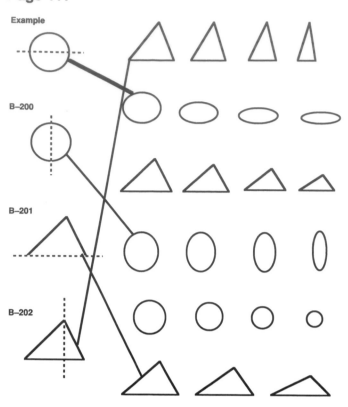

Page 112
B-203: 1, 3
B-204: 1, 4
B-205: 1, 5
B-206: 2, 3

Page 113
B-207: 5
B-208: 3
B-209: 4

Page 114

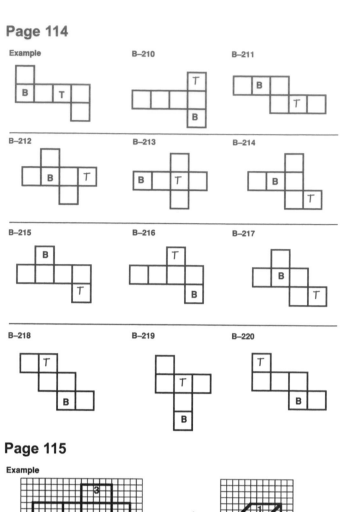

Page 115

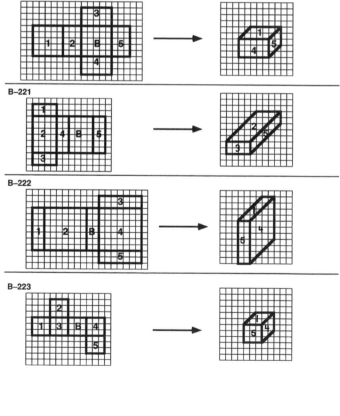

Page 116

B-224: b

B-225: d

B-226: a

Page 117

Example   4

B–227   3

B–228   3

B–229   4

B–230   5

B–231   4

B–232   5

B–233   6

B–234   4

Page 118

Example   4 regions
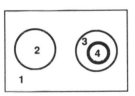

B–235   5 regions
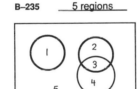

B–236   6 regions

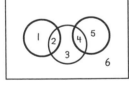

B–237   5 regions
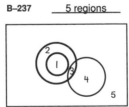

B–238   6 regions
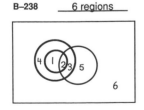

B–239   8 regions
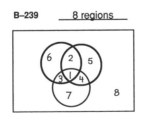

Page 119

Example   7
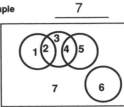

B–240   6
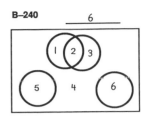

B–241   7
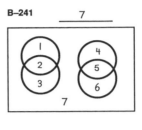

B–242   6
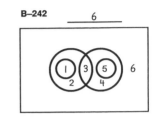

B–243   10
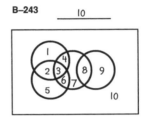

B–244   8
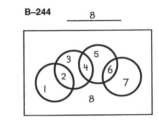

Page 120

Example   5 regions
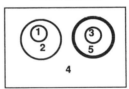

B–245   6 regions
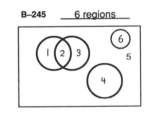

B–246   7 regions
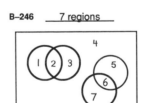

B–247   10 regions
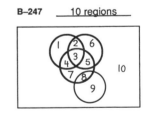

B–248   9 regions
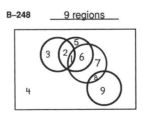

B–249   11 regions
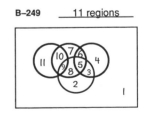

Page 121

Example

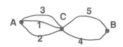

Is it possible? **YES**   Is it possible? **NO**

B–250

Is it possible? YES   Is it possible? NO

B–251

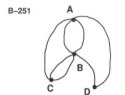

Is it possible? NO   Is it possible? YES

Page 122

Example

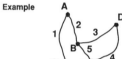

Is it possible? **YES**   Is it possible? **NO**

Starting Point **C** End Point **B**   Starting Point ___ End Point ___

B–252

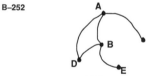

Is it possible? NO   Is it possible? YES

Starting Point ___ End Point ___   Starting Point **C** End Point **E**

B–253

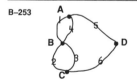
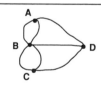

Is it possible? YES   Is it possible? NO

Starting Point **A** End Point **C**   Starting Point ___ End Point ___

Page 123

Example   B–254

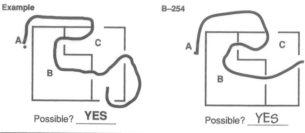

Possible? **YES**   Possible? YES

B–255   B–256

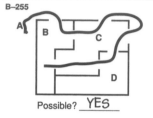

Possible? YES   Possible? YES

B–257   B–258

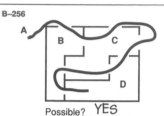

Possible? YES   Possible? NO

Page 124

Example   B–259

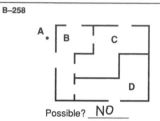

Possible? **YES**   Possible? YES

B–260   B–261

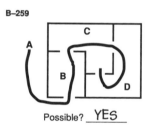

Possible? YES   Possible? YES

B–262   B–263

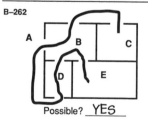
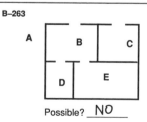

Possible? YES   Possible? NO

Page 125

C-1: 4 × 5, 5 + 5 + 5 + 5, 5 × 4, 4 + 4 + 4 + 4 + 4

C-2: 5 × 6, 6 + 6 + 6 + 6 + 6, 5 + 5 + 5 + 5 + 5 + 5, 6 × 5

C-3: 8 + 8 + 8 + 8, 4 × 8, 8 × 4, 4 + 4 + 4 + 4 + 4 + 4 + 4 + 4

Page 126
C-4: b, d

C-5: a, c

C- 6: b, c, d

Page 127
C-7: c, d, e

C-8: b, e, f

C-9: a, c, d, f

C-10: a, c, d

Page 128
C-11: a, b, e, f

C-12: a, c, d, e

C-13: b, d, e, f

C-14: a, c, d, f

Page 129
C-15: b

C-16: d

C-17: a

C-18: c

Page 130
C-19: d

C-20: a, c

C-21: c, d

C-22: b, d

Page 131

Example

$\frac{1}{4} \times 1 = \frac{1}{4}$

C–23

$\frac{2}{3} \times 1 = \frac{2}{3}$

C–24

$\frac{6}{24} \times 1 = \frac{6}{24}$

C–25

$\frac{4}{6} \times 1 = \frac{4}{6}$

C–26

$\frac{2}{5} \times 1 = \frac{2}{5}$

C–27

$\frac{3}{4} \times 1 = \frac{3}{4}$

C–28

$\frac{12}{20} \times 1 = \frac{12}{20}$

C–29

$\frac{5}{20} \times 1 = \frac{5}{20}$

Page 132
C-30: $\frac{1}{3}, \frac{1}{3}, \frac{1}{3} \times \frac{1}{3} = \frac{1}{9}$

C-31: $\frac{2}{4}, \frac{2}{6}, \frac{2}{6} \times \frac{2}{4} = \frac{4}{24}$

C-32: $\frac{3}{5}, \frac{2}{3}, \frac{2}{3} \times \frac{3}{5} = \frac{6}{15}$

Page 133
C-33: a

C-34: c

C-35: c

C-36: a

Page 134

Example

$\frac{3}{5} \times \frac{3}{4} = \frac{9}{20}$

C-37

$\frac{3}{4} \times \frac{1}{4} = \frac{3}{16}$

C–38

$\frac{3}{6} \times \frac{1}{4} = \frac{3}{24}$

C–39

$\frac{1}{4} \times \frac{2}{5} = \frac{2}{20}$

C–40

$\frac{1}{3} \times \frac{2}{4} = \frac{2}{12}$

C–41

$\frac{1}{4} \times \frac{1}{4} = \frac{1}{16}$

C–42

$\frac{5}{6} \times \frac{4}{4} = \frac{20}{24}$

C–43

$\frac{4}{4} \times \frac{2}{3} = \frac{8}{12}$

Page 135

Example   A taxi service sends 6 vans to transport 24 people to a meeting. How many people should ride in each van?

⑥ ⑥ ⑥ ⑥   24 ÷ 6 = 4   ④④④ / ④④④

C–44   A bottled water distributor is able to pack 6 jugs of water in each box. How many boxes will be needed to package 2 dozen jugs of water?

⑥ ⑥ ⑥ ⑥   24 ÷ 6 = 4   ④④④ ④④④

C–45   A local newspaper purchases 24 tons of paper. If its trucks can carry 6 tons of paper, how many trips are needed to deliver the paper to its printing plant?

⑥ ⑥ ⑥ ⑥   24 ÷ 6 = 4   ④④④ ④④④

C–46   A butcher wants to divide 24 pounds of hamburger into 6 packages. How many pounds should be placed in each package?

⑥ ⑥ ⑥ ⑥   24 ÷ 6 = 4   ④④④ / ④④④

Page 136

Example   A cake recipe requires 8 eggs.
If a chef has 2 dozen eggs, how many cakes can she make?

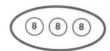 $24 \div 8 = 3$

C–47   Each student needs 4 cubes to make a pattern.
If the teacher has a set of 20 cubes, how many students can make the pattern?

 $20 \div 4 = 5$

C–48   A chef wants to make 8 omelets from 2 dozen eggs.
How many eggs can he put in each omelet?

 $24 \div 8 = 3$

C–49   A teacher wants to divide a set of 20 cubes between 4 students.
How many cubes will each student receive?

   $20 \div 4 = 5$

C–50   Books are on sale for $5.00 per book. How many books
could be purchased with $30.00?

$30 \div 5 = 6$

Page 137

C-51: 4
C-52: 40
C-53: 16
C-54: 30
C-55: 30
C-56: 18

C-57: 22
C-58: 3
C-59: 12
C-60   192
C-61: 192

Page 138

Example
$24 + (4 \div 2) = 26$

C–62
$(24 + 4) \times 2 = 56$

C–63
$(24 \times 4) - 2 = 94$

C–64
$24 + (4 - 2) = 12$

C–65
$24 \times (4 \div 2) = 48$

C–66
$6 = 12 \div (4 - 2)$

C–67
$27 = 28 - (4 - 3)$

C–68
$4 = 28 \div (4 + 3)$

C–69
$3 + (4 \times 2) = 8 + 3$

C–70
$12 + 2 = (5 \times 0) + 6$

C–71
$(3 + 4) \times 2 = (18 \div 2) + 5$

C–72
$12 - (8 - 4) = 16 \div (4 \div 2)$

Page 139

C-73: 2
C-74: 2 and 3, 4 and 6, 8 and 12
C-75: 12 and 0
C-76: 6 and 1, 4 and 3, 3 and 4, 1 and 6
C-77: 6 and 0, 12 and 2
C-78: 8, 2, and 0; 8, 3, and 1; 8, 4, and 2; 8, 6, and 4; 12, 6, and 0; 12, 8, and 2
C-79: 2, 0 and 1; 4, 0 and 2; 4, 6, and 1; 6, 0, and 3; 6, 3, and 2; 6, 12, and 1; 8, 6, and 2; 8, 2, and 3; 8, 0, and 4; 12, 6, and 3; 12, 3, and 4; 12, 0, and 6

Page 140

C-80: 6
C-81: 2
C-82: 8
C-83: 5
C-84: 6

C-85: 1
C-86: 1
C-87: 8
C-88: 2

Page 141

C-89: 7 and 4
C-90: 57
C-91: 10
C-92: 3
C-93: 3 and 5, 5 and 3, 15 and 1

Page 142
C-94: (1 × 100) + (4 × 10) + (3), 143
C-95: (2 × 100) + (0 × 10) + (7), 207
C-96: (2 × 100) + (6 × 10) + (6), 266

Page 143
C-97: b   C-100: b
C-98: a   C-101: c
C-99: a

Page 144
C-102: 3, 1, 1, 1, 2   C-105: 1, 3, 1, 1, 1
C-103: 1, 0, 0, 0, 3   C-106: 0, 3, 1, 0, 0
C-104: 5, 3, 1, 1, 0   C-107: 9, 3, 2, 0, 4

Page 145
C-108: c   C-111: b
C-109: c   C-112: b
C-110: a

Page 146
C-113: 0, 9, 8, 8, 0   C-116: 0, 7, 9, 8, 0
C-114: 1, 0, 1, 0, 0   C-117: 0, 1, 0, 1, 0
C-115: 0, 0, 7, 9, 8

Page 147
C-118: 2, 1, 2, 3, and 2.123
C-119: 0, 1, 3, 2, and 0.132

Page 148
C-120: 7, 3, 1, 1, 4   C-123: 1, 0, 1, 0, 0
C-121: 9, 3, 2, 0, 3   C-124: 0, 1, 1, 1, 1
C-122: 6, 2, 0, 0, 0   C-125: 0, 3, 1, 0, 2

Page 149
C-126: 5, 1, 1, 1, 0   C-129: 3, 0, 0, 0, 0
C-127: 0, 1, 1, 0, 2   C-130: 0, 0, 1, 1, 0
C-128: 4, 0, 0, 0, 2

Page 150
C-131: $\frac{9}{25}$, $\frac{16}{25}$ C-134: $\frac{2}{5}$, $\frac{3}{5}$

C-132: $\frac{3}{5}$, $\frac{2}{5}$ C-135: $\frac{9}{25}$, $\frac{16}{25}$

C-133: $\frac{6}{25}$, $\frac{19}{25}$

Page 151
C-136: $4\frac{1}{3}$, $1\frac{2}{3}$ C-138: $4\frac{1}{2}$, $1\frac{1}{2}$

C-137: $1\frac{2}{3}$, $2\frac{1}{3}$ C-139: $2\frac{1}{4}$, $3\frac{3}{4}$

Page 152
C-140: $\frac{2}{5}$ C-145: $7\frac{3}{5}$

C-141: $1\frac{7}{12}$ C-146: $\frac{1}{4}$

C-142: $2\frac{1}{8}$ C-147: $1\frac{3}{4}$

C-143: $1\frac{3}{8}$ C-148: $1\frac{1}{2}$

C-144: $\frac{2}{9}$

Page 153
C-149: 0.40, 0.60   C-151: 0.60, 0.40
C-150: 0.74, 0.26

Page 154
C-152: 0.3   C-157: 1.64
C-153: 0.64   C-158: 2.61
C-154: 0.93   C-159: 3.2
C-155: 0.61   C-160: 1.36
C-156: 1.00

Page 155
C-161: 4.2904, 42.904, 47.1944
C-162: 0.1703, 1.703, 1.8733
C-163: 33.67, 336.7, 370.37
C-164: 5.06, 50.6, 55.66
C-165: 852.08527, 8520.8527, 9372.93797

Page 156
C-166: 94.   C-167: 56.   C-168: 33.
      49.   65.   3.3
      9.4   6.5   .33
      4.9   5.6   sum = 36.63
      .94   .56
      .49   .65
sum = 158.73   sum = 134.31

Page 157
C-169: 3 + 5 = 8
C-170: 30 − 12 = 18
C-171: 3 × 5 = 15
C-172: 2 + 3 = 5
C-173: 4 + 8 = 12
C-174: 1 × 1 = 1 and 0 × 0 = 0

Page 158

Example

Properties of N

N is odd.
N > 3.
N < 12.
3 does not divide N.
N does not divide 5.

Possible Values of N

7, 11

C–175

Properties of N

N < 10.
2 does not divide N.
3 does not divide N.
N is not prime.

Possible Values of N

1

C–176

Properties of N

N is a two-digit number.
N < 40.
9 divides the sum of the two digits.

Possible Values of N

18, 27, 36

C–177

Properties of N

N < 40.
N is a multiple of 3.
N is odd.
9 does not divide N.

Possible Values of N

3, 15, 21, 33, 39

C–178

Properties of N

N > 10.
N < 40.
N is prime.
The sum of the digits of N is less than 10.

Possible Values of N

11, 13, 17, 23, 31

C–179

Properties of N

N is even.
N < 50.
N is a multiple of 3.
9 divides the sum of its digits.

Possible Values of N

18, 36

Page 159

Example

If N is between 0 and 10, then N − 1 is

____even
____odd
____not zero
✓ less than N
✓ less than 10

C–180

If N > 5, then 2 × N is

✓ even
____odd
✓ not zero
✓ greater than N
✓ greater than 10

C–181

If N is even, then N + N is

✓ even
____odd
____not zero
____greater than N

C–182

If N is odd, then N + 2 is

____even
✓ odd
✓ not zero
✓ greater than N
____greater than 3

C–183

If N is even, then 3 × N is

✓ even
____odd
____not zero
____greater than N
✓ divisible by 2
✓ divisible by 3
✓ divisible by 6

C–184

If N is odd, then 3 × N is

____even
✓ odd
✓ not zero
✓ greater than N
____divisible by 2
✓ divisible by 3
____not a prime number

Page 160

C-185: 4, 8, 12, 16, 20, 24, 28, 32, 36, 40, 44, 48, 52, 56, 60, 64, 68, 72, 76, 80, 84, 88, 92, 96, 100

C-186: 6, 12, 18, 24, 30, 36, 42, 48, 54, 60, 66, 72, 78, 84, 90, 96

C-187: 9, 18, 27, 36, 45, 54, 63, 72, 81, 90, 99

Page 161

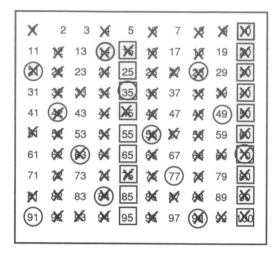

C–188 What numbers in the list are divisible by 10?
10, 20, 30, 40, 50, 60, 70, 80, 90, 100

C–189 What numbers in the list can be divided by both 5 and 7?
35, 70

C–190 List all the prime numbers that are less than 100.
2, 3, 5, 7, 11, 13, 17, 19, 23, 29, 31, 37, 41, 43, 47, 53, 59, 61, 67, 71, 73, 79, 83, 89, 97

Page 162

C-191: 1 × 4, 2 × 2

C-192: 1 × 12, 2 × 6, 3 × 4

C-193: 24 tiles, 1 × 24, 2 × 12, 3 × 8, 4 × 6

C-194:
    a. 1 × 2
    b. 1 × 10, 2 × 5
    c. 1 × 45, 3 × 15, 5 × 9
    d. 1 × 34, 2 × 17
    e. 1 × 7
    f. 1 × 21, 3 × 7
    g. 1 × 30, 2 × 15, 3 × 10, 5 × 6
    h. 1 × 41

Page 163

C-195:   4 = 1 × 4, 2 × 2   9 = 1 × 9, 3 × 3
           25 = 1 × 25, 5 × 5   49 = 1 × 49, 7 × 7

C-196:   20 = 1 × 20, 2 × 10, 4 × 5
           30 = 1 × 30, 2 × 15, 3 × 10, 5 × 6
           48 = 1 × 48, 2 × 24, 3 × 16, 4 × 12, 6 × 8
           50 = 1 × 50, 2 × 25, 5 × 10
           42 = 1 × 42, 2 × 21, 3 × 14, 6 × 7
           60 = 1 × 60, 2 × 30, 3 × 20, 4 × 15, 5 × 12, 6 × 10

C-197:   10, 27, and 35 are examples

Page 164

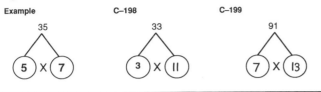

Example
35
(5) X (7)

C–198
33
(3) X (11)

C–199
91
(7) X (13)

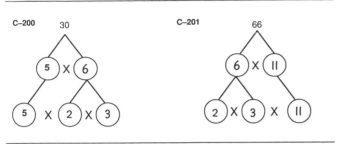

C–200
30
(5) X (6)
(5) X (2) X (3)

C–201
66
(6) X (11)
(2) X (3) X (11)

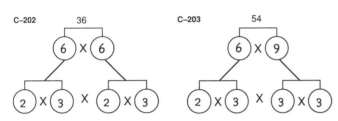

C–202
36
(6) X (6)
(2) X (3) X (2) X (3)

C–203
54
(6) X (9)
(2) X (3) X (3) X (3)

Page 165

For a roll of 3 and 5:

C-204: A= 3
C-205: B = 4
C-206: C = 5
C-207: D = 2
C-208: 6

C-209: 20
C-210: 15
C-211: 8
C-212: S = 49

Page 166

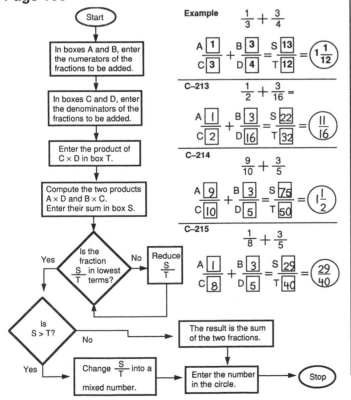

Example $\frac{1}{3} + \frac{3}{4}$

$A\boxed{1} + B\boxed{3} = S\boxed{13} = \left(1\frac{1}{12}\right)$
$C\boxed{3} \quad D\boxed{4} \quad T\boxed{12}$

C–213 $\frac{1}{2} + \frac{3}{16} =$

$A\boxed{1} + B\boxed{3} = S\boxed{22} = \left(\frac{11}{16}\right)$
$C\boxed{2} \quad D\boxed{16} \quad T\boxed{32}$

C–214 $\frac{9}{10} + \frac{3}{5}$

$A\boxed{9} + B\boxed{3} = S\boxed{75} = \left(1\frac{1}{2}\right)$
$C\boxed{10} \quad D\boxed{5} \quad T\boxed{50}$

C–215 $\frac{1}{8} + \frac{3}{5}$

$A\boxed{1} + B\boxed{3} = S\boxed{29} = \left(\frac{29}{40}\right)$
$C\boxed{8} \quad D\boxed{5} \quad T\boxed{40}$

Page 167

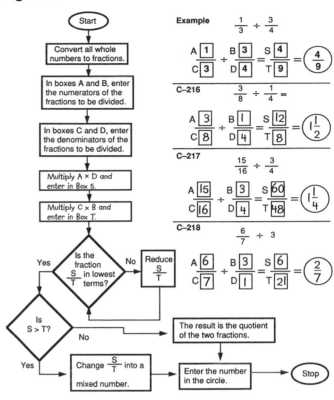

Example $\frac{1}{3} \div \frac{3}{4}$

$A\boxed{1} \div B\boxed{3} = S\boxed{4} = \left(\frac{4}{9}\right)$
$C\boxed{3} \quad D\boxed{4} \quad T\boxed{9}$

C–216 $\frac{3}{8} \div \frac{1}{4} =$

$A\boxed{3} \div B\boxed{1} = S\boxed{12} = \left(1\frac{1}{2}\right)$
$C\boxed{8} \quad D\boxed{4} \quad T\boxed{8}$

C–217 $\frac{15}{16} \div \frac{3}{4}$

$A\boxed{15} \div B\boxed{3} = S\boxed{60} = \left(1\frac{1}{4}\right)$
$C\boxed{16} \quad D\boxed{4} \quad T\boxed{48}$

C–218 $\frac{6}{7} \div 3$

$A\boxed{6} \div B\boxed{3} = S\boxed{6} = \left(\frac{2}{7}\right)$
$C\boxed{7} \quad D\boxed{1} \quad T\boxed{21}$

Page 168

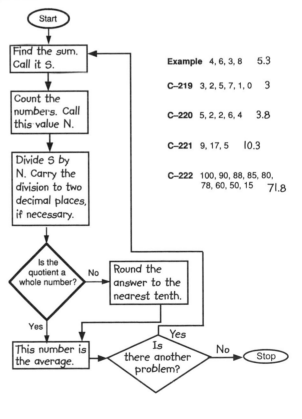

Example 4, 6, 3, 8   5.3

C–219 3, 2, 5, 7, 1, 0   3

C–220 5, 2, 2, 6, 4   3.8

C–221 9, 17, 5   10.3

C–222 100, 90, 88, 85, 80,
         78, 60, 50, 15   71.8

Page 169

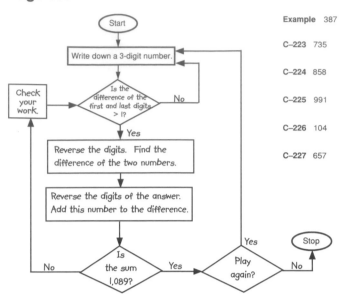

Example	387
C–223	735
C–224	858
C–225	991
C–226	104
C–227	657

Page 170

$$C = \frac{5}{9} \times (F - 32)$$

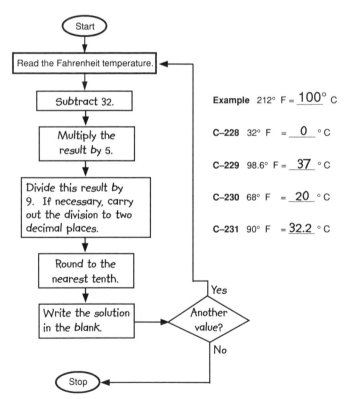

Example   212° F = **100°** C

C–228   32° F   = **0** °C

C–229   98.6° F = **37** °C

C–230   68° F   = **20** °C

C–231   90° F   = **32.2** °C

Page 171

Example   Jim purchased 3 books that normally sell for $5.99.

3 × $5.99   (3 × $4.99)   3 × $3.69

C–232   Sally purchased 4 books that normally sell for $4.99.

4 × $4.99   4 × $5.99   (4 × $ 3.69)

C–233   Hector purchased 3 books that normally sell for $5.99 and 4 books that normally sell for $4.99.

(3 × $4.99) + (4 × $3.69)   (3 × $5.99) + (4 × $4.99)

7 × $4.99   (4 × $4.99) + (3 × $3.69)

C–234   Sam bought 4 books that normally sell for $6.99 and 2 books that normally sell for $4.99.

(4 × $4.99) + (2 × $4.99)   (4 × $5.99) + (2 × $3.69)

(4 × $4.99) + (2 × $3.69)   6 × $4.99

C–235   Juanita bought 3 books that normally sell for $6.99, 2 books that normally sell for $5.99, and 1 book that normally sells for $4.99.

(3 × $4.99) + (3 × $4.99)   (3 × $5.99) + (2 × $4.99) + $3.69

(5 × $4.99) + $3.69   (3 × $4.99) + (2 × $4.99) + $3.69

Page 172

Example
Jim purchased 3 books that normally sell for $6.99.
How much money did he save?

3 × (**$6.99** – **$4.99**) = **$6.00**

C–236
Hector purchased 2 books that normally sell for $5.99.
How much money did he spend?

2 × ($5.99 – **1.00**) = **$9.98**

C–237
Juanita purchased 3 books that normally sell for $4.99, and 1 book that normally sells for $6.99.
How much money did she spend?

3 × (**4.99** – **1.30**) + (**6.99** – **2.00**) = **$16.06**

C–238
Mary bought 2 books that normally sell for $6.99, and 3 books that normally sell for $5.99.
How much money did she save?

2 × (**6.99** – $4.99) + **3** × (**5.99** – $4.99) = **$7.00**

2 × (**2.00**) + 3 × (**1.00**) = **$7.00**

C–239
Sally bought 3 books.
What is the most money that she could have saved on the books?

3 × (**6.99** – **4.99**) = **$6.00**

Page 173

C-240: d, $3.25   C-242: b or d, $1.10

C-241: c or d, $4.95

Page 174

C-243: c, $14.98   C-245: d, $47.73

C-244: d, $39.83   C-246: d, $4.10

Page 175
D-1: =   D-5: >
D-2: =   D-6: <
D-3: <   D-7: >
D-4: =

Page 176
D-8: <   D-12: =
D-9: >   D-13: >
D-10: >   D-14: <
D-11: =

Page 177
D-15: $\overline{AB}, \overline{AC}$ D-18: $\overline{AD}, \overline{CD}$
D-16: $\overline{CD}, \overline{AB}$ D-19: $\overline{AC}$, or $\overline{AB}, \overline{BC}$
D-17: $\overline{AD}$ or $\overline{CD}, \overline{AB}$

Page 178
D-20: =   D-23: >
D-21: <   D-24: >
D-22: <

Page 179
D-25: A   D-27: A
D-26: C

Page 180
D-28: 12   D-32: 13
D-29: 9   D-33: 9
D-30: 11   D-34: 9
D-31: 12

Page 181
D-35: >   D-39: <
D-36: =   D-40: >
D-37: >   D-41: <
D-38: >

Page 182
D-42: =   D-46: >
D-43: >   D-47: =
D-44: <   D-48: >
D-45: <

Page 183
D-49: 18   D-52: 18
D-50: 18   D-53: 18
D-51: 18

Page 184
D-54: 17.8   D-57: 14.8
D-55: 18.8   D-58: 16.2
D-56: 15.6

Page 185
D-59: 21.6   D-62: 16.8
D-60: 13.68   D-63: 19.2
D-61: 18.48

Page 186
D-64: 20   D-67: ?
D-65: 15   D-68: 16
D-66 : 20   D-69: 12

Page 187

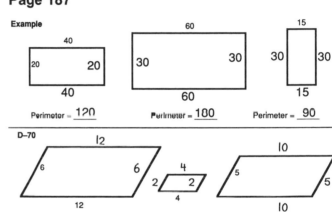

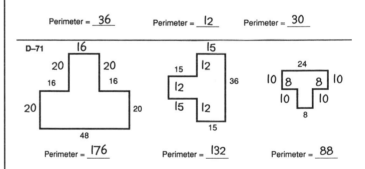

Page 188

Example

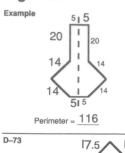

Perimeter = __116__

D–72

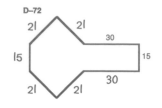

Perimeter = __174__

D–73

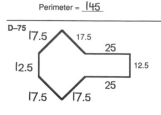

Perimeter = __145__

D–74

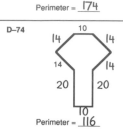

Perimeter = __116__

D–75

17.5 17.5
25
12.5   12.5
25
17.5 17.5

Perimeter = __145__

D–76

30 21 21
15   15
30 21 21

Perimeter = __174__

Page 189

D-77: EC = 3.75, BC = 10.5, Perimeter = 26.25
D-78: AC = 12, DE = 7.5, AG = 5, Perimeter = 30
D-79: AD = 1.4, BF = 1.4, AB = 4.2, BC = 3,
       Perimeter = 10.2

Page 190

D-80: BF = 6, DF = 2.5, DE = 6, EF = 6.5,
       Perimeter = 15
D-81: AE = 6.5, EF = 6, DA = 5, DB = 13,
       Perimeter = 15
D-82: GH = 4, BE = 6, DF = 6, EF = 2, DH = 4,
       Perimeter = 26

Page 191

D-83: 3.4   D-89: 18.4
D-84: 3.2   D-90: 6.8
D-85: 9.2   D-91: 9.6
D-86: 6.4   D-92: 10.2
D-87: 4.6   D-93: 5.2
D-88: 13.6

Page 192

D-94: 14.4   D-97: 17.6
D-95: 8.8   D-98: 8.4
D-96: 12.4   D-99: 16.8

Page 193

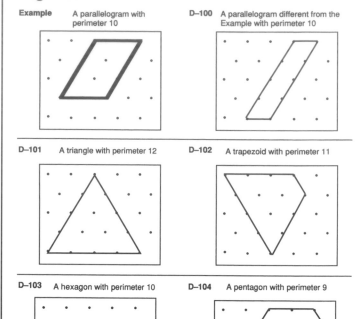

Example — A parallelogram with perimeter 10

D–100 — A parallelogram different from the Example with perimeter 10

D–101 — A triangle with perimeter 12

D–102 — A trapezoid with perimeter 11

D–103 — A hexagon with perimeter 10

D–104 — A pentagon with perimeter 9

Page 194

Example

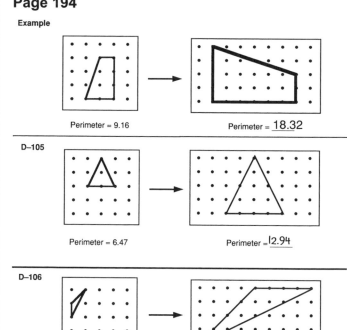

Perimeter = 9.16   Perimeter = __18.32__

D–105

Perimeter = 6.47   Perimeter = __12.94__

D–106

Perimeter = 4.65   Perimeter = __18.60__

Page 195

D-107: P = 11.6, C = 13.5, P = 15.4
D-108: P = 12.4, C = 13.1, P = 13.8

Page 196

D-109: P = 11.5, C = 13.25, P = 15
D-110: P = 12, C = 12.9, P = 13.8

Page 197

D:111: C, E, F, J, K, L
D-112: B, D, G, H, I

Page 198

D-113: B, F, J, K
D-114: C, E, G, H
D-115: A, D, I, L

Page 199

D-116: <   D-119: ? or =
D-117: >   D-120: ? or =
D-118: <

Page 200

Example

Area of figure = $8\frac{1}{2}$

D–121

Area of figure = 8

D–122

Area of figure = $6\frac{1}{2}$

D–123

Area of figure = $9\frac{1}{2}$

D–124

Area of figure = 8

D–125

Area of figure = 9

Page 201

Example

AREA

Completed figure   9
Added regions   6
Original figure   3

D–126

AREA

Completed figure   12
Added regions   4
Original figure   8

D–127

AREA

Completed figure   12
Added regions   9
Original figure   3

D–128

AREA

Completed figure   12
Added regions   6
Original figure   6

D–129

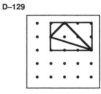

AREA

Completed figure   6
Added regions   4
Original figure   2

D–130

AREA

Completed figure   12
Added regions   8
Original figure   4

Page 202

Example   Parallelogram ABCD with
area of 6 square units

D–131   Rectangle ABCD with
area of 6 square units

D–132   Triangle ABC with
area of 8 square units

D–133   Square ABCD with
area of 8 square units

D–134   Trapezoid ABCD with
area of 7 1/2 square units

D–135   Isosceles triangle ABC with
area of 6 square units

Page 203

Example	Triangle ABC with the smallest possible area	D–136	Rectangle ABCD with the largest possible area

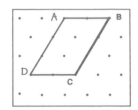

D–137	Quadrilateral ABCD with the smallest possible area	D–138	Triangle ABC with the largest possible area

D–139	Triangle ABC with the largest possible area	D–140	Quadrilateral ABCD with the smallest possible area

Page 204

Example		D–141

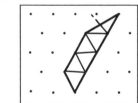

Area = 11

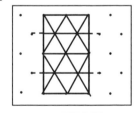

Area = 12

D–142		D–143

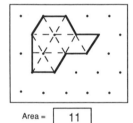

Area = 6

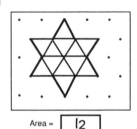

Area = 16

Page 205

Example		D–144

Triangle ABC with an area of 9

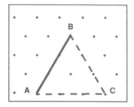

Parallelogram ABCD with an area of 12

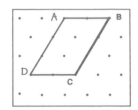

D–145		D–146

Rectangle ABCD with an area of 8

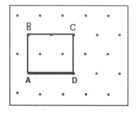

Right triangle ABC with an area of 8

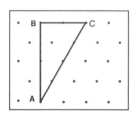

Page 206

D-147: 24, 20   D-150: 24, 35
D-148: 24, 36   D-151: 24, 33.75
D-149: 24, 32   D-152: 24, 29.75

Page 207

D-153: 29, 30   D-155: 23, 30
D-154: 26, 30   D-156: 22, 30

Page 208

Example	A rectangle with one side equal to 2 units

Perimeter = 40

D–157	D–158
A rectangle with one side equal to 3 units	A rectangle with one side equal to 6 units

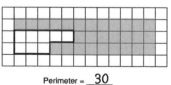

Perimeter = 30

Perimeter = 24

D–159	D–160
A rectangle with one side equal to 8 units	A rectangle with one side equal to 9 units

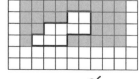

Perimeter = 25

Perimeter = 26

Page 209

Example

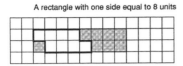

A rectangle with one side equal to 8 units

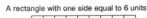

Area = 16

D–161

A rectangle with one side equal to 6 units

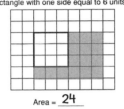

Area = 24

D–162

A rectangle with one side equal to 3 units

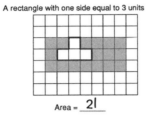

Area = 21

D–163

A rectangle with one side equal to 5 units

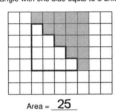

Area = 25

D–164

A rectangle with one side equal to 4 1/2 units

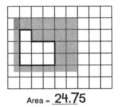

Area = 24.75

Page 210

D-165: 15   D-167: 25
D-166: 20   D-168: 30

Page 211

Example

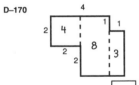

Area of figure = 20

D–169

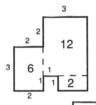

Area of figure = 13

D–170

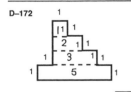

Area of figure = 15

D–171

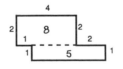

Area of figure = 13

D–172

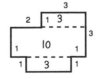

Area of figure = 11

D–173

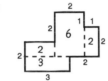

Area of figure = 16

Page 212

Example

Completed rectangle   25

Added regions   5

Original figure   20

D–174

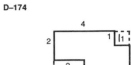

Completed rectangle   20

Added regions   5

Original figure   15

D–175

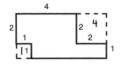

Completed rectangle   18

Added regions   5

Original figure   13

D–176

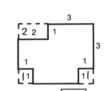

Completed rectangle   20

Added regions   4

Original figure   16

Page 213

Example

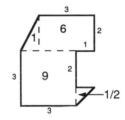

Area of figure = 16 1/2

D–177

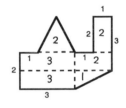

Area of figure = 13

D–178

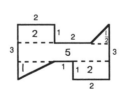

Area of figure = $10\frac{1}{2}$

D–179

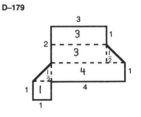

Area of figure = 12

Page 214

D-180: 16, best estimate = 12
D-181: 32
D-182: 60, best estimate = 50

Page 215

D-183: 24, best estimate = 16
D-184: 52
D-185: 80, best estimate = 64

Page 216

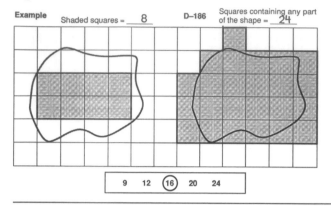

Example   Shaded squares = __8__   **D–186**   Squares containing any part of the shape = __24__

9   12   (16)   20   24

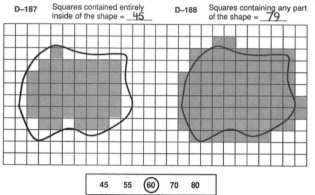

D–187   Squares contained entirely inside of the shape = __45__   **D–188**   Squares containing any part of the shape = __79__

45   55   (60)   70   80

Page 217

D-189: A: 0.75, 1.5, 4.71, 1.77
        B: 1.5, 3, 9.42, 7.07
D-190: A: 1, 2, 6.28, 3.14
        B: 2, 4, 12.56, 12.56
D-191: A: 1, 2, 6.28, 3.14
        B: 1.5, 3, 9.42, 7.07

Page 218

D-192: 6.28   D-195: 3.14
D-193: 4.71   D-196: 6.28
D-194: 9.42

Page 219

D-197: 10   D-200: 10
D-198: 16   D-201: 18
D-199: 36

Page 220

D-202: 6   D-204: 3
D-203: 4   D-205: 2

Page 221

D-206: 10   D-209: 14
D-207: 24   D-210: 8
D-208: 24

Page 222

D-211: 20   D-214: 32
D-212: 32   D-215: 23
D-213: 12

Page 223

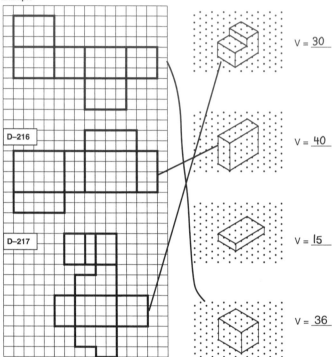

Example

D–216

D–217

v = __30__

v = __40__

v = __15__

v = __36__

Page 224

D-218: 6, 3, 7$\frac{1}{2}$ D-221: 12, 6, 15

D-219: 15, 3, 16$\frac{1}{2}$ D-222: 12, 6, 15

D-220: 0, 3, 1$\frac{1}{2}$

Page 225

Example

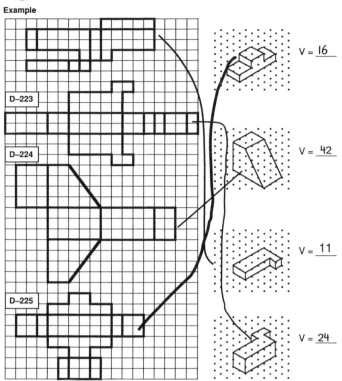

D–223

D–224

D–225

V = 16

V = 42

V = 11

V = 24

Page 226

Example   16 Cubes

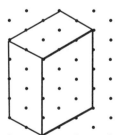

D–226   27 Cubes

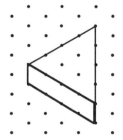

D–227   24 Cubes

D–228   8 Cubes

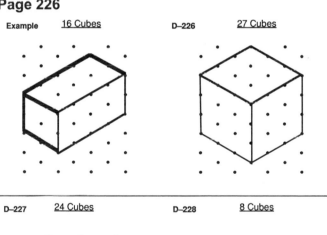

Page 227

D-229: 64   D-233: 238
D-230: 140   D-234: 236
D-231: 98   D-235: 204
D-232: 96   D-236: 160

Page 228

D-237: 144
D-238: 204
D-239: 280
D-240: 204
D-241: 128

Page 229

Example

g   V = 240
4   10
6

D–242

e   V = 96
2   6
8

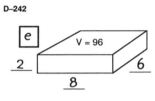

D–243

c   V = 90
3
6
5

D–244

a   V = 250
5   10
5

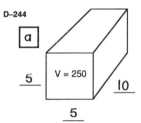

D–245

d   V = 90
3   3
10

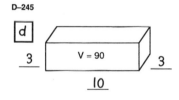

D–246

b   V = 72
6   4
3

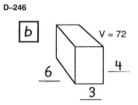

Page 230

D-247: 72
D-248: 80
D-249: 250
D-250: 40
D-251: 90

Page 231

Example

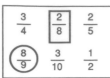

E–1

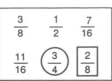

E–2

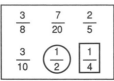

E–3

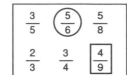

E–4

E–5

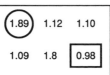

E–6 Which is the largest number in all the sets? _____ $\frac{8}{9}$

E–7 Which is the smallest number in all the sets? _____ $\frac{1}{6}$

Page 232

Example

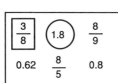

E–8

E–9

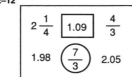

E–10

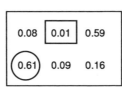

E–11

E–12

E–13 Which is the largest number in all the sets? _____ $\frac{7}{3}$

E–14 Which is the smallest number in all the sets? _____ 0.01

Page 233

E-15: <
E-16: =
E-17: >
E-18: >

E-19: <
D-20: =
E-21: <

Page 234

Example

6 and 9

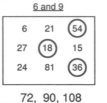

72, 90, 108

E–22

3 and 4

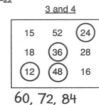

60, 72, 84

E–23

8 and 12

72, 120, 144

E–24

10 and 15

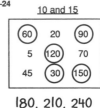

180, 210, 240

What is the smallest number that is a common multiple of each of the following pairs of numbers?

E–25 6 and 9   18

E–26 3 and 4   12

E–27 8 and 12   24

E–28 10 and 15   30

Page 235

Example	72	④ 5 ⑥ 7 ⑧ ㊱ 48
E–29	80	④ 6 7 ⑧ 12 ⑯ 24
E–30	256	④ ⑧ 12 14 ⑯ ㉜ 48
E–31	144	④ 7 ⑨ 32 ㊽ ㊲ 81
E–32	81	③ 6 ⑨ 12 15 ㉗ 31
E–33	360	7 ⑧ ⑨ 14 ㊱ ㊲ 108

E–34 $\frac{72}{80} = \frac{9}{10}$

E–35 $\frac{256}{360} = \frac{32}{45}$

E–36 $\frac{81}{144} = \frac{9}{16}$

E–37 $\frac{80}{256} = \frac{5}{16}$

E–38 $\frac{144}{360} = \frac{2}{5}$

E–39 $\frac{81}{360} = \frac{9}{40}$

Page 236

E-40: 4

E-41: $1\frac{1}{2}$

E-42: $\frac{3}{4}$, $\frac{4}{5}$

E-43: $2\frac{1}{2}$, $2\frac{2}{3}$, $1\frac{3}{8}$

E-44: $1\frac{1}{8}$, $\frac{7}{8}$

E-45: $8\frac{3}{8}$

E-46: $\frac{5}{13}$, $3\frac{1}{8}$

Page 237

E-47: (4.25, 3.15), (6.08, 9.50)

E-48: (1.25, 20), (7.25, 19.50)

E-49: (5, 6), (5, 7)

Page 238

Example $3 \boxed{+} (4+2) < 9 \boxed{\times} 2$

E-50 $(5 \boxed{+} 7) \boxed{+} 9 > 7 \boxed{+} (9 \boxed{-} 5)$

E-51 $3 \boxed{\times} (4 \boxed{+} 5) = (3 \boxed{\times} 4) \boxed{+} (3 \boxed{\times} 5)$

E-52 $1.85 \boxed{\div} 3.75 < 1.85 \boxed{+} 3.75$

E-53 $\frac{7}{8} \div 1\frac{1}{2} < \frac{2}{3} \boxed{+} \frac{7}{8}$

E-54 $3\frac{3}{4} \boxed{\times} 4\frac{1}{4} = 4\frac{1}{4} \boxed{\times} 3\frac{3}{4}$

Page 239

Example $3 \boxed{+} 2 \boxed{<} 7 + 4$

E-55 $9 \times 7 \boxed{=} 7 \boxed{\times} 9$

E-56 $\frac{3}{8} + \frac{5}{8} \boxed{>} \frac{7}{8} \div \frac{8}{7}$

E-57 $4.54 - 3.85 \boxed{=} 4.54 \boxed{-} 3.85$

E-58 $3 \boxed{\div} 4 \boxed{<} 5 \boxed{\div} 6$

E-59 $12.75 \boxed{-} 9.50 \boxed{<} 6.75 \boxed{+} 4.95$

E-60 $1 \boxed{-} 0 \boxed{>} 0 \boxed{\div} 1$

Page 240

E-61: 20, 26, 33

E-62: 26, 37, 50

E-63: 21, 28, 36

E-64: 36, 49, 64

E-65: 17, 18, 20

E-66: 49, 67, 88

E-67: 70, 92, 117

E-68: 44, 61, 80

Page 241

E-69: b, d

E-70: b, c

E-71: b

E-72: a, d

E-73: a, d

Page 242

E-74: c

E-75: b

E-76: b, c

E-77: a, c

Page 243

E-78: 53, 67, 83

E-79: 57, 69, 108

E-80: 59, 71, 110

E-81: 27, 61, 77

Page 244

E-82: 122, 257, 485

E-83: 288, 578, 1250

E-84: 143, 288, 624

E-85: 289, 579, 1251

Page 245

E-86: 9, 16, 23

E-87: 16, 36, 52

E-88: 7, 20, 26

E-89: 6, 8, 17

Page 246

E-90: d

E-91: a

E-92: b

E-93: c

E-94: d

Page 247

Example

L=33

Rule	Table		Rule	Table	
	A	B		A	B
B = 2 × A	0	0	B = A − 3	7	4
	2	4		9	6
	3	6		10	7
	5	10		17	14
	8	16		33	30

E–96

E–97

Rule	Table		Rule	Table	
	A	B		A	B
$\frac{A}{B} = \frac{1}{2}$	6	12	B = (2 × A) − 1	1	1
	8	16		3	5
	1	2		4	7
	3	6		7	13
	4	8		5	9

E–98

E–99

Rule	Table		Rule	Table	
	A	B		A	B
A < B + 2	0	1	B = A²	0	0
	1	1		1	1
	3	2		3	9
	4	3		7	49
	1	12		10	100

Page 248

Example   (1, 4)   (2, 7)   (3, 10)   (4, 13)   (5, 16)   (6, 19)

E–100   (3, 5)   (4, 6)   (5, 7)   (6, 8)   (7, 9)   (8, 10)

E–101   (1, 3)   (2, 6)   (3, 9)   (4, 12)   (5, 15)   (6, 18)

E–102   (2, 1)   (3, 1.5)   (4, 2)   (5, 2.5)   (6, 3)   (7, 3.5)

E–103   (3, 11)   (4, 14)   (5, 17)   (6, 20)   (7, 23)   (8, 26)

E–104   (1, 1)   (2, 4)   (3, 9)   (4, 16)   (5, 25)   (6, 36)

E–105   (3, 1)   (6, 2)   (9, 3)   (12, 4)   (15, 5)   (18, 6)

E–106   (1, 4)   (2, 8)   (3, 12)   (4, 16)   (5, 20)   (6, 24)

Page 249

Example   (4, 1)   (5, 1.25)   (6, 1.5)   (7, 1.75)   (8, 2) • • • (15, 3.75)

E–107   (2, 7)   (3, 8)   (4, 9)   (5, 10)   (6, 11) • • • (12, 17)

E–108   (1, 5)   (2, 10)   (3, 15)   (4, 20)   (5, 25) • • • (19, 95)

E–109   (3, 7)   (4, 9)   (5, 11)   (6, 13)   (7, 15) • • • (10, 21)

E–110   (1, 4)   (2, 7)   (3, 10)   (4, 13)   (5, 16) • • • (11, 34)

E–111   (4, 2)   (9, 3)   (16, 4)   (25, 5)   (36, 6) • • • (144, 12)

E–112   (2, 3)   (4, 6)   (6, 9)   (8, 12)   (10, 15) • • • (24, 36)

E–113   (5, 1)   (6, 1.2)   (7, 1.4)   (8, 1.6)   (9, 1.8) • • • (12, 2.4)

Page 250
E-114: (1, 1), (3, 9), (0, 0), (12, 144)
E-115: (5, 11), (3, 7), (1, 3), (0, 1)
E-116: (2, 6), (1, 3), (12, 36), (3, 9)
E-117: (6, 3), (2, 1), (10, 5)

Page 251
E-118: b   E-120: b
E-119: d   E-121: c

Page 252

Example The product of the numbers is less than 24 and their sum is 10.
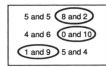

E–122 Both numbers are multiples of 3 and their difference is greater than 6.
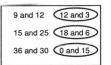

E–123 One number is 2 more than the other and their product is an odd number.
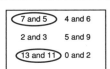

E–124 Both numbers are prime numbers and their product is less than 20.
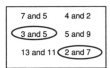

E–125 The sum of the two numbers is less than 9 and one number is twice the other.
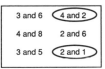

Page 253

E-126: 8 and 9, 6 and 7, 10 and 12,
        $3 \times (A + B) < A \times B$
E-127: 5 and 1, 4 and 2, 6 and 0, $A + 3 > 2 \times B$
E-128: 6 and 18, 4 and 8, 0 and 0, $A^2 = 2 \times B$
E-129: 1 and 2, 1 and 3, 0 and 2, $A^2 + B^2 < 13$

Page 254

E-130: True   E-135: False
E-131: Indeterminate   E-136: Indeterminate
E-132: False   E-137: True
E-133: Indeterminate   E-138: True
E-134: True

Page 255

E-139: True   E-144: False
E-140: Indeterminate   E-145: False
E-141: False   E-146: True
E-142: Indeterminate   E-147: True
E-143: False

Page 256

F-1: e
F-2: b
F-3: d
F-4: a or f

Page 257

F-5: 20 million   F-8: about 250 million
F-6: 1950s   F-9: about 90 million
F-7: 1930s

Page 258

F-10: 30, 1, 2, 3, 4, 5   F-12: 6, 1, 2
F-11: 20, 1, 2, 3, 4   F-13: 3, 6, 10, 15, 21, 28

Page 259

F-14: 2   F-17: 4, 3, 2, 1
F-15: 1   F-18: 5, 4, 3, 2, 1
F-16: 3, 2, 1

Page 260

F-19: 9   F-21: 9
F-20: 9   F-22: 9, 9, 9, 9, 9, 9, 54

Page 261

F-23: 64
F-24: 37
F-25: 16
F-26: 16
F-27: 16, 16, 16, 16, 16, 16, 96

Page 262

F-28: 8   F-31: Yes
F-29: 12   F-32: 1
F-30: 6   F-33: 8, 12, 6, 1

Page 263

F-34: $2\frac{1}{2}$ hours, $2.75

F-35: 4 hours, $2.50
F-36: 7 hours, $4.25

F-37: $2\frac{1}{2}$ hours, free

F-38: 11 hours, $5.25

Page 264

F-39: 2 hours 13 minutes, $1.75
F-40: 25 hours 24 minutes, $10.00
F-41: 13 hours 59 minutes, $6.00
F-42: 17 hours 43 minutes, $3.00
F-43: 50 hours 29 minutes, $18.75

Page 265

F-44: $15.95, $6.83, $16.62, $39.40, $5.00, $34.40
F-45: $11.78, $16.62, $14.49, $42.89, $8.00, $34.89

Page 266

F—46

3 A books	$11.78
3 B books	$13.57
1 F book	$8.25
Subtotal	$33.60
Discount	$4.50
Total	$29.10

F—47

3 A books	$11.78
4 B books	$17.96
1 F book	$8.25
Subtotal	$37.99
Discount	$7.00
Total	$30.99

F—48

4 A books	$15.58
3 B books	$13.57
1 F book	$8.25
Subtotal	$37.40
Discount	$7.00
Total	$30.40

F—49

3 D books	$20.22
1 C book	$5.95
1 A book	$3.99
2 B books	$8.98
Subtotal	$39.14
Discount	$5.00
Total	$34.14

F—50

3 C books	$16.62
2 F books	$15.95
3 A books	$11.78
2 B books	$8.98
Subtotal	$53.33
Discount	$8.00
Total	$45.33

F—51

3 F books	$24.20
2 D books	$13.39
1 C book	$5.95
1 A book	$3.99
Subtotal	$47.53
Discount	$6.00
Total	$41.53

Page 267

F-52: 10,500
F-53: 11,200
F-54: 14,100
F-55: 14,600
F-56: 21,000

Page 268

F-57: line connecting (1, 5) and (5, 1)
F-58: (1, 5), (2, 4), (3, 3), (4, 2), (5, 1)
F-59: 5
F-60: 1, 2, 3, 4, 5, 6, 5, 4, 3, 2, 1
F-61: 36
F-62: 7

Page 269

F-63: line connecting (5, 6) and (8,3)
F-64: (5, 6), (6, 5), (7, 4), (8, 3)
F-65: 4
F-66: 1, 2, 3, 4, 5, 6, 6, 6, 5, 4, 3, 2, 1
F-67: 48
F-68: the sums of 7, 8, and 9 each occur 6 times

Page 270

F-69: 36
F-70: 48
F-71: d
F-72: a
F-73: e
F-74: c
F-75: g
F-76: h
F-77: f

Page 271

F-78: (4, 8), (5, 7), (6, 6), (7, 5), (8, 4)
F-79: 16
F-80: 2
F-81: 7
F-82: 1, 2, 3, 4, 5, 6, 7, 8, 7, 6, 5, 4, 3, 2, 1

Page 272

Example

(0, 0), (1, 2), (2, 4), (3, 6), (4, 8)

RULE: a. A = B + 2
        b. A = 2 × B
        c. B = A + 2
        d. B = 2 × A

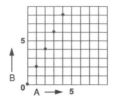

F—83

(0, 1), (1, 4), (2, 7), (3, 10), (4, 13)

RULE: a. A = (3 × B) + 1
        b. A = 3 × B
        c. B = (3 × A) + 1
        d. B = A + 3

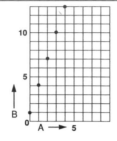

F—84

(0, 3), (1, 5), (2, 7), (3, 9), (4, 11)

RULE: a. B = (2 × A) + 3
        b. B = (3 × A) + 2
        c. A = (2 × B) + 3
        d. B = A + 4

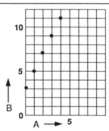

Page 273

F–85

(0, 0), (1, 3), (2, 6), (3, 9), (4, 12)

RULE: a. B = A + 2

b. A = B – 3

c. B = 3 × A ⟵(circled)

d. A = 3 × B

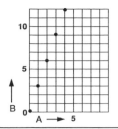

F–86

(0, 7), (1, 6), (2, 5), (3, 4), (4, 3)

RULE: a. B = A + 7

b. B = 6 × A

c. A = 7 – B

d. B = 7 – A ⟵(circled)

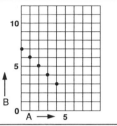

F–87

(0, 9), (1, 7), (2, 5), (3, 3), (4, 1)

RULE: a. A = 9 – (2 × B)

b. A + B = 9

c. B = 9 – (2 × A) ⟵(circled)

d. B = (2 × A) + 5

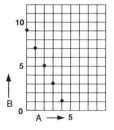

Page 274

Example B = (2 × A) + 1

A	B
0	1
1	3
2	5
3	7
4	9

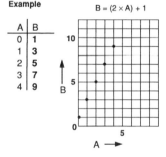

F–88 B = (2 × A) + 2

A	B
0	2
1	4
2	6
3	8
4	10

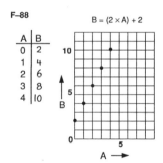

F–89 A + B = 10

A	B
0	10
1	9
2	8
3	7
4	6

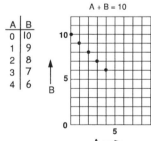

F–90 B = 2 × A

A	B
0	0
1	2
2	4
3	6
4	8

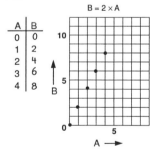

Page 275

F-91: 5, 4, 3, 2, 1, 0, and choice d

F-92: 10, 8, 6, 4, 2, 0, and choice c

Page 276

F-93: 4, 5, 6, 7, 8, 9, 10, 11, and choice c

F-94: 1, 2, 3, 4, 5 and choice b

F-95: 0, 3, 6, 9, 12, and choice d

Page 277

F-96: f

F-97: a

F-98: b

Page 278

F-99: 81

F-100: mile

F-101: 0.62

F-102: 90

F-103: 37

Page 279

F-104: 10

F-105: 69

F-106: 38

F-107: 122

F-108: 37

F-109: 158

F-110: -40°

Page 280

F-111: 300

F-112: 60

F-113: 5.7

F-114: 17.1

F-115: 122

F-116: 16.1

Page 281:

F-117: the traveller stopped

F-118: 65 miles

F-119: first 3 hours

F-120: about 13 miles per hour

F-121: about 5 miles per hour

F-122: bicycle, motor boat

Page 282:

F-123: stop periods, loading and unloading at ferry

F-124: 100 miles

F-125: 1 hour

F-126: Kim

F-127: Jones

F-128: 40 miles per hour

Page 283:

F-129: b

F-130: c

F-131: a

F-132: f